Gerrish's

Technical

Dictionary

Technical Terms Simplified

by

HOWARD H. GERRISH

Professor, Industrial Arts
San Jose State College, San Jose, California
Member of Institute of Electrical and Electronics
Engineers

WA6DBM

SOUTH HOLLAND, ILLINOIS
THE GOODHEART-WILLCOX COMPANY, INC.
Publishers

INTRODUCTION

The purpose of this Dictionary is to clarify definitions and obscure meanings of technical words and phrases that form our vast technical vocabulary.

Many of the words defined are common words, which have been given unusual meanings by industrial craftsmen. Some of the words find their roots in the "slang of the trade," and have become accepted through repeated usage.

After each word, the trade or craft in which the word is used is identified, in the following manner:

TRADE	IDENTIFIED BY
Aero Space Technology	(space)
Air Conditioning	(air cond.)
Architectural Drafting Machine Drafting	(draft.)
Arts and Crafts Ceramics Jewelry	(crafts)
Automation	(automation)
Automotive	(auto.)
Building Trades	(const.)
Cabinet Making Carpentry Woodworking	(wood.)
Electricity Electronics	(elec.)

Introduction

Foundry
Machine Tools
Metal Work, general   (metal)
Sheet Metal

Graphic Arts and Printing   (graphics)

Painting and Decorating   (painting and dec.)

Plumbing and Heating   (plumb.)

Welding   (welding)

Technical Dictionary

AAA (auto.): American Automobile Association.

AARON'S ROD (const.) aar' on's rod: An architectural ornamentation, consisting of scroll work and leafage representing a rod with a serpent twined about it.

ABACUS (const.) ab' a cus: A slab on the top of a column. It may be curved or square and it supports the architrave.

ABAMPERE (elec.) ab' am pere: A CGS (centimeter-gram-second) electromagnetic unit. It is equal to ten amperes.

A-BATTERY (elec.) a-bat' tery: A battery used to supply the heater voltage for electron tubes.

ABBREVIATION (graphics) ab bre vi a' tion: Part of a word used as a substitute for the whole word.

ABCOULOMB (elec.) ab cou' lomb: A CGS electromagnetic unit. It is equal to a charge of ten coulombs.

ABLATION (space) a bla' tion: Melting of nose cone materials during reentry of spacecraft or other vehicles into the earth's atmosphere at hypersonic speeds.

ABOHM (elec.) ab ohm': A unit of resistance in the CGS electromagnetic system. It is equal to 10^{-9} ohms.

ABORT (space) a bort': Failure of an aerospace vehicle to accomplish its purposes.

A-B POWER PACK (elec.) a-b pow' er pack: A compact battery for use in portable radios that supplies both heater and B plate voltages for the electron tubes.

ABRASION (welding) a bra' sion: The wearing away of a surface by rubbing.

ABRASIVE (metal) a bra' sive: Materials used for grinding, polishing and lapping.

ABRASIVE COATING, CLOSED (painting and dec.) a bra' sive coat' ing, closed: In closed coating of paper no adhesive is exposed as surface of paper is completely covered with abrasive. In open coating, surface of backing paper is covered with regulated amount of abrasive exposing the adhesive. Space between the abrasive grains reduces loading and filling when sanding gummy or soft materials.

ABRASIVE CUTTING TOOLS (automation) a bra' sive cutting tools: Tools used for grinding, buffing, lapping, honing, super finishing and brushing.

ABRASIVE PAPER (const.) a bra' sive pa' per: Paper or cloth coated with abrasive materials.

ABSOLUTE (const.) ab' so lute: Exact; complete.

ABSOLUTE ZERO (air cond.) ab' so lute zero: The temperature at which the molecular motion of a substance ceases; 459.7 below zero Fahrenheit; the point at which no heat exists in a substance.

ABSORB (paint. and dec.) ab sorb': To assimilate, to swallow up or suck in, like wood absorbing a finishing material such as paint or stain.

ABSORBENT (air cond.) ab sorb' ent: A compound or substance that takes up liquid or vapor, and changes physically or chemically during the process.

ABSORPTION SYSTEM (air cond.) ab-sorp' tion sys' tem: A refrigeration system in which the refrigerant gas from the evaporator is absorbed and released in a generator when heat is applied.

ABSORPTION WAVEMETER (elec.) ab-sorp' tion wave 'me ter: An electronic device used to measure frequency and wave length by the tuning of a resonant circuit until maximum energy is absorbed from the circuit being measured.

ABUT (const.) a but': One timber touching or meeting another.

ABUTTALS (const.) a but' tals: The boundaries of a parcel of land to other lands, streets, rivers, etc.

ABVOLT (elec.) ab' volt: A unit of voltage measurement in the CGS electromagnetic system; it is equal to 10^{-8} volt.

AC (elec.) ac: Alternating current.

A-C (elec.) a-c: Alternating current, used as an adjective.

ACANTHUS (const.) a can' thus: A decorative carved molding.

ACCELERATE (auto.) ac cel' er ate: To increase speed or velocity.

ACCELERATING ELECTRODE (elec.) ac cel' er a ting   e lec' trode: An electrode in a cathode-ray tube used to increase the velocity of the electrons in the beam.

ACCELERATING JET (auto.) ac cel'-er a ting jet: A jet in the carburetor that supplies additional fuel to the incoming air stream during acceleration.

ACCELERATION (auto.) ac cel' er a-tion: The rate of increase of velocity or speed.

ACCELERATOR (auto.) ac cel' er a-tor: A foot pedal in an automobile that controls the speed of the engine.

ACCELERATOR (const.) ac cel' er a-tor: Any substance added to plaster or Portland cement during mixing, which will speed up its setting time.

ACCELERATOR-PUMP SYSTEM (auto.) ac cel' er a' tor-pump sys' tem: A pump in the carburetor that (momentarily) enriches the air-fuel mixture to the engine and causes a rapid gain of speed.

ACCELEROMETER (elec.) ac cel' er-om' e ter: An instrument used to measure acceleration.

ACCENT (graphics) ac' cent: A mark designating the letter or symbol upon which accent is placed in pronunciation.

ACCEPTOR CIRCUIT (elec.) ac cep'-tor cir' cuit: A series tuned circuit at resonance; accepts signals at resonant frequency.

ACCEPTOR IMPURITY (elec.) ac cep'-tor im pu' ri ty: An impurity added to a semiconductor material that creates holes for current carriers.

ACCESS TIME (elec.) ac' cess time: The time required to obtain a word from the memory section of a computer.

ACCUMULATOR (air cond.) ac cu' mu-la' tor: A storage chamber for the low-side liquid refrigerant.

ACCUMULATOR (elec.) ac cu' mu la'-tor: A storage battery (British): The section of a computer, consisting of a modified binary counter with input terminals, in which the stored count is increased to a new total each time a pulse is applied to the counter.

AC-DC (elec.) ac-dc: Referring to a device which will operate on either ac or dc current.

ACETATE CELLULOSE (elec.) ac' e-tate cel' lu lose: A plastic base used in the manufacturing of magnetic recording tape.

ACETIC ACID (paint. and dec.) a ce'-tic ac' id: A sour, colorless compound. (Vinegar contains 4 to 12 percent acetic acid.)

ACETONE (paint. and dec.) ac' e tone: A water-white volatile solvent with ether-like odor, Acetone is made by destructive distillation of hardwood, fermentation of butyl alcohol and from petroleum sources. Used extensively in making paint removers.

ACETYLENE (welding) a cet' y lene: Gas composed of two parts of carbon and two parts of hydrogen. When burned in an atmosphere of oxygen, it produces one of the highest flame temperatures obtainable.

ACETYLENE CYLINDER (welding) a-cet' y lene cyl' in der: Specially built container manufactured according to I.C.C. standards. Used to store and ship acetylene, it is occasionally called "tank" or "bottle."

ACETYLENE GAS (metal) a cet' y lene gas: An illuminating gas made by treating calcium carbide with water. Used in oxyacetylene welding.

ACETYLENE GENERATOR (metal) a-cet' y lene gen' er a' tor: A tank type generator in which calcium carbide and water are mixed to provide acetylene gas at a constant pressure.

ACETYLENE HOSE (welding) a cet' y-lene hose: See HOSE.

ACETYLENE REGULATOR (welding) a cet' y lene reg' u la' tor: An automatic valve used to reduce acetylene cylinder pressures to torch pressures and to keep the pressures constant.

AC GENERATOR (elec.) ac gen' er a-tor: A generator using slip rings and brushes to connect armature to external circuit. It produces an alternating current.

ACHROMATIC (crafts) ach ro mat' ic: A lens that refracts light of all colors equally; a lens designed to minimize chromatic aberration.

ACHROMATIC (paint. and dec.) ach-ro mat' ic: Colorless; without color.

ACID (metal) ac' id: A substance which dissolves in water with the formation of hydrogen ions; a substance containing hydrogen that may be chemically replaced with metals to form salts.

ACID BATH (metal) ac' id bath: An acid mixture, called a pickling bath for removing oxidation and cleaning metal parts in preparation for electroplating.

ACID NUMBER (paint. and dec.) ac' id num' ber: A designation of the amount of free acid in oils, flats, waxes and resins, expressed as the number of milligrams of potassium hydroxide required to neutralize one gram of the material being tested. Also called acid value.

ACLINIC LINE (elec.) a clin'ic line: An imaginary line around the earth, approximately at the equator, where all points have a zero magnetic inclination.

ACME THREAD (metal) ac'me thread: A thread system used extensively for feed mechanisms. It is between a

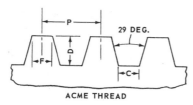

ACME THREAD
D = .5 x P (MINIMUM DEPTH)
F = .3707 x P
C = F (MINIMUM DEPTH)

square thread and a V thread with a 29 deg. included angle.

ACORN TUBE (elec.) a'corn tube: A small acorn shaped electron tube without a base. Connections to elements are made through pins extending radially from the tube. It is used in high frequency applications.

ACOUSTICAL FEEDBACK (elec.) a-cous'ti cal feed'back: The reflection of, and return of, a part of a sound wave to the input of an amplifier in phase with original sound input so that the amplification of the system is increased.

ACOUSTICAL PLASTER (const.) a-cous'ti cal plas'ter: A finishing type of plaster used with certain aggregate materials that absorb sound waves.

ACOUSTICS (elec.) a cous'tics: The science of sound and hearing; the qualities of a room or device as it affects the reception and/or transmission of sound.

ACOUSTIC TILE (const.) a cous'tic tile:

Tile made of sound absorbing materials.

AC PLATE RESISTANCE, Symbol r_p (elec.) ac plate re sist'ance: A variational characteristic of a vacuum tube representing the ratio of a change of plate voltage to a change in plate current, while the grid voltage is constant.

ACROSS (const.) a cross': A term used to describe cutting across the grain of a board, usually at a right angle.

ACRYLIC RESINS (painting and dec.) a cry'lic res'ins: A group of transparent thermoplastic resins made by polymerization of esters of acrylic acid. It is used in emulsion and solvent based paints.

ACTINIC (space) ac tin'ic: Pertaining to electromagnetic radiation capable of initiating photochemical reactions.

ACTIVATED ALUMINA (air cond.) ac-ti vated a lu'mi na: Aluminum oxide used as an absorbent.

ACTUAL THROAT (welding) ac'tu al throat: Distance from face of a weld to the root of the weld.

ACTUATION (automation) ac'tu a'tion: Directing energy; put into action.

ACUTE ANGLE (metal) a cute' an'gle: An angle less than 90 deg.

AD (graphics) ad: An abbreviation for advertisement.

AD COPY (graphics) ad cop'y: Copy or content of an advertisement.

ADDENDUM (metal) ad den'dum: The distance from pitch line to outside diameter of a gear.

ADDENDUM CIRCLE (draft.) ad den'-dum cir'cle: The outer circumference of a gear.

ADDER (elec.) ad' der: Circuit in electronic computer that registers the sum of two or more numbers or quantities.

ADDITION (const.) ad di' tion: A change in the structure of a building in which the exterior dimensions are increased.

ADDITIVES (auto.) ad' di tives: Chemicals added to lubricating oils to produce desired characteristics.

ADDRESS (automation) ad dress': A number identifying a location.

ADHERENCE (const.) ad her' ence: The property of materials or substances causing them to stick together.

ADHESIVE (const.) ad he' sive: A cement; glue; any substance that causes bodies to stick together.

ADIABATIC (air cond.) ad i a bat' ic: A change in volume or pressure without a change in heat.

ADIABATIC PROCESS (air cond.) ad i-a bat' ic proc' ess: A process in which a change in pressure or volume occurs without gain or loss of heat.

ADJACENT ANGLE (draft.) ad ja' cent an' gle: One angle is adjacent to another angle if one leg is common to both angles.

ADJACENT-CHANNEL INTERFERENCE (elec.) ad ja' cent chan' nel inter fer' ence: Interference from a signal originating in an authorized adjacent channel, such as in TV.

ADJUSTABLE WRENCH (const.) adjust' able wrench: An open end wrench with an adjustable jaw.

ADMITTANCE, (Symbol Y), (elec.) admit' tance: The reciprocal of impedance.

ADOBE (const.) a do' be: Clay; aluminous earth; brick made by mixing earth and straw and baking in the sun.

ADOBE CONSTRUCTION (const.) a do'-be con struc' tion: A building which has exterior walls made of adobe brick. These bricks are made of soil and straw and baked in the sun.

ADSORBENT (air cond.) ad sorb' ent: A substance which has the ability to cause liquid vapor or gas to adhere to its surfaces without a chemical or physical change during the process.

ADVANCE (auto.) ad vance': A term used in automotive electricity to indicate that ignition occurs before piston reaches top dead center; to adjust ignition to fire earlier.

ADVANCING COLORS (paint. and dec.) ad vanc' ing col' ors: Colors that give illusion of being closer to the observer. Warm colors in which red-orange predominates are advancing colors.

ADZ (const.) adz: An ax-like tool used for rough-shaping a wood timber.

ADZ BLOCK (const.) adz block: The head which holds the cutting blades in a wood planer machine.

ADZ HAMMER (const.) adz ham' mer: A hammer with an extended claw and eye which gives a greater bearing on the handle.

AERATION (air cond.) aer a' tion: A process of cooling or mixing by air circulation or ventilation.

AERIAL (elec.) aer' i al: An antenna.

AEROBALLISTIC MISSILE (space) aer-o bal lis' tic mis' sile: A wingless vehicle employing the boostglide and continuous roll technique for flight at hypersonic speeds within the earth's atmosphere.

AERODYNAMICS (space) aer o dy nam'ics: That field of dynamics which considers the motion of bodies relative to the air and the forces that act upon the bodies, especially as these forces relate to flight through the air.

AEROELASTICITY (space) aer o e lastic' i ty: The effect of aerodynamic forces on elastic bodies.

AEROSOL (air cond.) aer o sol: Small particles suspended in air. Example: dust, fog, smoke.

AEROSPACE (space) aer o space': An operationally indivisible medium consisting of the total expanse beyond the earth's surface.

AEROSPACE FORCES (space) aer o-space' forces: Includes all vehicles, their equipment and, where applicable, weapons and crews that operate in aerospace for military purposes. This includes aircraft, missiles, aerospacecraft and spacecraft.

AEROSPACE VEHICLE (space) aer o-space've' hi cle: Specifically, an aerospace vehicle is one that functions both in the sensible atmosphere and in the space equivalent or space environment. In its general sense, any vehicle manned or unmanned that operates in the aerospace environment.

AF (elec.) af: Abbreviation for audio frequency.

AFC (elec.): Abbreviation of Automatic Frequency Control.

AFTER IMAGE (crafts) af ter im' age: An impression of a visual image which

remains on the retina of the eye momentarily after the stimulus is removed.

AGAINST THE GRAIN (graphics) against' the grain: Opposite to the direction to which fibers run in a sheet of paper.

AGATE (crafts) ag' ate: A semiprecious stone; variegated quartz in which colors are in bands.

AGATE (graphics) ag' ate: A size of type now called 5 1/2 point. Agate is composed 14 lines to the inch. It is the basis for newspaper and magazine advertising space sold by the line.

AGC (elec.): Abbreviation for AUTOMATIC GAIN CONTROL. A circuit employed to vary the gain of an amplifier in proportion to the input signal strength so that its output remains at a constant level.

AGGREGATE (const.) ag' gre gate: Materials such as sand, rock and gravel used in making concrete.

AGING (const.) ag' ing: A process used to make materials or surfaces appear old or antique.

AGING (metal) ag' ing: The change in the structure of a metal or alloy that takes place slowly at room temperature.

AGITATOR (air cond.) ag' i ta tor: A mechanical device to produce turbulence in a liquid storage tank.

AGONIC LINE (elec.) a gon' ic line: An imaginary line around the earth's surface in a north-south direction, on which all points have a zero declination.

AGRAVIC (space) a grav' ic: A condition of no gravity; weightlessness.

AGRICULTURAL VARNISHES (painting

and dec.) ag ri cul' tur al var' nishes: Varnishes designed to protect and
beautify farm implements and machinery.

AIEE (elec.): American Institute of Electrical Engineers.

AIR BLAST (air cond.) air blast: Forced
air.

AIR BLEED (auto.) air bleed: A device
to permit additional air to enter the
main nozzle of the carburetor to balance
the air-fuel ratio at higher speeds.

AIR BOUND (metal) air bound: A term
used to describe a condition when air
pressure prevents a machine from
operating properly.

AIR BREAKUP (space) air break' up:
The breakup of a body after reentry
into the atmosphere.

AIR BREATHER (space) air breath' er:
A missile or vehicle propelled by fuel
oxidized by intake from the atmosphere.

AIR BRUSH (painting and dec.) air brush:
A device used to spray paint by means
of compressed air.

AIR CAPACITOR (elec.) air ca pac' i-
tor: A capacitor employing air as a
dielectric.

AIR CHAMBER (plumb.) air cham' ber:
A chamber installed on the discharge
end of a piston pump to minimize the
pulsating discharge.

AIR CHANGES (air cond.) air chang' es:
An expression used to denote the change
of air in a building in terms of building
or room volumes.

AIR CLEANER (const.) air clean' er: A
device to remove impurities, such as

smoke, dust, cinders, fumes, etc., from
the air.

AIR CLEANER (auto.) air clean' er: See
INTAKE SILENCER.

AIR CONDITIONING (air cond.) air con-
di' tion ing: The control of the temperature, humidity, motion, dust and distribution of the atmosphere in a building.

AIR-COOLED ENGINE (auto.) air-cooled
en' gine: An internal combustion engine
cooled by forced air; an engine with
individual cylinders cooled by a series
of fins around the head. Air is blown
through and around the cooling fins.

AIR COOLER, Types of (air cond.) air
cool' er:
   CONVECTION: Similar to the dry
type cooler but depending upon the
natural circulation of air.
   DRY TYPE: A cooler using forced
air circulation without liquid spray.
   PRESSURE TYPE: A cooler depending upon air resistance.
   SPRAY TYPE: A forced air circulation cooler using a liquid spray in
addition to cooling coils.

AIR-CORE INDUCTOR (elec.) air-core
in duc' tor: An inductor wound on an
insulated form without a metallic core.
A self-supporting coil without a core.

AIR DRIED (const.) air dried: Lumber
dried naturally in stacks in lumber
storage yards.

AIR DRY (painting and dec.) air dry: To
dry a coating at ordinary room conditions.

AIR DUCT (const.) air duct: See DUCT.

AIRFOIL (space) air' foil: Any aerodynamic surface designed to obtain a
reaction from the air through which it
moves.

AIRFRAME (space) air' frame: The assembled structural and aerodynamic components of an aircraft or missile that support the different systems and subsystems integral to the missile or aircraft.

AIR-FUEL RATIO (auto.) air-fuel ra'- tio: The ratio of the weight of air to the weight of fuel, as used in internal combustion engines.

AIR GAP (auto.) air gap: The air space between spark plug electrodes; the space between the armature and coil of a relay.

AIR GAP (elec.) air gap: The space between magnetic poles; the space between the contact points of a relay; space between rotating and stationary assemblies in a motor or generator.

AIR GAP (plumb.) air gap: The vertical distance through free atmosphere between the lowest opening of a water supply system and the flood level of the receptacle.

AIR GUN (const.) air gun: A device designed to apply adhesive materials to a surface by means of air pressure.

AIR-HARDENING (metal) air-har' dening: A process of hardening steel by heating and cooling rapidly in a blast of air.

AIR HORN (auto.) air horn: The air entrance to the carburetor.

AIR INDUCTOR (elec.) air in duc' tor: An inductor without a magnetic core.

AIR LOCK (plumb.) air lock: Air, gas or vapor trapped in a pipe supplying a liquid.

AIR LOCKING (const.) air lock' ing: Weather stripping; any materials used to make a building airtight.

AIR POCKET (const.) air pock' et: An air space; a space in a concrete wall resulting from improper pouring.

AIR RESISTANCE (auto.) air re sist- ance: The resistance to the movement of a vehicle through air.

AIR SEASONED (const.) air sea' soned: See AIR DRIED.

AIR SHOWER (space) air show' er: A group of cosmic ray particles observed in the atmosphere.

AIR SLAKING (const.) air slak' ing: The exposure of quicklime to air for gradual absorption of moisture.

AIR SPACE (const.) air space: The space between the inner and outer walls of a building.

AIR STANDARD (air cond.) air stan'- dard: Air weighing .075 lb. per cu. ft. at 68 deg. F. dry bulb and containing 50 percent humidity at barometric pressure of 29.92 in. of mercury. Dry air at 70 deg. F. and the same pressure.

AIR TUNNEL (air cond.) air tun' nel: A refrigerated tunnel with forced air circulation for rapid cooling and freezing of products passed through it.

AIR WASHER (air cond.) air wash' er: A water spray system for washing and humidifying the air.

AISLE (const.) aisle: A passageway or walk between seats in a theater or a church.

ALABASTER (const.) al' a bas ter: A fine-grained white gypsum material.

ALBANY SAND (metal) al' ba ny sand: A sand used for molding.

ALBEDO (space) al be' do: A numerical ratio expressing the amount of electromagnetic radiation reflected by the body to the amount falling upon it.

ALBERTITE (const.) al' bert ite: A black asphalt found in Nova Scotia.

ALBUMEN PLATE (graphics) al bu'_men plate: A plate sensitized with bichromated egg solution used in lithography.

ALCOHOL (crafts) al' co hol: Ethyl hydroxide made from grain; C_2H_5OH.

ALCOHOL RESISTING (painting and dec.) al' co hol   re sist' ing: Showing no damage when in contact with alcohol.

ALCOVE (const.) al' cove: A recess opening off a room.

ALGAE (air cond.) al' gae: Minute fresh water plant growth.

ALIGNMENT (auto.) a lign' ment: The mechanical adjustment to bring parts in line; the adjustment of the front wheel suspension system to conform to certain specifications.

ALIGNMENT (elec.) a lign' ment: The adjustment of tuned circuits in amplifier and/or oscillator circuits so that they will produce a specified response at a given frequency.

ALIGNMENT (graphics) a lign' ment: When different size types are so justified that their faces all line up at the bottom.

ALIGNMENT CHART (draft.) A lign'_ment chart: See NOMOGRAPH.

ALIGNMENT TOOL(elec.) a lign' ment tool: A special non-conductive screwdriver-type tool for adjusting cores and capacitors during alignment of tuned circuits.

ALIPHATIC (painting and dec.) al i_phat' ic: Fatty; a class of organic compounds used as solvents.

ALIVE (graphics) a live': A printing term describing a form of type after it has been set and until it is ready to be distributed.

ALIZARIN (painting and dec.) a liz' a_rin: Pigment that is bright red with blue undertone, made by complicated chemical process.

ALIZARIN LAKE (painting and dec.) a liz' a rin lake: A red pigment made from the organic coal tar dyestuff, alizarin. The color is dark bluish-red. Some purple pigments are also marketed under this name.

ALKALINE BATTERY (elec.)al' ka line bat' ter y: A battery known as the Edison Cell that uses sodium or potassium hydroxide as an electrolyte and active plates of nickel-oxide flakes and powdered iron.

ALKYD (paint. and dec.) al' kyd: Resins made from phthalic acid or phthalic anhydride and glycerol. These resins are used in paints.

ALLEN SCREWS (metal) Al' len screws: Cap screws and setscrews with a hexagonal socket in the head. They are tightened with an Allen wrench or hexagonal key.

ALLEN WRENCH (auto.) Al' len wrench: A special wrench used for setscrews with a hexagonal recessed hole in the head.

ALLEY (const.) al' ley: A narrow passageway between two buildings.

ALLEY (graphics) al' ley: A walking or working space between facing type cabinets or case racks in the composing room.

ALLIGATOR CLIP (elec.) al' li ga tor clip: A spring activated clip for temporary wire connections. It resembles a miniature alligator's jaws.

ALLIGATORING (paint. and dec.) al'-li ga tor ing: Condition of paint film in which the surface is cracked and develops an appearance somewhat similar to skin on the back of an alligator.

ALLIGATOR WRENCH (metal) al' li ga-tor wrench: A wrench with toothed V-shaped jaws.

ALLOTROPIC (metal) al lo trop' ic: The phenomena of an element existing in two or more different forms.

ALLOWANCE (metal) al low' ance: An intentional difference in dimensions between mating parts.

ALLOY (metal) al' loy: A mixture of two or more metals; white metal; babbitt.

ALLOY STEEL (metal) al' loy steel: A steel alloyed with a small percentage of another metal such as manganese, nickel, tungsten vanadium, chromium, etc.

ALL-ROWLOCK WALL (const.) all-row' lock wall: A brick wall built with two courses entirely of stretchers on edge alternating with one course of headers on edge.

ALLUVIAL (const.) al lu' vi al: Sand and clay deposited by flowing water.

ALMANDITE (metal) al' man dite: Mineral garnet used as an abrasive.

ALNICO (elec.) al' ni co: A special alloy used to make small permanent magnets.

ALPHA (elec.) al' pha: Greek letter α, represents the current gain of a transistor. It is equal to the change in collector current caused by a change in emitter current for a constant collector voltage.

ALPHABET OF LINES (draft.) al' phabet of lines: The type and weight of lines used in drafting.

ALPHA CUT-OFF FREQUENCY (elec.) al' pha cut-off fre' quen cy: The frequency at which the current gain drops to .707 of its maximum gain.

ALPHA PARTICLE (elec.) al' pha par'-ti cle: The emission from a nuclear reaction consisting of two protons and two neutrons that is essentially a free helium nucleus.

ALPHA PARTICLE (space) al' pha par'-ti cle: A positively charged particle emitted from the nuclei of certain atoms during radioactive disintegration.

ALTERATION (const.) al ter a' tion: Any changes in the structural parts of a building without an increase in the cubical content of the building.

ALTERNATE POSITION (draft) al' ter-nate po si' tion: A drawing made of a moving part of an object to show the limits of movement. Outline of objects in alternate position is drawn with broken lines.

ALTERNATING CURRENT (elec.) al'-ter nat ing cur' rent (ac): A current of electrons that moves first in one direction and then in the other.

ALTERNATOR (elec.) al' ter na tor: An a-c generator.

ALTIMETER (space) al tim' e ter: An instrument that indicates altitudes by means of atmospheric pressure.

ALUMINA (metal) a lu' mi na: Triox-
ide of aluminum, AL_2O_3; an important
constituent of all clays, which determines their suitability for fire brick;
an abrasive.

ALUMINUM (metal) a lu' mi num: A
silvery-white and very light metal.
Used as an alloy and as an independent
metal. Symbol AL.

ALUMINUM LEAF (painting and doc.)
a lu' mi num leaf: Very thin hammered
or rolled aluminum sheets.

ALUMINUM OXIDE (painting and dec.)
a lu' mi num ox' ide: Hard and sharp
abrasive made by fusing mineral bauxite at high temperature.

ALUMINUM PAINT (painting and dec.)
a lu' mi num paint: Mixture of finely
divided aluminum particles in flake
form combined with vehicle.

ALUMINUM SILICATE (painting and
dec.) a lu' mi num sil' i cate: White
extender pigment made from China
clay, field-spar, etc., which provides
very little color or opacity.

AM (elec.) AM: Abbreviation for Amplitude Modulation.

AMALGAM (elec.) a mal' gam: A compound or mixture containing mercury.

AMALGAMATED LITHOGRAPHERS OF
AMERICA (graphics) A mal' ga mated Li thog' ra phers of America: A
trade union of journeymen lithographers.

AMALGAMATION (elec.) a mal ga ma'-
tion: The process of adding a small
quantity of mercury to zinc during
manufacture.

AMBER (elec.) am' ber: A yellowish
translucent fossil resin that becomes

electrified by friction with another
object.

AMBER & AMBER SCALE (automation)
Am' ber & Am' ber scale: A scale expressing the class or order of automation for A_0 to A_9, named for George
H. and Paul S. Amber, consulting engineers.

AMBIENT (space) am' bi ent: Environ-
mental conditions such as the pressure
or temperature.

AMBIENT AIR (air cond.) am' bi ent air:
The air surrounding a machine or device.

AMBIENT TEMPERATURE (elec.) am'-
bi ent tem' per a ture: The temperature of the surrounding air about a
component or device.

AMERICAN BOND (const.) A mer' i-
can bond: A method of laying bricks
in which every fifth, sixth and seventh
course consists of headers.

AMERICAN PROCESS ZINC OXIDE
(paint. and dec.) A mer' i can pro'-
cess zinc ox' ide: Zinc oxide pigment
made directly from zinc ores.

AMERICAN SCREW GAUGE (const.)
A mer' i can screw gauge: A standardized system of dimension for wood
screws and machine screws.

AMERICAN STANDARD PIPE THREADS

$E_0 = D - (0.050D + 1.1)p$
$E_1 = E_0 + 0.0625 L_1$
$L_2 = (0.80D + 6.8)p$
$H = 0.866p$

AMERICAN STANDARD PIPE THREADS (const.) A mer' i can stan' dard pipe threads: A standardized system of dimensioning steam, gas and water pipe threads. (See illustration, page 15.)

AMERICAN VERMILLION (paint.,dec.) A mer' i can ver mil' lion: Chrome orange pigment.

AMERICAN WIRE GAUGE (metal) A- mer' i can wire gauge: The accepted standard for sizing copper wire, brass wire, German silver wire and also the thickness of sheets of these materials. (Also Brown and Sharpe.)

AMES INSTRUMENT (draft.) Ames in'- stru ment: A device to produce letter- ing guide lines.

AMMETER (elec.) am' me ter: A meter used to measure current.

AM MODULATION, Types of, (elec.) am mod u la' tion:
GRID: Audio signal is applied in series with the grid of the power ampli- fier.
PLATE: Audio signal is injected into plate circuit of modulated stage.

AMMONIA (air cond.) am mon' i a: A colorless pungent gas, NH_3, composed of nitrogen and hydrogen. It is used extensively as a refrigerant.

AMORPHOUS (metal) a mor' phous: A material having no regular form or structure.

AMORTIZATION (const.) a mor ti za'- tion: The scheduled and progressive liquidation of a long-term debt or obligation.

AMPERE, Symbol I, (elec.) am' pere: Electron or current flow representing the flow of one coulomb per second past a given point in a circuit.

AMPERE, ANDRE MARIE (1775-1836) (elec.): The French scientist noted for his work in mathematics and electri- city. He made the distinction between electrostatics and electrodynamics and was one of the first scientists to con- ceive "currents" of electricity. He was a professor at the College de France in Paris.

AMPERE-HOUR (elec.) am' pere-hour: The capacity rating measurement of batteries. A 100 ampere-hour battery will produce, theoretically, 100 am- peres for one hour.

AMPERE-HOUR CAPACITY (auto.) am'- pere-hour ca pac' i ty: A term used to describe the capacity of a storage bat- tery. A 100 amp-hour battery theo- retically should supply 100 amperes for one hour.

AMPERE-HOUR METER (elec.) am'- pere-hour me' ter: Electrical instru- ment used to measure ampere hours.

AMPERE TURN (elec.) am' pere turn: Unit of measurement of magnetomotive force. Represents product of amperes times number of turns in coil of an electromagnet. F in Gilberts = 1.257 In. or 1.257 Ampere Turns.

AMPERITE TUBE (elec.) am' per ite tube; See BALLAST TUBE.

AMPERSAND (graphics) am' per sand: The character &; a sign meaning AND.

AMPLIDYNE (elec.) am' pli dyne: A synchro control system employing a dc generator in such a way that a small variation in the field current produces a great variation in power output; to operate an ac servomotor with suffi- cient torque to move a large load.

AMPLIFICATION (elec.) am pli fi ca'- tion: The ability to control a relatively large force by a small force. In a vacuum tube, a relatively small variation in grid input signal is accompanied by a relatively large variation in output signal.

AMPLIFICATION FACTOR (elec.) ampli fi ca' tion fac' tor: Expressed as μ (mu). The characteristic of a vacuum tube to amplify a voltage. The mu is equal to the change in plate voltage as a result of a change in grid voltage while the plate current is constant.

AMPLIFIERS, Types of, (elec.) am' pli fi ers:

AF: Used to amplify audio frequencies.

CLASS A: An amplifier, so biased that plate current flows during the entire cycle of input signal.

CLASS B: An amplifier, so biased that plate current flows for approximately one half the cycle of input signal.

CLASS C: An amplifier so biased that plate current flows for appreciably less than half of each cycle of applied signal.

CLASS AB: A compromise between class A and class B.

CLASS AB_1: Same as class AB, only grid is never driven positive and no grid current flows.

CLASS AB_2: Same as AB except that signal drives grid positive and grid current does flow.

DC: Directly coupled amplifiers used to amplify direct current.

IF: Used to amplify intermediate frequencies.

LINEAR: An amplifier which has a flat or uniform response over its frequency range.

MAGNETIC: An amplifier based upon the principle of core saturation of a transformer. The signal is applied in such a manner as to increase or decrease the saturation of the core and thus vary the output.

MONAURAL: A single channel amplification system.

POWER: An electron tube used to increase power output. Sometimes called a current amplifier.

PULSE: Used to amplify pluses.

RF: Used to amplify radio frequencies.

STEREOPHONIC: A binaural amplification system employing two amplifiers. Each amplifier is fed to its respective speakers placed several feet apart. By this method a more realistic sound reproduction is achieved by imparting a directional quality to the sound as it appears to originate from a source similar to that used during recording.

VIDIO: Used to amplify video frequencies.

VOLTAGE: An electron tube used to amplify a voltage.

AMPLITUDE (elec.) am' pli tude: The extreme range of a varying quantity. Size, height of.

AMPLITUDE MODULATION (elec.) am'-pli tude mod u la' tion (AM): Modulating a transmitter by varying the amplitude of the r-f carrier at an audio rate.

AMYL ACETATE (painting and dec.) am' yl ac' e tate: Solvent for nitrocellulose, formed by esterification of acetic acid with amyl alcohol. (Banana Oil.)

ANACOUSTIC ZONE (space) an a cous'-tic zone: The zone of silence in space; the region above 100 miles altitude.

ANALOG SIGNAL (automation) an' a log sig' nal: A signal used for computation and control. An analog signal is continuous in time and proportional to the variable it represents.

ANALOGOUS HARMONY (painting and dec.) a nal' o gous har' mo ny (related harmony): Colors which are related by containing one color in common.

ANALOGY (elec.) a nal' o gy: Comparison to a familiar practice or operation for purposes of clarification.

ANALYZER (auto.) an' a lyz er: A combination of automotive test instruments enclosed in a movable cart. Instruments diagnose troubles in charging circuits, engine and ignition efficiency and compression tests.

ANALYZER (elec.) an' a lyz er: A test instrument, usually combining several basic instruments, which may be quickly attached to specified type of electronic equipment. Many special purpose instruments have been designed to assist the technician in service and maintenance.

ANCHOR (elec.) an' chor: A rod or stake driven into the ground to which guy wires for a tower are attached.

ANCHOR BOLT (const.) an' chor bolt: A bolt, one end of which is imbedded in concrete. It is used to bolt wood and steel parts to the concrete.

AND CIRCUIT (elec.) and cir' cuit: A circuit with two or more inputs and all inputs must be present to produce an output signal.

ANEMOMETER (air cond.) an e mom'- e ter: An instrument used to measure the velocity of air or gas.

ANGEL (space) an' gel: A radar echo from some object not discernible to the human eye.

ANGLE (draft.) an' gle: A geometric figure formed by two lines meeting at a point.

ANGLE BRACE (const.) an' gle brace: A bar or support member across the inside angle in framework to stiffen the structure; a special tool used to hold and drive a wood bit when boring a hole in a corner.

ANGLE CLOSER (const.) an' gle clos'- er: Part of a brick used to close the bond of brickwork at a corner.

ANGLE DIVIDERS (wood.) an' gle divid' ers: A tool used for bisecting angles.

ANGLE FLOAT (const.) an' gle float: A plastering tool used to shape inside corners.

ANGLE GAUGE (const.) an' gle gauge: A tool used to set off and test angles.

ANGLE IRON (const.) an' gle iron: A piece of iron shaped like a right angle; L-shaped iron reinforcement.

ANGLE JOINT (const.) an' gle joint: Two structural members which meet at an angle.

ANGLE NEWEL (const.) an' gle newel: A newel post located at the angle of a well in a staircase.

ANGLE OF COMPENSATION (elec.) an' gle of com pen sa' tion: A correction angle applied to a compass reading to compensate for local magnetic influence.

ANGLE OF DECLINATION (elec.) an' gle of dec li na' tion: See DECLINATION.

ANGLE OF INCIDENCE (elec.) an' gle of in' ci dence: The angle between a beam of light striking a surface and an imaginary line perpendicular to the surface.

ANGLE OF LEAD OR LAG (elec.) an'-gle of lead or lag: The angle between voltage and current vectors describing an ac circuit expressed in degrees. Example: In a capacitive circuit the current leads the voltage by a certain angle.

ANGLE OF REFLECTION (elec.) an' gle of re flec' tion: The angle between the reflected beam of light from a surface and an imaginary line perpendicular to the surface. The angle of reflection is equal to the angle of incidence.

ANGLE OF REFRACTION (elec.) an' gle of re frac' tion: A light ray is bent slightly as it passes from one optical medium to another of different density. The angle between the refracted ray and the normal line perpendicular to the surface is the angle of refraction.

ANGLE PLATE (metal) an' gle plate: Accurately machined L-shaped blocks to support work at right angles to base.

ANGLE POST (const.) an' gle post: A newel post located in the angle of a staircase.

ANGLE TIE (const.) an' gle tie: See ANGLE BRACE.

ANGSTROM (space) ang' strom: A unit of length; ten billion angstroms equal one meter.

ANGULAR GEARS (metal) an' gu lar gears: Bevel gears designed to run at angles other than a right angle.

ANGULAR PHASE (elec.) an' gu lar phase: The position of a rotating vector in respect to a reference line.

ANGULAR VELOCITY (elec.) an' gu lar

ve loc' i ty: The speed of a rotating vector in radians per second. ω (omega) $= 2\pi f$.

ANHYDROUS (painting and dec.) an hy'-drous: Free from moisture.

ANHYDROUS LIME (const.) an hy' drous lime: Unslaked lime made from pure limestone; quicklime; common lime.

ANILINE (painting and dec.) an' i line: A colorless, oily poisonous liquid.

ANILINE COLORS (painting and dec.) an' i line col' ors: See ANILINE DYES.

ANILINE DYES (painting and dec.) an' i-line dyes: A synthetically produced dye from coal tar products.

ANION (elec.) an' i on: A negative ion; an ion which moves toward the positive electrode in electrolysis.

ANNEAL (metal) an neal': To soften metals by heating to remove internal stresses caused by rolling and forging.

ANNEALING (metal) an neal' ing: To soften metals by uniformly heating and cooling at predetermined rate.

ANNUAL RINGS (wood.) an' nu al rings: Rings or layers of wood which represent one growth period of a tree. In cross section the rings may be used to determine the age of the tree.

ANNULAR BALL BEARING (const.) an'-nu lar ball bear' ing: A bearing in which the balls are held in a ring type container.

ANNULET (const.) an' nu let: A ring-like molding encircling a column or capital.

ANNUNCIATOR (elec.) an nun' ci a tor: A remote communication device used to announce signals from a number of locations.

ANODE (elec.) an' ode: The positive terminal, such as the plate in the electron tube.

ANODIZE (metal) an' od ize: The process of protecting aluminum by oxidizing in an acid bath using a d-c current.

ANOXIA (space) an ox' i a: The complete lack of oxygen available for physiological use within the body.

ANTECHAMBER (const.) an' te chamber: A small connecting room to the main room; a waiting room; a vestibule.

ANTENNA (elec.) an ten' na: A device for radiating or receiving radio waves.

ANTENNA EFFICIENCY (elec.) an ten'-na ef fi' cien cy: The field strength produced at one mile along the ground by an antenna with one kilowatt input compared to the field strength in a standard reference antenna.

ANTENNA GAIN (elec.) an ten' na gain: The gain in the radiation effectiveness compared to a standard antenna.

ANTENNA POWER (elec.) an ten' na pow' er: The antenna resistance multiplied by the square of the antenna current.

ANTENNAS (elec.) an ten' nas, Types of:
  BEAM: An antenna made up of two or more horizontal elements spaced along a beam. Elements other than the radiator are reflectors and directors. This antenna is directional and a means of rotation is provided.
  CLOVER LEAF: An antenna with four curved elements at each layer resembling a four leaf clover.
  DIPOLE: A half-wave center-fed antenna. Since it is made up of two poles,

each one quarter wave in length, it is called a dipole.
  DUMMY: A resistor that duplicates the electrical characteristics of an antenna. It is a non-radiating device connected to a transmitter during tune-up and adjustment.
  HERTZ: An antenna one-half wave length long or any even multiple thereof.
  HORIZONTALLY POLARIZED: An antenna whose radiation elements are parallel to the ground.
  LOOP: A closed circuit antenna formed by one or more loops of wire so that its ends are close together.
  MARCONI: A grounded antenna whose length is one-quarter wave or any odd multiple.
  PARABOLIC: A disk shaped reflector antenna used at microwave frequencies. Its principle of operation is similar to a light. The light source is replaced by a small dipole antenna.
  RHOMBIC: Four long wire radiating elements arranged in the shape of a rhombus.
  SUPER-TURNSTILE: A more efficient antenna made up of sheets of radiating elements arranged turnstile fashion. It radiates efficiently a wide band of frequencies and is ideal for TV transmitters.
  TURNSTILE: A non-directional antenna made up of a number of dipoles arranged as turnstiles in a baseball park. The dipoles are assembled in spaced layers on a vertical tower or mast.
  VERTICALLY POLARIZED: An antenna whose radiating element is perpendicular to the ground.

ANTI-CORROSIVE PAINT (painting and dec.) an' ti-cor ro' sive paint: Metal paint designed to inhibit corrosion. Applied directly to the metal.

ANTI-FLOODING AGENT (painting and dec.) an' ti-flood' ing a' gent: A synthetic organic product used to reduce floating and flooding of iron blues, carbon blacks, chrome greens, etc.

ANTIFOULING PAINT (painting and dec.) an' ti foul' ing paint: A special coating for ship bottoms. It contains poison like copper or mercury, formulated to release the poison at a controlled rate, to prevent attachment and growth of marine organisms such as barnacles and algae.

ANTIFREEZE (auto.) an' ti freeze: Solution added to water in cooling system to lower freezing temperature.

ANTI-G SUIT (space) an' ti-g suit: A tight flying suit that covers parts of body below the heart and is designed to retard the flow of blood to the lower body in reaction to acceleration or deceleration. An antiblackout suit.

ANTIGRAVITY (space) an' ti grav' i ty: Effect upon masses, such as rocket vehicles and human bodies by which some (still-to-be-discovered) energy field would cancel or reduce gravitational attraction of earth.

ANTIHUNT DEVICE (elec.) an' ti hunt de vice': A device or circuit used to prevent hunting.

ANTIKNOCK VALUE (auto.) an' ti knock val' ue: The grading of engine fuels according to their ability to perform without knocking; the octane number of a gasoline.

ANTIMISSILE MISSILE (space) an' ti-mis sile mis' sile: A defensive missile launched to intercept and destroy other missiles in flight.

ANTIMONIAL LEAD (metal) an' ti mo-ni al lead: An alloy of 90 to 95 percent lead and 5 to 10 percent antimony. Used for storage battery plates.

ANTIMONY (graphics) an' ti mo ny: A metallic element used to give hardness to type. Antimony does not contract when cooled, thus giving a sharp outline to a letter.

ANTIMONY (metal) an' ti mo ny: A bluish-white, hard crystalline metallic element. Symbol Sb. It is mostly used as an alloy. When alloyed with tin or lead, it gives hardness.

ANTIMONY OXIDE (painting and dec.) an' ti mo ny ox' ide: Pure white pigment that provides about the same hiding power as lithopone.

ANTINODE (elec.) an' ti node: A point on a waveform of maximum current or voltage.

ANTIPERCOLATOR (auto.) an' ti per'-co la tor: A small vent in the high speed circuit of a carburetor to relieve vapor pressure caused by excessive heat.

ANTIQUE (graphics) an tique': The name of a heavy Roman type of even thickness and heavy serifs; a finish on paper that has little or no calendering.

ANTIQUE (painting and dec.) an tique': Furniture finishing technique intended to give appearance of age or wear.

ANTIQUE FINISH (graphics) an tique' fin' ish: A low finish on paper described as rough, soft, uneven and with little calendering.

ANTISATELLITE MISSILE (space an'-ti sat' el lite mis' sile: A missile designed to destroy an orbiting satellite.

ANTISKINNING AGENT (painting and dec.) an' ti skin' ning a' gent: A synthetic organic product, used to prevent forming of surface skin in packaged varnishes and paints.

ANTISYPHON TRAP (const.) an' ti sy-
phon trap: A trap used in a sink drain
with sealing ability increased by enlarging the volume of water in the trap
by means of a bowl or tank.

ANVIL (metal) an' vil: A heavy block of
steel or iron for use as a hammering
or forging work surface.

APERIODIC (elec.) a pe ri od' ic: Occuring at irregular intervals.

APERTURE (const.) ap' er ture: An
opening in a wall for a door or window.

APERTURE (elec.) ap' er ture: A gap;
opening; passage.

APERTURE MASK (elec.) ap' er ture
mask: A thin sheet of perforated material placed directly behind the viewing screen in a three-gun color picture
tube.

APEX (const.) a' pex: The topmost point
in any structure.

APEX STONE (const.) a' pex stone: The
triangular stone at the apex of a gabled
wall.

APHELION (space) aph e' lion: Point on
an elliptical orbit around the sun that
is farthest from the sun. (The earth's
aphelion is about 94,500,000 miles from
the sun.)

APOGEE (space) ap' o gee: The point
or position at which a moon or an
artificial satellite in its orbit is farthest from its primary.

APPARENT POWER (elec.) ap par' ent
pow' er: The power apparently used in
a circuit as the product of current
times voltage.

APPLIANCES (elec.) ap pli' an ces: A
general term describing the many electric labor-saving devices used around
the home such as washers, mixers,
toasters, etc.

APPRENTICE ap pren' tice: A beginner
in a trade, usually serving several
years as a helper to a journeyman.

APPRENTICESHIP ap pren' tice ship:
The period of training for a skilled
trade; a period of employment during
which the employer promises to teach
an employee the fundamental skills of
a trade.

APRON (const.) a' pron: A part of the
interior trim of a window. It is placed
beneath the stool.

APRON (metal) a' pron: The lower part
of the lathe carriage, containing the
gears and locking mechanisms to control the feed.

AQUA DAG (elec.) aq' ua dag: A colloidal suspension of graphite in water;
the deposit or carbon coating on the
glass envelope of a vacuum tube or CRT
for shielding the electrodes from light,
absorption of heat or collecting stray
electrons.

AQUA REGIA (crafts) aq' ua re' gi a: A
mixture of hydrochloric and nitric acid.

AQUASTAT (const.) aq' ua stat: A ther-
mostatic device for controlling the temperature of water.

AQUEDUCT (const.) aq' ue duct: A water
conductor made of masonry, channels or
pipes through which water is supplied
to a community.

AQUEOUS (const.) aq' ue ous: Watery.

ARABESQUE (const.) ar' a besque: An
ornamentation of plants, fruit, figures
of men and animals, carved or painted
in low relief; a decorative design of
interlocking curves.

ARABIC NUMERAL (graphics) ar' a bic nu' mer al: Any figure between one and ten.

ARBOR (const.) ar' bor: A latticework archway.

ARBOR PRESS (metal) ar' bor press: A mechanical press for straightening work in auto, farm and machine shops. The work is supported on blocks or V-blocks and the press applies extreme force at the point to be bent.

ARC (draft.) arc: A part of a circle.

ARC (welding) arc: Term given to the flow of electricity through a gaseous space or air gap. In arc welding, it is this flow of electricity through the air which produces high temperatures.

ARCADE (const.) ar cade' : A passageway having an arched roof.

ARCBACK (elec.) arc' back: Current flowing the opposite direction in a diode, when the plate has a high negative voltage.

ARC BLOW (welding) arc blow: Tendency for an arc to wander or whip from its normal course during arc welding.

ARC CUTTING (welding) arc cut' ting: Cutting metal by means of an electric arc, generally using carbon electrodes.

ARCH (const.) arch: A curved structure supported at its ends.

ARCH BRICK (const.) arch brick: Wedge shaped bricks used in constructing arches and curved masonry work.

ARCHIMEDEAN PRINCIPLE (const.) ar- chi me' de an prin' ci ple: A body wholly or partially submerged in a liquid is buoyed up by a force equal to the weight of the liquid displaced.

ARCHITECT (const.) ar' chi tect: A professional person skilled in the design the preparation of plans and the supervision of building construction.

ARCHITRAVE (const.) ar' chi trave: Wooden casing or trim around a door or window; a beam resting on columns.

ARCING (elec.) arc' ing: The forming of an electric arc across contacts of a switch or of motor or generator brushes.

ARC-JET ENGINE (space) arc-jet en'-gine: A rocket engine in which the propellant gas is heated by passing through an electric arc.

ARC VOLTAGE (welding) arc volt' age: Electrical potential (pressure or voltage) across the arc.

ARC WELDING (metal) arc weld' ing: Welding by means of an electrode and an electric current. The electric arc is produced by bringing the electrode In contact with work and then separated a distance such that the current continued to flow through the gaseous medium between the electrode and the work. Electric energy is transformed into heat at the arc and is concentrated within a small area.

AREA (const.) ar' e a: An open court or section of ground designated for a special purpose such as a play area.

AREAWAY (const.) a' re a way: A space around the foundation walls of a building to permit light and air to reach the basement.

ARGON (elec.) ar' gon: A colorless inert gas. It is used to fill electric incandescent lamps. It is present in ordinary air to the extent of .9 percent.

ARITHMETIC UNIT (elec.) a rith' me-tic u' nit: The section of a computer that performs the arithmetic operations.

ARMATURE (elec.) ar' ma ture: The revolving part in a generator or a motor. The vibrating or moving part of a relay or buzzer.

ARMATURE REACTION (elec.) ar' mature re ac' tion: The effect on the main field of a generator by the armature acting as an electromagnet.

ARMATURE SLOTS (elec.) ar' ma ture slots: Slots, channels or pockets in an armature to hold the windings.

ARMATURE SPIDER (elec.) ar' ma ture spider: A framework to support the shaft of a motor or generator armature. The bearings are held in the center of the radial spider.

ARMATURE VARNISH (elec.) ar' mature var' nish: Special insulating varnish applied to generator and motor windings to hold them in place and protect them from moisture.

ARMORED CABLE (elec.) ar' mored ca' ble: See BX CABLE.

ARMSTRONG, EDWIN HOWARD (1890-1954) (elec.): A famous American inventor in the field of radio. He is famous for feedback oscillating circuits that improved radio sensitivity, the superheterodyne receiver and FM radio.

AROMATIC (painting and dec.) ar o-mat' ic: Derived from or belonging to a major class of organic compounds, many of which are useful as solvents.

ARRIS (const.) ar' ris: The point at which two surfaces meet to form an angle, such as the edge of a board.

ARRL (elec.): Abbreviation for the American Radio Relay League. It is the parent organization of the radio amateurs of the U. S. and Canada and the publisher of QST magazine. It serves as a voice in legal aspects of operation and experimentation in radio for the amateur. It renders public service by training and organizing amateur communications during emergencies.

ART GUM (draft.) art gum: An eraser in drafting.

ARTIFICER ar tif' i cer: An inventor; a man skilled in the use of tools.

ARTIFICIAL MAGNETS (elec.) ar ti-fi' cial mag' nets: Man-made magnets.

ARTISAN ar' ti san: A craftsman; a man who makes things with tools.

ART METAL HAMMERS (metal) art met' al ham' mers: The variety of special hammers used in art metal work for chasing, forming, planishing and raising.

ART METAL (metal) art met' al: The processes and skills involved in shaping metal artistically; artistic work using nonferrous metals such as copper, brass and silver.

ART METAL STAKES (metal) art metal stakes: Steel stakes made in a

variety of shapes and sizes on which nonferrous metals are shaped and finished.

ASA (draft.): Abbreviation for American Standards Association.

ASBESTINE (painting and dec.) as bes-tine: Having the properties of asbestos; natural fibrous white magnesium silica used as an extender pigment in paints.

ASBESTOS (const.) as bes' tos: A min-eral fiber; a silicate of calcium and magnesium that occurs in long thread-like fibers.

ASBESTOS PAPER (const.) as bes' tos pa' per: An asbestos building paper that will not burn and is a poor con-ductor of heat.

ASBESTOS SHINGLES (const.) as bes'-tos shin' gles: Shingles made of Port-land cement and asbestos.

ASCENDER (graphics) as cend' er: The part of a lower case letter that extends above the body of the letter. The letters b, d, f, h, k, l, and t have ascenders.

ASH (wood.) ash (Fraximus Americana): An extremely tough and elastic wood. It is straight grained, heavy, hard and strong and has excellent bending quali-ties. Ideal for tool handles and athletic equipment.

ASH DUMP (const.) ash dump: A cov-ered opening in the bottom of a fire-place for disposal of ashes. Ashes usually fall into a pit at the base of the chimney and may be removed from an outside door.

ASHLAR BRICK (const.) ash' lar brick: Brick which is made to resemble stone on its face.

ASHLAR MASONRY (const.) ash' lar ma-son ry: Walls built with stone prepared by sawing, dressing and facing.

ASPECT RATIO (elec.) as' pect ra' tio: The ratio of the width to the height of a TV picture. This is standardized as 4:3.

ASPECT RATIO (air cond.) as' pect ra-tio: The relationship between the width and depth in a rectangular air duct.

ASPEN (const.) as' pen: A species of tree commercially valuable as pulp in the manufacturing of paper.

ASPHALT (const.) as' phalt: A mineral pitch used as a waterproofing mater-ial. It is extensively used in construc-tion on roofs, exterior walls and in paints.

ASPHALT (painting and dec.) as' phalt: Black solid bitumen found naturally. Also the residue from distillation of petroleum.

ASPHALT MASTIC (const.) as' phalt mas' tic: A paste-like material made of asphalt and other mineral materials.

ASPHALT ROOFING (const.) as' phalt roof' ing: A roofing material made by saturating an asbestos or rag felt with asphalt.

ASPHALTUM (const.) as phal' tum: A black tar-like substance found in its natural state or by evaporating petro-leum.

ASPHALTUM VARNISH (const.) as-phal' tum var' nish: A black fast-dry-ing varnish, used principally for its ability to resist heat and acids.

ASPIRATION (air cond.) as pi ra' tion: The movement of a liquid by suction.

ASSEMBLY (automation) as sem' bly: The fitting together of individual parts to make a fabricated product.

ASSEMBLY DRAWING (draft.) as sem'-bly draw' ing: A drawing showing vari-our parts of a machine assembled in their relative positions.

ASTEROID (space) as' ter oid: One of many thousands of minor planets which revolve around the sun between the orbits of Mars and Jupiter.

ASTM (auto.): American Society for Testing Materials.

ASTRAGAL (const.) as' tra gal: A small convex or beaded molding used to cover the joint between two doors.

ASTRIONICS (space) as tri on' ics: The science of adapting electronics to aerospace flight.

ASTROBIOLOGY (space) as tro' bi ol_o gy: A branch of biology concerned with the discovery and study of life on planets.

ASTROGATION (space) as tro ga' tion: Navigating in space.

ASTRONAUT (space) as' tro naut: One who flies or navigates through space.

ASTRONAUTICS (space) as tro' nautics: The art or science of designing, building or operating space vehicles.

ASTYLAR (const.) a sty' lar: Having no columns or pilasters; a plain wall.

A_SUPPLY (elec.) a_sup' ply: Voltages supplied for heater circuits of electron tubes.

ASYMMETRICAL (elec.) a sym met' rical: A multivibrator producing unequal waves from each tube due to unequal conduction periods.

ASYNCHRONOUS (elec.) a syn' chronous: Out of step or phase; not having the same frequency.

AT_CUT CRYSTAL (elec.) at_cut crys'_tal: A crystal cut at approximately a 35 deg. angle with the Z axis.

ATLAS (space) At' las: An Air Force strategic bombardment missile whose range is 5,500 nautical miles. The Atlas, America's first intercontinental ballistic missile, had its first successful flight, using North American liquid rocket engines in August, 1958.

ATMOSPHERE (space) at' mo sphere: The envelope of gases which surrounds the earth and certain other planets.

ATMOSPHERICS (elec.) at mo spher'_ics: Interference to communication resulting from static electricity in the atmosphere.

ATOM (elec.) at' om: The smallest particle that makes up an element, a type of matter.

ATOMIC ARC WELDING (welding) a tom' ic arc' weld' ing: An arc welding process in which the welding heat is created by hydrogen becoming atomic hydrogen as it passes through the electric arc and then being converted back to molecular hydrogen. The hydrogen also forms a shield over the weld and prevents oxidation.

ATOMIC CLOCK (space) a tom' ic clock: A precision clock that is operated by an electrical oscillator and regulated by the natural vibration frequency of an atomic system.

ATOMIC HYDROGEN WELDING (welding) a tom' ic hy' dro gen weld' ing: Electric welding done in an atmosphere of hydrogen.

ATOMIC NUMBER (elec.) a tom' ic number: The number of protons in the nucleus of a given atom.

ATOMIC WEIGHT (elec.) a tom' ic weight: The mass of the nucleus of an atom in reference to oxygen, which has weight of 16.

ATOMIZATION (auto.) at' om i za tion: The process of spraying or breaking up a liquid into small particles.

ATOMIZE (air cond.) at' om ize: To reduce a liquid to a fine spray.

ATRIUM (const.) a' tri um: The central court or main room of a Roman house.

ATTENUATION (elec.) at ten u a' tion: A decrease in amplitude or intensity.

ATTENUATOR (elec.) at ten' u a tor: Networks of resistance used to reduce voltage, power or current to a load.

ATTIC (const.) at' tic: The part of a building immediately below the roof.

ATTIC FAN (air cond.) at' tic fan: An exhaust fan in the upper part of a building used for cooling the building by discharging the warm air.

ATTIC STORY (const.) at' tic sto' ry: The top story of a building which encloses the attic space.

ATTITUDE (space) at' ti tude: The position or orientation of a space craft.

ATTITUDE JETS (space) at' ti tude jets: Sometimes called steering jets, attitude control jets, or roll, pitch and yaw jets.

AUDIO (elec.) au' di o: Pertaining to sound.

AUDIO FREQUENCY (elec.) au' di o fre' quen cy: Frequencies to which the human ear responds. Frequencies up to 30,000 cps. are classified as audio although humans cannot hear vibrations exceeding 18,000 cps. (approx.).

AUDIOMETER (elec.) au di om' e ter: An instrument used to measure the intensity of sound waves.

AUDION (elec.) au' di on: The name of the first triode vacuum tube invented by Dr. Lee deForest.

AUGER BIT (wood) au' ger bit: A spiral

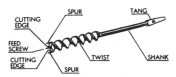

shaped tool with screwpoint and cutting lips for boring holes in wood.

AURAL (elec.) au' ral: Pertaining to sound.

AURAL TRANSMITTER (elec.) au' ral trans mit' ter: The transmitter in a TV station which broadcasts the sound information.

AURORA (space) au ro' ra: Commonly known as the northern and southern lights. A high altitude air glow caused by solar particles, predominantly protons, moving as charged particles in the earth's magnetic field and interacting with the earth's atmosphere.

AUSTENITE (metal) aus' ten ite: The transformed state of Pearlite above the decalescence point.

AUTHOR'S CORRECTIONS (graphics) au' thor's cor rec' tions: Changes and corrections made by author after composition errors have been corrected.

AUTODYNE RECEIVER (elec.) au' to-dyne re ceiv' er: A radio receiver circuit that employs a detector and an oscillator. The output signal is the difference signal between tuned signal and the oscillator frequency.

AUTOMATIC CHOKE (auto.) au to mat'-ic choke: A carburetor choke, usually controlled by engine temperature and vacuum.

AUTOMATIC COGNITION (automation) au to mat' ic cog ni' tion: The ability of a machine to recognize multiple conditions affecting its product. A machine's awareness to variables that affect its product.

AUTOMATIC FEEDER (graphics) au to mat' ic feed' er: A mechanical device for feeding paper at regular intervals into a printing press.

AUTOMATICITY A_0 (automation) au to ma tic' i ty: Zero order of automaticity, such as hand tools that always require human energy and brain control.

AUTOMATICITY A_1 (automation) au to ma tic' i ty: Powered machines are classified as first order of automaticity. Machines provide most of the energy for doing the work. Man's effort includes starting and stopping the machine, positioning the machine and the work, and frequently guiding and feeding the machine.

AUTOMATICITY A_2 (automation) au to ma tic' i ty: The second order of automaticity includes semi-automatic machines in which a single cycle of operations are performed without human interference. A coin operated, soft drink machine is an example.

AUTOMATICITY A_3 (automation) au to ma tic' i ty: A class of machines that are fully automated and can be entirely self acting for an extended period of time. These machines reload and recycle automatically.

AUTOMATICITY A_4 (automation) au to ma tic' i ty: A class of automated machines employing feedback systems so that the machine monitors its own performance and makes its own corrections. These machines make simple decisions.

AUTOMATICITY A_5 (automation) au to ma tic' i ty: Machines in this classification are computer controlled. The computer can sense several or more conditions that may affect the operation of the machine. Dependent and independent factors can be properly related. This class of machine possesses an awareness of the multiple conditions affecting its output.

AUTOMATICITY A_6 (automation) au to ma tic' i ty: This higher order of automation includes machines that learn by experience and attain their production goals by several different methods. Not yet a practical machine.

AUTOMATICITY A_7 (automation) au to ma tic' i ty: Machines capable of reasoning. Machines that would produce a planned operation as a result of known responses. It would program itself in response to past occurrences and operating variables. Not yet practical.

AUTOMATICITY A_8 (automation) au to ma tic' i ty: A class of machines that exhibit creativity. Such a machine could produce an original product when information is fed to the machine in general characteristics rather than specifics. Not yet practical.

AUTOMATICITY A_9 (automation) au to ma tic' i ty: This highest order of automaticity is called dominance and exceeds the ability of man. In science fiction only.

AUTOMATICITY SUPERSCRIPT (automation) au to ma tic' i ty su' per script: Indicates the intensity or degree of automation. Ex: $A^{3/8}$ indicates a machine has eight operations, three of which are automatic.

AUTOMATIC RESET (automation) au to mat' ic re' set: A self-correction operation of a machine by means of feedback.

AUTOMATIC SHIFT (auto.) au to mat'- ic shift: A transmission gear control in which gears are changed automat- ically to match the power and speeds required.

AUTOMATIC SPARK CONTROL (auto.) au to mat' ic spark con trol' : A me- chanical or vacuum control on the spark advance of an internal combustion en- gine, to match the change of speeds of the engine.

AUTOMATIC SURVEILLANCE (automa- tion) au to mat' ic sur veil' lance: The capability of a machine to oversee some of its operations as well as perform them.

AUTOMATIC WELDING (welding) au to- mat' ic weld' ing: Welding in which the work, the torch, and/or the arc is mechanically moved and controls are used to control the speed and/or the direction of travel.

AUTOMATION (automation) au to ma'- tion: A method or process of con- trolling and operating mechanical ma- chines by other than human manpower. Such operations include adjustment, feeding, production, movement and quality control of parts and materials.

AUTOMATION (elec.) au to ma' tion: An industrial technique of employing automatic self controlled machinery to replace human labor and control.

AUTOMATION SHOCK (automation) au- to ma' tion shock: The shock to em- ployees and management resulting from a fast radical change-over to auto- mation.

AUTOMATON au tom' a ton: A robot; a mechanical man.

AUTO MECHANICS (auto.) au' to me- chan' ics: The science of repair and maintenance of automobiles.

AUTO - QC (automation) auto - QC: Automatic Quality Control.

AUTOSYN (elec.) au' to syn: The trade name of a device that transmits me- chanical motion from one location to another by means of electricity.

AUTOTRANSFORMER (elec.) au to- trans form' er: A transformer with a common primary and secondary wind- ing. Step-up or step-down action is accomplished by taps on the common winding.

AUXILIARY AIR INTAKE (auto.) aux- il' ia ry air in' take: An air intake on a carburetor that provides additional air for high speed operation.

AUXILIARY VIEW (draft.) aux il' ia ry view: An additional view of parts of an object that are inclined to be one of the coordinate planes made by a pro- jection on a plane parallel to the in- clined surface of the object.

AVC (elec.) avc: Automatic volume control.

AVERAGE VALUE (elec.) av' er age val' ue: That value of alternating cur- rent or voltage of sine waveform that is found by dividing the area under one alternation by the distance along the X axis between 0 and 180 deg.
$$E_{avg} = .637 E_{max}$$

AVIARY (const.) a' vi ar y: An enclo- sure for keeping birds.

AVIONICS (elec.) a vi on' ics: A term used to designate aviation electronics.

AVODIRE (wood.) av o di re' : A fine cabinet wood from western Africa. It is dull white to golden cream in color with beautiful grain.

AWG (elec.): American Wire Gauge, used in sizing wire by numbers.

AWL (wood.) awl: A sharp pointed tool anchored in a handle. Used for scribing and marking holes.

AWL

AWL HAFT (const.) awl haft: The handle of an awl.

AXES (draft) ax' es: Plural of axis.

AXIAL LEADS (elec.) ax' i al leads: Leads connected on the axis of a component part.

AXIS (draft.) ax' is: An imaginary line around which parts rotate or are regularly arranged.

AXIS OF A WELD (welding) ax' is of a weld: An imaginary line along the center of gravity of the weld metal and perpendicular to a cross section of the weld metal.

AXLE (auto.) ax' le: A shaft on which wheels are mounted, such as an automobile axle.

AXONOMETRIC PROJECTION (draft.) ax o no met' ric pro jec' tion: An orthographic projection of an object tilted to show three faces of the object.

AZUSA (space) a zu' sa: A short range tracking system that gives position and velocity of an object being tracked.

B (elec.): Symbol for magnetic flux density.

b (elec.): Symbol for susceptance in an ac circuit; the reciprocal of reactance.

BABBITT (auto.) bab' bitt: An alloy of tin, antimony, copper and lead, used as a bearing material.

BACKBAND (const.) back' band: A molding used in carpentry to cover the joint between a wood frame and a masonry wall; the outer molding on the interior trim of a window or door.

BACK EDGE (graphics) back edge: The rear edge of a sheet as it goes through the press.

BACK EMF (elec.): See COUNTER EMF.

BACKFILL (const.) back' fill: To replace earth after excavation.

BACK FILLET (const.) back fil' let: The finished end of a projecting molding which returns the molding to the wall.

BACKFIRE (auto.) back' fire: The ignition of the air-fuel mixture in the intake manifold, usually caused by a leaking valve.

BACKFIRE (welding) back' fire: A short "pop" of the torch flame followed by extinguishing of the flame or continued burning of the gases.

BACKFLOW (plumb.) back' flow: The flow of water or liquids into a drinking water supply from some other nonintended source.

BACKFLOW VALVE (plumb.) back' flow valve: A device in the drainage system to prevent reversal of flow.

BACK GEARS (metal) back gears: A gear box to reduce the speed of the spindle in relation to the cone pulley.

BACKHAND WELDING (welding) backhand weld' ing: Welding in the direction opposite the direction the gas flame is pointing.

BACK HEARTH (const.) back hearth: The section of a fireplace hearth on which the fire is built.

BACKING (const.) back'ing: Broken stones and rubble used behind a finish facing on a masonry wall; nailing strips on walls and partitions for nailing the ends of plaster lath in corners.

BACKING (welding) back'ing: Some material placed on the root side of a weld to aid control of penetration.

BACKING BRICK (const.) back'ing brick: Usually cheaper bricks used in a wall in its center, behind the face.

BACKING LAMP (auto.) back'ing lamp: A backup light; a light at the rear of an automobile which turns on when the car is placed in reverse.

BACKING OFF (metal) back'ing off: To remove metal from behind the cutting edge of a machine cutting tool to reduce friction.

BACKING UP (const.) back'ing up: The use of cheaper bricks in the back side of a brick wall.

BACKLASH (metal) back'lash: The amount of lost motion between a freely revolving screw and a nut.

BACKOUT (space) back'out: Reverse countdown; undoing things already done in reverse order.

BACK PAINTING (const.) back paint'ing: To paint the unexposed surface of lumber before installation to protect against moisture.

BACK PORCH (TV SIGNAL) (elec.): The part of the pedestal blanking pulse after the sync pulse.

BACK PRESSURE (plumb.) back pres'sure: Pressure in drainage pipes greater than atmospheric pressure.

"BACK PRIMED" (painting and dec.) back primed: When a coat of paint is applied to the back of woodwork or exterior siding to prevent moisture from entering the wood.

BACK PUTTYING (const.) back put'tying: The filling of any space with putty after a sash has been face puttied.

BACK-RAKE (metal) back-rake: The angle a cutting tool slopes back from its nose.

BACKREST (metal) back'rest: A support placed behind long slender work in a lathe to prevent vibration or bending due to cutting pressure.

BACKSAW (wood) back'saw: A short crosscut saw with a stiff metal back. Used for accurate and precise cutting.

BACKSET (const.) back'set: In a lock set, it is the distance between the face of the lock and the center line through the knob or keyhole.

BACK SIPHONAGE (plumb) back'siphonage: Pressure in plumbing pipes less than atmospheric pressure; negative pressure.

BACK-STEP WELDING (welding) back-step weld'ing: A method of welding small sections of a joint in a direction opposite to the direction the weld is progressing.

BACKUP (const.) back'up: Material used behind the exterior facing of a masonry wall.

BACKUP (graphics) back'up: To print on the back side of an already printed sheet.

BACK VENT (plumb.) back vent: A vent pipe in a plumbing drainage system to relieve pressures above or below atmospheric pressure.

BACKWARD WELDING (welding) backward weld'ing: See BACKHAND WELDING.

BACK WAVE (elec.) back wave: An improper emission of a continuous wave transmitter while in the off position due to incorrectly neutralized amplifier circuits.

BADGER (const.) bad'ger: A tool used to clean out excess mortar at the joints of a newly laid drain.

BAFFLE (auto.) baf'fle: A plate, reflector or obstruction for checking and deflecting the flow of air, gases and sound.

BAFFLE (elec.) baf'fle: A partition or device in a loudspeaker cabinet to prevent the sound wave from the back of the speaker from cancelling the wave from the front of the speaker.

BAIL (graphics) bail: On a platen press, either of the metal bands hinged on the upper and lower edges of the platen which serve to hold the sheets of the tympan in place.

BAKELITE (const.) ba'ke lite: The trade name for a plastic material made by chemical condensation of phenol and formaldehyde.

BAKELITE (painting and dec.) ba'ke-lite: A synthetic resin made from formaldehyde and phenol; a registered trade name for phenolic resins.

BAKER-NUNN CAMERA (space) ba'-ker-nunn cam'er a: A large camera used in tracking satellites.

BAKING FINISHES (painting and dec.) bak'ing fin'ish es: Baking at elevated temperatures improves certain types of coatings used on metal articles, such as automobiles and refrigerators, etc. Baking may be done in an oven, under infrared lamps, or by induction heating according to the demands of shape, space, and other requirements.

BAKING JAPAN (painting and dec.) bak'-ing ja pan': An enamel in which artificial heat is used to attain maximum hardness and toughness of film.

BALANCE (graphics) bal'ance: Type composition when its various parts are so grouped that they are equalized in mass.

BALANCED AMPLIFIER (elec.) bal'-anced am'pli fi er: An amplifier employing two tubes as a push-pull or as a push-push amplifier.

BALANCED CIRCUIT (elec.) bal'anced cir'cuit: A circuit so adjusted that equal voltages appear across its branches or equal currents flow through its branches.

BALANCED MODULATOR (elec.) bal'-anced mod'u la tor: A modulator using two tubes in push-pull or push-push in which the carrier frequency is canceled and the output contains only the sum and difference frequencies of the carrier and the audio modulating signal.

BALANCE, STATIC (metal) bal'ance, stat'ic: The distribution of weight around a shaft so that it will remain in any position and not turn if supported on knife edge balancing ways.

BALANCE WHEEL (auto.) bal'ance wheel: A flywheel; a wheel in which energy of motion due to the weight insures smooth and regular motion of an engine.

BALANCING COIL (auto.) bal' anc ing coil: An electrical indicating device based upon the deflection of an indicating needle between two electromagnets. The electrical resistance of the sensing unit determines the current through the electromagnets and the position of the indicator.

BALCONET (const.) bal' co net: A small ornamental railing placed outside the sill of a window or door.

BALCONY (const.) bal' co ny: A porch-like projection from the face of a building. It may or may not be supported by columns. It is usually surrounded by a balustrade.

BALK (const.) balk: A large squared timber.

BALL AND CLAW (wood.) ball and claw: A decorative foot for a piece of furniture representing a ball grasped by a claw.

BALLAST (const.) bal' last: Gravel or broken stone fill.

BALLAST TUBE (elec.) bal' last tube: An iron wire enclosed in a hydrogen-filled envelope, used for voltage regulation.

BALL BEARING (auto.) ball bear' ing: Anti-friction bearing employing hardened steel balls between two races.

BALL CATCH (const.) ball catch: A door catch which holds the door closed by means of a small spring loaded ball engaging with the striking plate.

BALL-CHECK VALVE (plumb.) ball-check valve: A valve which permits flow in one direction only. Flow is

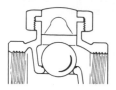

checked by a ball resting on a ground seat.

BALL COCK (plumb.) ball cock: A flow control valve or faucet depending upon the controlled rise and fall of a ball.

BALL CRANK (metal) ball crank: A crank shaped handle for manual movement of cutting tools, slides and tables.

BALLISTIC MISSILE (space) bal lis' tic mis' sile: Any missile which does not rely on aerodynamic surfaces for lift and which utilizes reaction propulsion as a power source.

BALLISTIC MISSILE EARLY WARNING SYSTEM (BMEWS) (space): The Ballistic Missile Early Warning System which the Air Force provides the North American Air Defense Command. It is an electronic system to provide detection and early warning of attack by enemy intercontinental ballistic missiles.

BALLISTIC MISSILE INTERCEPTOR (space) bal lis' tic mis' sile in ter-cep' tor: An interceptor, specifically, an explosive rocket missile, designed to home upon and destroy, a ballistic missile in flight.

BALLISTICS (space) bal lis' tics: The science or art that deals with the motion, behavior, appearance, or modification of missiles or other vehicles acted upon by propellants, wind, gravity, temperature or any other modifying substance, condition or force.

BALL JOINT (plumb.) ball joint: A flexible type joint in which a ball is held in a cup-like shell.

BALLOON FRAMING (const.) bal loon' fram' ing: A system of house framing in which all vertical structural elements extend from the sill to the roof plate.

BALLOON TIRE (auto.) bal' loon tire: A relatively large thin walled tire for an automobile designed for low air pressures. Provides a smoother ride.

BALL PEEN HAMMER (const.) ball peen ham' mer: A hammer having a semi-spherical head, used in the metal trades.

BALL RACE (metal) ball race: In a ball bearing, it is the groove in which the balls run.

BALL STAKE (metal) ball stake: A metal working stake with a rounded head for shaping curved surfaces.

BALSA (wood.) bal' sa: A wood grown in the West Indies and in Central America. It is very light and relatively strong. It is used extensively in model airplane construction.

BALUN (elec.) bal' un: An impedance-transforming and balancing device.

BALUSTER (const.) bal' us ter: A small column used as a rail support.

BALUSTRADE (const.) bal' us trade': A row of balusters with a common rail.

BAMBOO (wood.) bam boo': A tropical grass with a tree-like stem. Used for furniture, fishing poles, etc.

BANAK (Virola Koschnyi) (wood.) ba'-nak: A wood similar to African Mahogany but stiffer. It is pinkish brown

to brownish grey in color. It is straight grained and has uniform texture.

BANANA JACK (elec.) ba nana' jack: The female jack to take the banana plug.

BANANA OIL (paint. and dec.) ba nana' oil: A colorless liquid ester, amyl acetate, which has the odor of bananas. It is used as a mixer for certain wood and metal finishes, such as lacquers.

BANANA PLUG (elec.) ba nana' plug: A male connection plug.

BANCA TIN (metal) ban' ca tin: High grade tin from Banca and Malacca.

BAND (const.) band: A low flat molding.

BAND (elec.) band: A group of adjacent frequencies in the frequency spectrum.

BAND-PASS FILTER (elec.) band-pass fil' ter: A filter circuit designed to pass currents of frequencies within a continuous band and reject or attenuate frequencies above or below the band.

BAND REJECT FILTER (elec.) band re' ject fil' ter: A filter circuit designed to reject currents in a continuous band of frequencies, but pass frequencies above or below the band.

BAND SAW (wood.) band saw: A power saw employing a flexible endless steel saw blade running as a belt between two wheels. It will cut straight and curved lines.

BAND SHELL (const.) band shell: A bandstand with a large sound reflecting back shaped like a shell.

BANDSPREAD (elec.) band' spread: A fine-tuning control; a method employed to give a finer frequency adjustment by varying a small capacitor in parallel with the main tuning capacitor of a tuning circuit.

BANDSTAND (const.) band' stand: An elevated platform, usually covered but open on all sides, in which bands give outdoor concerts.

BAND SWITCHING (elec.) band switching: A receiver employing a switch to change its frequency range of reception.

BANDWIDTH (elec.) band' width: The band of frequencies allowed for transmitting a modulated signal; the range of frequencies over which a piece of equipment is designed to operate.

BANDY-LEG (wood.) ban' dy-leg: A cabriole leg; a curved or bowed leg on furniture.

BANISTER (const.) ban' is ter: The balustrade of a staircase.

BANKER (const.) bank' er: A stonecutter's workbench.

BAR (graphics) bar: A bar across a type chase to prevent it from spreading under pressure.

"BARBER-CHAIR" (space) bar' ber-chair: An adjustable type of seat that can quickly position the occupant from an upright seated position to a supine or semisupine position to increase his tolerance to high acceleration.

BARCH-PAYZANT (draft.) barch-pay'-zant: A special lettering pen.

BAR CLAMP (wood.) bar clamp: A

woodworker's clamp consisting of a screw clamp and an adjustable stop

mounted on a bar. They are made in a variety of lengths.

BAR FOLDER (metal) bar fold' er: A machine to bend sheet metal along a straight line.

BARGEBOARD (const.) barge' board: See VERGE BOARD.

BARGE SPIKE (const.) barge spike: A square chisel pointed spike used in heavy timber construction.

BARIUM SULPHATE (BARYTES) (painting and dec.) bar' i um sul' phate: Extender pigment made from mineral, barite.

BARIUM TITANATE (elec.) bar' i um ti' ta nate: A compound used for an electrostrictive transducer. It is shaped and kiln fired and polarized by a high voltage during cooling.

BARK (wood.) bark: The tough exterior coating which nature provides as protection for a tree.

BARLEY TWIST (wood.) bar' ley twist: Spiral wood turning.

BAR MAGNET (elec.) bar mag' net: A straight permanent magnet.

BARN SASH (const.) barn sash: Small window sash of four to six lights, used in farm building construction.

BARN SIDING (const.) barn sid' ing: Drop siding or tongue and groove boards used in farm building construction.

BAROGRAPH (draft.) bar' o graph: A bar chart by which statistical data may be represented diagrammatically and may be easily understood by the average person.

BAROMETER (air cond.) ba rom' e ter:

An instrument used to measure atmospheric pressure.

BAROQUE (draft.) ba roque': Later version of renaissance architecture using extremely elaborate ornamentation; Rococo.

BARREL BOLT (const.) bar'rel bolt: A round sliding bolt used as a door fastener or lock.

BARRIER REGION (elec.) bar'ri er re'gion: The potential difference across a PN junction due to diffusion of electrons and holes across the junction.

BAR SASH LIFT (const.) bar sash lift: A bar type handle by which a sash can be lifted.

BARYTES (painting and dec.) ba ry'tes: See BARIUM SULPHATE.

BASAL ANGLE (const.) ba'sal an'gle: The angle at the base of a structural member.

BASALT (const.) ba salt': A dark igneous rock used as road beds and rock fill.

BASE (elec.) base: The thin section between the emitter and collector of a transistor.

BASEBOARD (const.) base'board: The finish board around the base of a room covering the joint between floor and walls.

BASE CIRCLE (metal) base cir'cle: In the designing of gears, it is the circle on which the involute tooth is constructed.

BASE COURSE (const.) base course: The foundation or first course of bricks in a wall.

BASE LINE (draft.) base line: A system of dimensioning where all dimensions are given from base lines; an established line from which measurements are taken.

BASEMENT (const.) base'ment: The base story of a house, usually underground.

BASE METAL (welding) base met'al: Metal to be welded, cut or brazed.

BASE MOLDING (wood.) base mold'ing: A molding directly above the plinth or base of a piece of furniture, a column or a pedestal.

BASEPLATE (const.) base'plate: See SOLE PLATE.

BASE SHOE (const.) base shoe: See SHOE MOLD.

BASIC HOLE SYSTEM (draft.) ba'sic hole sys'tem: The system of determining proper allowances and tolerances computed from basic hole sizes.

BASIC SHAFT SYSTEM (draft.) ba'sic shaft sys'tem: The system of determining proper allowances and tolerances computed from basic shaft sizes.

BASIC SIZE (draft.) ba'sic size: The exact theoretical size from which variations are made.

BASIC WEIGHT (graphics) ba'sic weight: The weight of a sheet of paper in terms of its weight in a full ream in the size represented by its class.

BASIL (const.) ba'sil: The beveled edge of a cutting tool.

BASILICA (const.) ba sil'i ca: In ancient history, it was a large hall of justice; a meeting place; a Christian church building.

BAS-RELIEF (const.) bas-re lief': In sculpture, when figures project outward from the background; raised figures.

BASS (elec.) bass: Low frequency sounds in audio range.

BASS BOOST (elec.) bass boost: An audio circuit used to boost low frequency sound.

BASS COMPENSATION (elec.) bass com pen sa' tion: An electronic circuit which compensates for the inability of the human ear to respond to low frequency sound at low volume as well as to high frequency sound at the same volume.

BASSO-RELIEVO (const.) bas' so-re lie' vo: A form of bas-relief where the projected figures are not detached from the background.

BASS REFLEX (elec.) bass re' flex: A speaker enclosure designed to reproduce low frequency sounds and enhance the bass effect.

BASS RESPONSE (elec.) bass response': The ability of an audio amplifier system to amplify and reproduce the low frequency range of sound.

BASSWOOD (const.) bass' wood: The light brown, porous wood of the American Linden tree. Its fine texture and easy-to-work characteristics makes it adaptable for finish work and paneling.

BAST (wood.) bast: Fibrous and stringy wood which composes the bark of a tree.

BASTARD (graphics) bas' tard: Anything around a printing office which is not standard form or size.

BASTARD (metal) bas' tard: A course cut file.

BASTARD-SAWED (const.) bas' tard-sawed: A method of sawing timber into boards by cutting successive parallel slices lengthwise of the log; plain sawing.

BAT (const.) bat: A lump of clay; a type of insulating material.

BATAVIA (painting and dec.) Ba ta' vi-a: Short for Batavia dammar.

BATTEN DOWN (const.) bat' ten down: To fasten down a cover or canvas with strips or battens.

BATTENS (const.) bat' tens: Small strips of lumber, usually nailed over joints in sheathing to keep out the weather.

BATTER (const.) bat' ter: The gradual incline of a wall such as a wall which has a base wider than its top; inclined away from viewer.

BATTER BOARD (const.) bat' ter board: A temporary framework used to layout the corners of a new foundation.

BATTER BRACE (const.) bat' ter brace: An inclined brace at the end of a truss, for additional support.

BATTERY (elec.) bat' tery: Several voltaic cells connected in series or parallel. Usually contained in one case.

BATTERY CAPACITY (elec.) bat' tery ca pac' i ty: The ability of a battery to produce a given current over a period of time measured in ampere hours. A rated 100 amp. hr. battery will theoretically produce one ampere for one hundred hours or two amperes for fifty hours, etc.

BATTERY CHARGER (auto.) bat' tery charg' er: A rectifier to convert alternating current to direct current for charging a storage battery.

BATTERY CLIP (elec.) bat' tery clip: A relatively large spring clip for temporary connections to the terminals of a storage battery.

BATTERY RESISTANCE (elec.) battery re sist' ance: The internal resistance between plates and electrolyte in a cell or battery.

BAUD (elec.) baud: A unit used to measure signaling speed. It represents the number of code elements transmitted per second.

BAUXITE (metal) baux' ite: Hydrated oxide of alumina, mixed with iron oxide and silica. Aluminum ore.

BAY (const.) bay: A division of a roof; a wing; a storage compartment or area.

BAY (elec.) bay: A part or element of an antenna array.

BAYONET BASE (elec.) bay' on et base: A lamp base which is held in place by two pins which fit into slots in the socket.

BAY WINDOW (const.) bay win' dow: A window or group of windows set out from the regular building and supported on a foundation extending beyond the main wall.

B-BATTERY (elec.) b-bat' tery: A group of series cells in one container producing a high voltage for the plate circuits of electronic devices. Popular batteries include 22 1/2, 45 and 90 volts.

BEAD (const.) bead' : A circular molding.

BEAD (welding) bead': The ridge formed at a welded joint resulting from fusion and addition of welding rod.

BEAD (welding) bead' : Denotes the appearance of the finished weld; describes neatness of the ripples formed by the metal while it was in a semiliquid state.

BEADING (crafts.) bead' ing: An edge or border.

BEADING PLANE (const.) bead' ing plane: A carpenter's tool, used to cut beads on a board.

BEADWORK (const.) bead' work: Ornamental molding.

BEAKHEAD (const.) beak' head: A drip mold along the edge of a cornice.

BEAKHORN (metal) beak' horn: See STAKE.

BEAM (const.) beam: A term used to describe joists, rafters, girders and purlins.

BEAM (elec.) beam: A stream of electrons, protons or electromagnetic particles.

BEAM ANCHOR (const.) beam an' chor: An anchor used to secure and tie floor beams to the walls.

BEAM BENDER (elec.) beam bend' er: See ION TRAP.

BEAM CEILING (const.) beam ceil' ing: A method of finishing the ceiling of a room where beams, either false or solid, are exposed as a decorative feature.

BEAM COMPASS (draft.) beam com'-pass: A compass employing a bar and adjustable sliding points and markers.

Used for drawing large arcs and circles.

BEAM PATTERN (auto.) beam pat' tern: The light pattern or area covered by the automobile headlights.

BEAM POWER TUBE (elec.) beam pow' er tube: A tube so constructed that the electrons flow in concentrated beams from the cathode through the grids to the plate.

BEARER (graphics) bear' er: Various devices used to protect the type in a form.

BEARERS (graphics) bear' ers: Roller-bearers are useful in job-press forms when the roller-pins are broken, for they then cause the rollers to rotate. Electrotype bearers are pieces of metal, type-high, placed around type forms to protect them while making a mold in wax.

BEARING (const.) bear' ing: The portion of a beam that rests on its support.

BEARING CAP (metal) bear' ing cap: The top half of a journal bearing.

BEARING METAL (metal) bear' ing metal: Any of the antifriction metals used as bearing surfaces such as brass, white metal, babbitt, etc.

BEARING PARTITION (const.) bear' ing par ti' tion: A partition which supports a load.

BEARING WALL (const.) bear' ing wall: A wall which supports a load.

BEAT FREQUENCY (elec.) beat fre'-quen cy: Frequencies produced by addition and subtraction of intensities of two signals at regular intervals; the resultant frequency obtained by mixing two signals together.

BEAT FREQUENCY OSCILLATOR (elec.) beat fre' quen cy os cil la' tor: An oscillator whose output is beat with the continuous wave to produce a beat frequency in the audio range. Used in CW reception.

BEATING (elec.) beat' ing: The process of combining two signals in a nonlinear device such as an electron tube, to obtain a beat frequency.

BEAT NOTE (elec.) beat note: The difference frequency obtained when two different frequencies are beat together.

BEAUX ARTS (draft.) beaux arts: A famous French school of architecture and art.

BEAVER BOARD (const.) bea' ver board: An insulating board made of wood-fibre materials, used to finish interior walls.

BED (const.) bed: The lower surface of a brick, stone or tile.

BED (graphics) bed: The flat metal part of a press on which the form is placed.

BED (metal) bed: The foundation on which a machine is built.

BEDDING (const.) bed' ding: A filling and leveling with mortar or putty to secure a firm bearing.

BEDFORD STONE (const.) bed' ford stone: One of the finest building limestones, quarried in Bedford, Indiana.

BED JOINT (const.) bed joint: In masonry, it is the horizontal joint upon which bricks rest.

BED MOLD (const.) bed mold: A molding used to cover the joint between the plancier and frieze. Also used as a cornice mold.

BEDROCK (const.) bed' rock: The solid rock which underlies the earth's surface; a solid foundation on which to rest the foundations of a building.

BED STONE (const.) bed stone: A foundation stone.

BEESWAX (crafts.) bees' wax: Wax from the honeycomb. Used in art metal work and to coat foundry patterns to facilitate removal from sand mold.

BEESWAX (painting and dec.) bees' wax: Wax produced by honey bee.

BEL (elec.) bel: A unit of measurement of relative power equivalent to a 10 to 1 ratio of power gain. It represents the smallest difference in audio sound which can be detected by the human ear.

BELFRY (const.) bel' fry: A tower on a church in which a bell is hung.

B ELIMINATOR (elec.) b e lim' i na-tor: A power supply to replace the B batteries in a battery radio receiver.

BELL (plumb.) bell: The enlargement on the end of a piece of pipe, so that another pipe of the same size may be inserted and sealed with a satisfactory joint.

BELL AND SPIGOT JOINT (plumb.) bell and spig' ot joint: A joint where the straight end of one pipe (the spigot) fits into the bell of the next pipe. The joint is made tight by calking.

BELL, ALEXANDER GRAHAM (1847-1922) (elec.) The inventor of the telephone. This distinguished American scientist first conceived that "voice could be carried on wires." He was a regent of the Smithsonian Institute and president of the National Geographic Society.

BELL CRANK (metal) bell crank: A lever with two arms at a 90 degree angle.

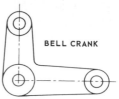

BELL HOUSING (auto.) bell hous' ing: The housing around the flywheel and clutch assembly in an automobile.

BELL METAL (metal) bell met' al: Bronze suitable for casting bells.

BELL MOUTHED (metal) bell mouthed: Shaped like a bell; having a bell shaped opening at an end.

BELLOWS (metal) bel' lows: Hand operated air pump used by foundry man to blow loose sand away from mold cavities; air supply for blacksmith's forge. See illustration, page 41.

BELL TRANSFORMER (elec.) bell trans form' er: A small transformer to change the power line voltage of 117 volts to 6 or 12 volts for operation of door bells or chimes.

BELL TRAP (plumb.) bell trap: A bell shaped trap with cover used in a floor drainage system.

BELLY (const.) bel' ly: To bulge out.

BELLY (graphics) bel' ly: A gradual depression formed in the center of a locked up type form due to binding of lines at each end. Belly is checked with a straight edge.

BELT (const.) belt: A decorative course of bricks projecting from a brick or stone wall, usually in line with window sills. It may be enriched by molds and

flutes or may be of an entirely different type of brick or stone.

BELT CONVEYER (const.) belt convey'er: An endless belt operating on
revolving rollers, to transport objects
or materials from one location to another.

BELT COURSE (const.) belt course: A
flat board and molding, horizontally
installed around or across a building.

BELT DRESSING (const.) belt dress'-
ing: Any of several substances used on
a machinery belt to prolong life and
improve its frictional grip.

BELT LACING (const.) belt lac'ing:
Narrow strips of leather used to lace
together the ends of belts.

BELT SANDER (wood.) belt sand'er:
A sanding machine in which an endless
abrasive belt is supported by two
drums. One of the drums is power
driven. Used for finishing flat surfaces on wood, metal and plastics.

BELVEDERE (const.) bel ve dere': A
lookout for scenic viewing; a small
house, with open sides, built to take
advantage of an attractive view.

BENCH DOG (const.) bench dog: A stop,
such as a pin or a block, inserted in
a bench top, to hold work from slipping.

BENCH GRINDER (wood.) bench grind'-
er: A double ended motor with provisions on each shaft end for mounting
wheels or buffers. It is mounted on a
bench. Tool rests, guards and eye
shields are usually included with the
complete grinder.

BENCH HOOK (const.) bench hook: A
hook-shaped device used to prevent
work from slipping on a bench; a board,

with cleats nailed on each side at opposite ends, used to hold work in place
on a bench.

BENCH LATHE (metal) bench lathe: A
small bench mounted machine lathe.

BENCH MARKS (const.) bench marks:
A permanent marker placed in the
ground from which differences in elevations are computed.

BENCH PLATE (metal) bench plate: See
surface plate.

BENCH SAW OR TABLE SAW (wood.)
bench saw or ta'ble saw: A woodworking machine. A stationary metal bench
in which is mounted a power driven
circular saw. The bench is equipped
with necessary gauges and fences for
cutting off or ripping lumber. The saw
blade or table may also be tilted for
bevel or compound cutting.

BENCH STOP (const.) bench stop: A
type of bench dog, usually made of
metal.

BENCH TABLE (const.) bench ta'ble: A
course of projecting stone around the
base of a building, which appear to form
a seat.

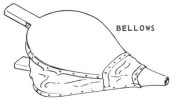

BELLOWS

BENCH VISE (metal) bench vise: A
small vise for metal work which may
be temporarily or permanently attached
to a bench; a small all purpose vise.
The vise may have a small anvil as
part of its body; it may also be
equipped with pipe jaws.

BENCHWORK   (metal)   bench'work:

Work in a machine shop consisting of layout, assembly and fitting of parts.

BEND (plumb.) bend: A short piece of curved pipe.

BEN DAY PROCESS (graphics) Ben Day pro' cess: A process invented by Ben Day, and used by photoengravers. The process consists in using gelatine films, with designs in relief, which are inked, and the designs transferred to metal plates. After being covered with a resin, which adheres to the ink and is burned on, the plate is etched.

BENDING JIG (crafts.) bend' ing jig: A device for shaping and bending sheet metal and wire.

BENDIX DRIVE (auto.) ben' dix drive: An inertia activated mechanism for engaging the pinion gear on the cranking motor with the ring gear on the engine flywheel.

"BENNY" (painting and dec.) ben' ny: Slang for benzine.

BENZENE (painting and dec.) ben' zene: Sometimes called "Benzol". A very powerful aromatic solvent for many materials. Its use is restricted, however, due to its toxicity and also due to the fact that it is a fire hazard.

BENZINE (VARNISH MAKERS' AND PAINTERS' NAPTHA - VM&P) (painting and dec.) Benzine Petroleum product used by painters as thinning solvent and diluent. Highly flammable.

BENZOL (auto.) ben' zol: An engine fuel; by-product from manufacturing of coke.

BENZOL (painting and dec.) ben' zol: See benzene.

BESSEMER PROCESS (metal) bes' semer pro' ces: A steel refining process, using air to remove impurities from the molten iron.

BETA (elec.) be' ta: Greek letter β, represents current gain of a common-emitter connected transistor. It is equal to the ratio of a change in collector current to a change in base current while the collector voltage is constant.

BETA PARTICLE (elec.) be' ta particle: An electron liberated by neutron decay.

BETA RAYS (elec.) be' ta rays: One of the types of rays emitted from radioactive materials.

BETRATRON (elec.) be' tra tron: A device used to accelerate the velocity of electrons by injecting a beam of electrons into a region of varying magnetic flux.

BEVATRON (elec.) bev' a tron: A proton synchrontron invented at the University of California in which particles are accelerated to energies of several billion electron volts.

BEVEL (welding) bev' el: The angle cut on the edge of metal plates in preparation for welding.

BEVEL BOARD (const.) bev' el board: A board used in roof framing to lay out bevels.

BEVEL GAUGE (wood.) bev' el gauge: A

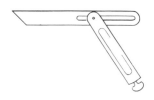

type of square with a blade which can be set at a desired angle for checking bevels.

BEVEL GEARS (metal) bev'el gears: Gears used to transmit power between two shafts at an angle to each other.

BEVELED RULE (graphics) bev'eled rule: When the face of a rule is at one side and the shoulder slopes to the other side.

BEVEL PROTRACTOR (metal) bev'el pro trac'tor: A tool used for measuring angles.

BEVEL SIDING (const.) bev'el sid'ing: Boards used as exterior wall covering and applied with an overlap, like shingling. The boards are sawed so that they are thicker along one edge.

BEZANT (const.) bez'ant: A flat disk, used in architectural ornamentation.

BEZEL (auto.) bez'el: A groove and flange to hold a transparent cover on an instrument.

BEZEL (const.) bez'el: The sloping cutting edge of a tool, such as a chisel.

BEZEL (crafts) bez'el: A metal collar that holds a stone in a ring or jewelry.

B. F. (graphics) b. f. : Abbreviation for BOLD-FACE type.

B-H CURVE (elec.) b-h curve: A graph showing the magnetic characteristics of a substance. H or magnetizing force is plotted on the X axis against B or density on the Y axis.

BIAS (elec.) bi'as: The dc potential applied to the input grid of an electron tube; the dc potential applied to elements of a transistor such as forward bias between emitter and base.

BIAS (elec.) bi'as:
CATHODE SELF-BIAS, Bias created by voltage drop across a cathode resistor.

FIXED, Voltage supplied by fixed sources.
GRID LEAK, Bias created by charging a capacitor in the grid circuit. Bias level is maintained by leak resistor.

BIAS, FORWARD (elec.) bi'as, forward: The connection of a potential to produce a current across a PN junction. The source potential connected so that it opposes the potential hill and reduces it.

BIAS REVERSE (elec.) bi'as re verse': The connection of a potential so that little or no current will flow across a PN junction. The source potential has the same polarity as the potential hill and adds to it.

BIBB OR BIB (plumb.) bibb or bib: A faucet, cock, tap or plug.

BIBLE PAPER (graphics) bi'ble paper: A thin, opaque, book paper of unusual strength and durability.

BIDET (plumb.) bi det': A small bathtub similar to a sitz bath and used for bathing the lower part of the body.

BIFILAR (elec.) bi fi'lar: A method of winding a coil by using a double wire so that the current in one turn is 180 deg. out of phase with the current in the next turn and therefore cancels the inductance.

BILATERAL TOLERANCE (draft.) bilat'er al tol'er ance: Tolerance permitted on both sides of basic size.

BILLET (metal) bil'let: A piece of steel having a cross sectional area of 4 to 36 square inches; in the preliminary stages of working steel, an ingot is gradually reduced to blooms, billets and slabs in the rolling mill.

BILLHEAD (graphics) bill'head: A

form of office stationary sent with delivered goods.

BILL OF MATERIAL (draft.) bill of mate' ri al: A stock list of part numbers, sizes, description and quantity of all parts and materials needed to make a given object.

BIMETAL (elec.) bi met' al: A temperature indicating or regulating device based on the principle that two dissimular metals having unequal expansion rates, when welded together, will tend to bend when heated.

BIMETALLIC ELEMENT (air cond.) bime tal' lic el' e ment: A device used in temperature control, consisting of two metals having different coefficients of thermal expansion.

BIMETAL-THERMOSTAT (auto.) bi'-met al-ther' mo stat: Device made of two different strips of metal welded together. Unequal expansion, when heated, causes the device to bend or curl.

BIMORPH CELL (elec.) bi' morph cell: Two crystals cemented together and used in crystal microphones, headphones and phono pickups.

BINARY (elec.) bi' na ry: A number system having a base of 2, using only the symbols 0 and 1.

BINARY DIGITS (elec.) bi' na ry digits: Numbers used in a digital computer such as 0 and 1 in the binary numbers system.

BINAURAL (elec.) bin au' ral: A sound reproduction system in which two sources of sound are amplified in separate amplifiers or channels and reproduced by individual speakers to give a stereophonic effect.
    AMPLIFIER, A dual channel amplifier used in stereophonic sound system.

BROADCAST, The transmitting of two separate sound signals for use in binaural reception.
    DISK, A recording disk with two separate sound signals, one on each side of the groove.
    TAPE, A two track magnetic tape on which two separate sound signals have been recorded.

BIND (graphics) bind: A term used to describe a condition when a type form cannot be locked-up square and even, due to the size and position of type.

BINDER (metal) bind' er: A material such as linseed oil, molasses and other preparations used to bind core sands and give the core strength. Used in the foundry.

BINDER (painting and dec.) bind' er: The non-volatile portion of a paint which serves to bind the pigment particles together.

BINDERS BOARD (graphics) bind' er's board: A tough fiberboard used for book binders and covers.

BINDING POST (elec.) bind' ing post: Spring loaded or screw terminals on equipment so that it may be attached to other equipment conveniently.

BIOASTRONAUTICS (space) bi o astro nau' tics: Astronautics considered for its effect upon animal or plant life.

BIONICS (space) bi on' ics: A study of systems which act like or resemble living systems.

BIRCH (Betual Lutea) (wood.) birch: A very hard, heavy, strong and close grain wood. It is a favorite American cabinet wood.

BIRD'S-EYE (const.) bird's-eye: A grain configuration appearing in some woods such as maple, that looks like an eye due to the elliptical arrangement of wood fibers around a central spot or eye.

BIRD'S-EYE VIEW (draft.) bird's-eye view: A perspective view looking down on an object.

BIRD'S MOUTH (const.) bird's mouth: The cut out at the bottom end of a rafter which fits over the plate.

BIRMINGHAM GAUGE (metal) bir'-ming ham gauge: A standard gauge for measuring iron wire and hot and cold rolled steel.

BISCUIT (const.) bis' cuit: Unglazed tile.

BISECT (draft.) bi sect' : To divide into two equal parts.

BISMUTH (metal) bis' muth: A metallic element with a low melting point. Used as an alloy and in safety devices. In a fire protection sprinkler system bismuth is used to detect heat. A rise in temperature will melt the bismuth and turn on the sprinkler system. Bismuth is also used as a safety plug in boilers and for electric fuses.

BIT (const.) bit: A cutting tool; the part of a key which projects from the key shaft and operates the tumblers on the lock.

BIT (elec.) bit: The abbreviation for Binary Digit; a unit of storage capacity of a computer; a single character of a language employing two kinds of characters only.

BIT BRACE (wood.) bit brace: A crank shaped tool used for holding various types of boring and utility bits.

BIT GAUGE (wood.) bit gauge: A device

fastened to an auger bit to limit the depth of the hole.

BITING (painting and dec.) bit' ing: Solvent in top coat dissolves or bites into the coat below. If lacquer solvent is too biting, dried lacquer surface may be rough or provide "orange peel effect."

BIT STOP (wood.) bit stop: A depth stop which attaches to an auger bit.

BITUMEN (painting and dec.) bi tu' men: Mineral pitch, any of several materials obtained as asphaltic residue in the distillation of coal tar products, natural asphalt.

BLACK BOX (elec.) black box: A box containing an unknown and possibly complicated circuit.

BLACK BOX (space) black box: A term used loosely to refer to any component, usually electronic, that can be readily inserted or removed from a specific place in a larger system without knowledge of its detailed internal structue.

BLACKDAMP (metal) black' damp: Gases formed in mines; carbon dioxide gas.

BLACKER THAN BLACK (elec.) black'-er than black: In television, it is the blackness of the picture which is beyond the black or blanking level of the CRT. It is during this region that retrace of beam occurs.

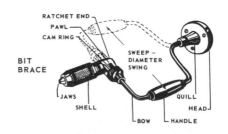

BLACK-LETTER (graphics) black-let'-ter: A black faced type called text. So named for its total black appearance when set in mass formation on a page of a book.

BLACK LEVEL (elec.) black lev'el: The reference level in the composite television signal which represents the black area of a picture. It also is considered as the blanking level of the TV picture and at this point the CRT is cutoff.

BLACK LIGHT (elec.) black light: A light emitting ultraviolet energy.

BLACK VARNISH (metal) black varnish: Shellac with lamp black. Used by the patternmaker.

BLACK WALNUT (wood.) black wal'-nut: A heavy hard, brownish wood from the black walnut tree. Used for furniture, gunstocks and interior finish.

BLANC FIXE (painting and dec.) blanc fixe: Artificially prepared barium sulphate. An extender pigment.

BLANCH (air cond.) blanch: The sterilization of certain vegetables to be canned by dipping in hot water.

BLANK (graphics) blank: A quad, slug, piece of furniture of other material used in type form to make a blank space on the printed space.

BLANK (metal) blank: A piece of flat steel stock cut and prepared for forming operations.

BLANKET (graphics) blan'ket: A sheet of rubber, reinforced with fabric which is clamped around offset cylinder and transfers ink from plate to paper.

BLANKET INSULATION (const.) blan'-ket in su la'tion: Insulation materials made in strips usually 15 or 23 inches wide to fit between studs. They may be composed of mineral wools, glass or wood fibers and the materials are fastened between heavy asphalt treated paper.

BLANKING DIE (metal) blank'ing die: A press using dies of specified size to cut out blanks. A strip or sheet is fed into the machine which punches out one or more blanks at one time.

BLANKING LEVEL (elec.) blank'ing lev'el: The level of the composite video signal during blanking. During the blanking period the sync pulse is transmitted.

BLANKING PULSE (elec.) blank'ing pulse: Pulses transmitted by the TV transmitter, which are used in the receiver to cutoff the scanning beam during retrace time.

BLANK-OUT (graphics) blank-out: The blank part of the last page of a chapter in a book.

BLAST FURNACE (metal) blast fur'-nace; A furnace used to refine iron ore.

BLAST HEATER (air cond.) blast heat'er: A heater employing an air blast through heated coils.

BLEACHING (wood.) bleach'ing: The cleaning and whitening of wood by oxalic acid or other substances.

BLEACHING (painting and dec.) bleaching: Restoring discolored or stained wood to its normal color or making it lighter by using bleaching agents.

BLEED (const.) bleed: In reference to wood, it is the bleeding of sap or pitch to the surface of the wood.

BLEED (graphics) bleed: A sheet or page is bled when it is trimmed into the printed portion.

BLEEDER (elec.) bleed' er: A resistor connected across a power supply to discharge filter capacitors.

BLEEDER TILE (const.) bleed' er tile: A tile pipe placed at the base of a foundation wall to allow surface water collected at the base of the wall to drain into the sewer system inside the wall.

BLEEDING (paint. and dec.) bleed' ing: A term which describes the effect when stain applied to a wood surface bleeds through the finish coat. Bleeding is prevented by applying a fast drying seal coat before finishing.

BLEEDING STAIN (painting and dec.) bleed' ing stain: Stain which "bleeds" through succeeding coats of finishing materials.

BLEMISH (const.) blem' ish: An imperfection in a wood which mars its appearance.

BLEND (paint. and dec.) blend: To mix together such as in pigments of paint, to pass gradually from one shade of color to another; to go well together.

BLENDING (painting and dec.) blend'- ing: Mixing one color with another so the colors mix or merge gradually.

BLIND (const.) blind: An outside window covering, usually made of wood, to protect the glass and shut out light. It is now used for ornamental purposes.

BLIND ARCH (const.) blind arch: A closed arch in a building, usually for ornamentation only and to harmonize with open arches in other parts of the building.

BLIND CASING (const.) blind cas' ing: A rough casing for a window frame; a subcasing.

BLIND HEADER (const.) blind head' er: Stones or bricks which appear to be a header, but are only short pieces.

BLIND HOLE (wood.) blind hole: A partially drilled hole; not a through hole.

BLIND MORTISE (const.) blind mor'- tise: A mortise which is not cut completely through the material.

BLIND NAILING (const.) blind nail' ing: Nailing so that heads do not appear on finished surface of work.

BLIND STOP (const.) blind stop: A rectangular molding used in a window frame.

BLIND TENON (const.) blind ten' on: A tenon in a mortise which extends only part way through the wood.

BLIP (elec.) blip: A spot of light on a radar screen caused by the presence of a reflecting object.

BLIP (space) blip: A spot of light or other indicator on a radar scope indicating the relative position of a reflecting object such as a missile in flight.

BLISTER (paint. and dec.) blis' ter: A defect in paint when paint lifts off surface due to moisture or direct heat.

BLISTERING (paint. and dec.) blis'- ter ing: Formation of bubbles on surface of paint or varnish film.

BLISTER STEEL (metal) blis' ter steel: Steel bars made by the cementation process. Used mostly for cutlery.

BLOCK (auto.) block: The basic framework of an engine. All other engine parts are attached to it. It is usually an iron or aluminum casting, machined for cylinders, valve ports, bearings and cooling passages.

BLOCK (automation) block: A group of words considered as a unit.

BLOCK (const.) block: A building unit of concrete or tile, somewhat larger than a brick; a piece of wood placed behind a base or molding to hold it in place and provide a nailing ground.

BLOCK AND TACKLE (metal) block and tack'le: One or more pulley blocks or sheaves and the rope or cable to operate same.

BLOCK FLOORING (const.) block floor'ing: Flooring made from small blocks of wood.

BLOCKING (elec.) block'ing: See KEYING, GRIDBLOCK.

BLOCKING CAPACITOR (elec.) block'ing ca pac'i tor: A capacitor used to block a d-c voltage.

BLOCKHOUSE (space) block'house: A concrete protective structure to protect personnel from blast, heat or explosions during rocket launchings. It houses the electronic control instruments.

BLOCKING COURSE (const.) block'ing course: A course of stones placed on top of a cornice crowning a wall.

BLOCKING OUT (graphics) block'ing out: Removing or eliminating undesired copy or illustrations.

BLOCK PLANE (wood.) block plane: A short plane used for planing end grain wood.

BLOCKS (graphics) blocks: Used to temporarily mount electrotypes.

BLOCK TIN (const.) block tin: Pure tin.

BLOOM (const.) bloom: An efflorescence which sometimes appears on brick walls; a cloudy appearance on a varnished surface due to moisture.

BLOOM (metal) bloom: A block of steel as it is in an intermediate rolling process and its cross sectional area is more than 36 square inches.

BLOOM (painting and decorating) bloom: Clouded appearance on varnished surface.

BLOOMING (elec.) bloom'ing: The defocusing of a television picture due to an increase in signal intensity.

BLOW-BY (auto.) blow-by: The condition when engine pressure and explosion pressure passes the piston rings.

BLOW HOLE (metal) blow hole: Holes in castings resulting from improper venting of gases.

BLOWHORN (metal) blow'horn: See STAKE.

BLOWOFF (plumb.) blow'off: A discharge outlet in a pipeline to release water, steam or other fluids.

BLOWOFF (space) blow'off: Separation of an instrument section or package from the remainder of the rocket vehicle by application of explosive force, in order to retrieve the instruments after they have collected the required information.

BLOWOUT (auto.) blow'out: The rupture of a tire.

BLOWPIPE (welding) blow'pipe: A gas welding torch.

BLOWPIPE (welding) blow'pipe: A

term used to describe an oxyacetylene torch.

BLOWTORCH (plumb. - paint. and dec.) blow' torch: A gasoline fired portable torch which produces intense heat.

BLOWN OIL (painting and dec.) blown oil: A vegetable or fish oil which has been thickened by air blown through it.

BLUEING (metal) blue' ing: Oxidizing the surface of steel by heating in bath of sodium and potassium nitrate which produces a coating having a dark blue color.

BLUE LEAD (painting and dec.) blue lead: Sulphate of lead containing small amounts of lead sulphide and carbon that impart a bluish-gray color.

BLUE PRINT (draft.) blue print: A photographic copy of an original tracing.

BLUESTONE (const.) blue' stone: A grayish blue sandstone from the Hudson River region. It is used as a building stone and as door and window sills.

BLUNGING MACHINE (crafts) blung'-ing   ma chine': A machine to mix clays for ceramics.

BLUSHING (painting and dec.) blush'-ing: A whitish spot appearing on lacquers and varnishes due to humidity and rapid evaporation of solvents; a clouded appearance on varnished surfaces.

BOARD (const.) board: Lumber less than 2 inches thick.

BOARDFOOT (wood.) board' foot: The unit of measure of lumber representing a board 1 inch thick, 12 inches wide and 12 inches long.

BOARDING IN (const.) board' ing in:

The nailing of boards on the outside of a building.

BOARD MEASURE (wood.) board mea'-sure: The measuring system by which lumber is designated and priced.

BOARD RULE (const.) board rule: A measuring device with various scales to determine the board feet in lumber without mathematical calculations.

BOASTER (const.) boast' er: A tool used to smooth the surface of hard stone.

BOASTING (wood) boast' ing: Roughing out a carving.

BOAT SPIKE (const.) boat spike: See BARGE SPIKE.

BOAT TAIL (space) boat tail: The cylindrical section of a ballistic body that continually decreases in diameter toward the tail to reduce overall aerodynamic drag.

BODKIN (graphics) bod' kin: A long, tapered sharp-pointed tool useful for removing type from a line when making corrections.

BODONI (graphics) bo do' ni: The designer of the first modern Roman type face. This type is named in his honor.

BODY (welding) bod' y: The main structure or enclosure of a regulator.

BODY (painting and dec.) bod' y: Thickness of a fluid.

BODY COAT (painting and dec.) bod' y coat: Intermediate coat of paint between priming and finishing coats.

BODY MATTER (graphics) bod' y mat'-ter: The part of a display advertisement which is not set in display type.

BOILED OIL (paint. and dec.) boiled oil: A linseed oil, used in painting, which has been heated to a temperature between 400-600 deg. and to which has been added a small amount of drier.

BOILER HORSEPOWER (const.) boil'er horse'pow er: The equivalent evaporation of 34.5 pounds of water per hour at 212 deg. F. This is equal to 33,475 Btu per hour.

BOILER PLATE (metal) boil'er plate: Steel sheets and plates used in the construction of tanks and boilers.

BOILING POINT boil'ing point: Temperature at which a liquid boils. Water boils at 100 deg. C. or 212 deg. F.

BOILOFF (space) boil'off: The vaporization of liquid oxygen as the temperature of the propellant mass rises during exposure to ambient conditions of the missile tank or other containers.

BOLD (graphics) bold: Heavy face type, prominent; stands out.

BOLD-FACED (graphics) bold-faced: Type which is heavier than the text type in which it is used.

BOLECTION (wood.) bo lec'tion: A molding around a panel usually projecting beyond the face of the framing which holds the panel.

BOLOMETER (elec.) bo lom'e ter: A resistive component which varies with temperature.

BOLT (const.) bolt: A threaded metal fastener consisting of a round metal rod with head and threaded to receive a nut.

BOMARC (space) bomarc: An Air Force surface-to-air guided missile whose range is 200-400 miles. Bomarc is an area defense interceptor missile. The Bomarc is powered by twin ramjet engines with either liquid or solid rocket booster.

BOMBARDMENT (elec.) bom bard'-ment: The striking of a surface by high speed electrons, ions or particles resulting in secondary emission or fluorescence.

BOND (const.) bond: The connection of stones and bricks in a wall to form a strong and decorative mass. It is formed by overlapping bricks and by laying some bricks at right angles to the wall face.

BOND (graphics) bond: A general class of hard, tough textured paper.

BOND (welding) bond: Junction of the weld metal and the base metal.

BOND COURSE (const.) bond course: A course of header or bondstones in a masonry wall.

BOND INK (graphics) bond ink: Ink used in a letterpress for printing on highly sized paper.

BONDED LINING (auto.) bond'ed lin'-ing: Brake lining cemented to the brake shoes to eliminate rivets.

BONDING (const.) bond'ing: Any materials used to join two surfaces together.

BONDSTONES (const.) bond'stones: stones or bricks in a wall running through the thickness of wall to bond it together.

BONE BLACK (painting and dec.) bone black: Pigment made from calcined animal bones.

BONE FOLDER (graphics) bone fold'er

A piece of flat polished bone with rounded edges, used to fold sheets by hand.

BONNET (plumb.) bon' net: The housing of a gate valve into which the disc rises when the valve is opened.

BOOK CHASE (graphics) book chase: A large chase with shifting bars.

BOOK CLOTH (graphics) book cloth: A woven material, pressed and embossed in many finishes, and made in numerous colors, shades and designs, used in binding books.

BOOM (elec.) boom: A mechanical support or arm for a microphone so that it may be suspended above an actor, yet out of the view of the camera.

BOOSTER-GLIDE VEHICLE (space) boost' er-glide ve' hi cle: A rocket-boosted winged vehicle capable of leaving the atmosphere and re-entering under aerodynamic control in an unpowered or gliding mode.

BOOSTER ROCKET (space) boost' er rock' et: A rocket motor, usually a solid rocket, that assists the normal propulsive system of a rocket or other aerospace vehicle in some phase of its trajectory or flight path.

BOOST VOLTAGE (elec.) boost volt'-age: In a television set, it is the additional voltage produced in the damper circuit and represents the average charge on boost capacitor. The boost voltage is added to the B+ voltage for the plate of the horizontal output tube.

BOOTSTRAP OSCILLATOR (elec.) boot' strap os' cil la tor: A saw tooth wave generator producing an extremely linear sweep and a high amplitude sweep voltage.

BORAX (metal) bo' rax: A flux used in brazing and hard soldering.

BORAX SLATE (crafts) bo' rax slate: A slate slab used for mixing a flux of borax and water.

BORDER (const.) bor' der: A decorative or ornamental edge around anything.

BORDER (graphics) bor' der: An ornamentation or space enclosing a job.

BORE (auto.) bore: The diameter of an engine cylinder.

BORE (const.) bore: The internal diameter of a pipe, cylinder or hole.

BORING (const.) bor' ing: The process of making holes in wood or metal.

BORING BAR (metal) bor' ing bar: A bar with a tool bit fastened in one end. Used for internal cutting and boring on a lathe.

BORING MILL (metal) bor' ing mill: A machine used for enlarging holes to a finished size, usually by single cutting tool.

BORING MILL, HORIZONTAL (metal) bor' ing mill, hor i zon' tal: A boring mill in which the tool revolves on a horizontal axis. The spindle holding the tool may be fed longitudinally and sometimes vertically to the work. The work table also may be fed transversely and longitudinally.

BORING MILL, VERTICAL (metal) bor'-ing mill, ver' ti cal: A boring mill in which the work holding table revolves and the cutting tool is fed either up and down or laterally to the work.

BORING TOOL (metal) bor' ing tool: A single pointed tool forged or clamped

to a bar. Used for enlarging an existing hole or opening.

BORT (metal) bort: Industrial diamonds
used as an abrasive.

BOSS (const.) boss: An enlarged portion
of a shaft.

BOSSING (const.) boss' ing: The process of shaping malleable metals to
conform to irregular surfaces.

BOSSING MALLET (const.) boss' ing
mal' let: A mallet used in shaping
sheet lead.

BOSTON HIP ROOF (const.) bos' ton hip
roof: A method of laying shingles over
a hip or joint of a hip roof.

BOSTON RIDGE (const.) bos' ton ridge:
A method of laying shingles along the
ridge of a roof to make it watertight.
Shingles are saddled over the ridge and
and intersect with shingles from both
sides of the roof.

BOTCH (metal) botch: to do a poor job.

BOTTLED (graphics) bot' tled: Worn
type which will not stand upright on its
feet.

BOTTOM DEAD CENTER (auto.) bot'-
tom dead cen' ter: The lower limit of
piston movement. Abbrev. BDC.

BOTTOM RAIL (wood.) bot' tom rail:
The lowest horizontal member of a
door or a window.

BOURDON TUBE (auto.) bour' don tube:
A hollow curved tube closed at one
end. Liquid under pressure applied to
open end of tube has a tendency to
straighten tube. The device may be calibrated to measure oil pressure.

BOURGEOIS (graphics) bour' geois:
Nine point type.

BOW (const.) bow: Projecting in the
form of an arch.

BOWER (const.) bow' er: A private
room; a retreat.

BOW INSTRUMENTS (draft.) bow in-
stru' ments: Drafting instruments, including the compass and divider, which
employ spring tension for steady setting of the instrument. Accurate setting is made by a screw adjustment.

BOW PEN (draft.) bow pen: A bow compass with a pen in one leg.

BOW PENCIL (draft.) bow pen' cil: A
bow compass using a pencil lead fastened to one leg.

BOW SAW (const.) bow saw: A special
saw employing a thin blade held in tension by rods and turn buckles. It is
used to make curved cuts.

BOX AND PAN BRAKE (metal) box and
pan brake: A machine for bending
sheet metal to form boxes. Adjustable
fingers on the brake fit the size of the
box to be folded.

BOX BEAM (const.) box beam: A hollow
beam formed like a box.

BOX CASING (const.) box cas' ing: The
blind or sub casing of a window frame.

BOX COLUMN (const.) box col' umn: A
built-up hollow column used in porch
construction.

BOX CORNICE (const.) box cor' nice:
A completely inclosed cornice by
means of shingles, fascia and plancier.

BOXES (graphics) box' es: The compartments in a type case for individual letters.

BOX FRAME (const.) box frame: A window frame which has box-like sides for holding sash weights.

BOX GUTTER (const.) box gut' ter: A concealed gutter built into the roof.

BOX SILL (const.) box sill: A foundation sill in which the sole plate rests on the floor joists rather than on the sill; a sill made by nailing a header across the ends of the floor joist and resting on a wall plate.

BOX STRING (const.) box string: See CLOSE STRING.

"BOX THE PAINT" (painting and dec.) box the paint: After the paint has been thoroughly mixed by stirring, boxing consists of pouring it back and forth from one pail to another.

BOX UNION (plumb.) box un' ion: See UNION.

BOYLE'S LAW Boyle's law; The volume of a gas varies inversely as pressure, at a constant temperature.

BRACE (const.) brace: An inclined timber used to strengthen and stiffen the frame of a building.

BRACED FRAMING (const.) braced fram' ing: A system of framing in which all vertical structural elements except the corner posts extend one story only. Corner posts are diagonally braced extending full height of story and crossing several studs in each outer wall.

BRACE FRAME (const.) brace frame: A type of building framework where the corner posts are braced to sills and plates.

BRACES (graphics) bra' ces: Individual characters which may be joined together such as { } or ( ) which are braces.

BRACE TABLE (wood.) brace ta' ble: A table usually found on the tongue of the carpenter's square which shows the length of common braces.

BRACKET (const.) brack' et: A shelf support; a projection on the face of a wall to support a cornice or ornamental feature.

BRAD (const.) brad: A small headless nail.

BRADAWL (const.) brad' awl: A short straight awl with a chisel point, used to make holes for screws and brads.

BRADDOCK TRIANGLE (draft.) brad'-dock tri' an gle: A triangle which has a series of holes punched through its face, graduated to produce guide lines for lettering when a pencil is inserted in a hole and the triangle moved back and forth.

BRAIDED WIRE (elec.) braid' ed wire: A wire made of several small wires twisted or braided together.

BRAIN (space) brain: Generally refers to the man-made kind, the navigational units or electronic data processing systems.

BRAKE BAND (auto.) brake band: A semi-flexible band of metal to which is fastened a brake lining material.

BRAKE DRUM (auto.) brake drum: A steel drum, approximately 10 to 20 inches in diameter and 2 to 3 inches wide attached to the wheels of a car, against or around which the brake shoes or bands act. The friction between a shoe and the drum causes the braking action.

BRAKE HORSEPOWER (auto.) brake horse' power: The power that an engine actually delivers. So called, because this measurement was made with a prony brake.

BRAKE LINING (auto.) brake lin' ing: Woven or formed materials such as cotton or asbestos, interwoven with fine wire, used to cover brake shoes and bands.

BRAKE SHOE (auto.) brake shoe: A curved casting, matching the brake drum, which is forced against the drum for braking action. The shoe is lined.

BRAKING ELLIPSES (space) brak' ing el lipses' : A series of orbital approaches to the Earth's or any other planet's atmosphere for the purpose of slowing up a rocket preparatory to landing.

BRAKING SURFACE (auto.) brak' ing sur' face: The area in square inches of contact between the stationary and moving parts of a brake through which braking friction is obtained.

BRANCH (plumb.) branch: A horizontal drainage pipe.

BRANDERING (const.) bran' der ing: The operation of nailing furring strips to girders, joists and surfaces. This provides a space between lath and any surface so that plaster can be keyed.

BRASS (metal) brass: An alloy of copper and zinc.

BRASS FOIL (metal) brass foil: Very thin rolled brass.

BRASS THIN SPACES (graphics) brass thin spaces: Pieces of brass, one point thick, used for justifying lines.

BRAYER (graphics) bray' er: A small hand roller used to spread ink on the inking table or to apply it to the distributing plates or rollers of a press.

BRAZE WELDING (welding) braze weld' ing: The joining of metals together by a brazing alloy. The base metal is not fused in this process.

BRAZING (metal) braz' ing: A process of joining metals, similar to soldering, except that spelter is used instead of solder.

BRAZING (metal) bra' zing: Making an adhesion between two close fitting metal parts by using a low melting point brazing alloy. As the metal parts are heated the brazing metal is drawn into the joint by capillary action.

BRAZING METAL (metal) braz' ing met' al: An alloy of 98 percent copper and 2 percent tin.

BRAZING SOLDER (metal) braz' ing sol' der: A solder alloy of about 50 percent copper and 50 percent zinc with small percentages of lead and iron. It melts at 1500-1600 degrees.

BREADBOARD(elec.) bread' board: The system of laying out and wiring electronic components and circuits on a board for the purpose of designing, experimentation and testing.

BREAK (const.) break: Any projection or irregularity from the general surface of a building.

BREAK (draft.) break: A line used to show that a part of a long object has been removed so that the object can be represented within the limits of the drawing paper.

BREAKDOWN (elec.) break' down: A sudden and usually destructive flow of current due to failure of insulation under electrostatic stress.

BREAKER (auto.) break' er: An electric switch activated by a gear from the camshaft of an automotive engine. The switch opens the primary circuit of the ignition coil and induces the high voltage in the secondary circuit.

BREAKER POINTS (auto.) break' er points: The metal switch contacts on the breaker.

BREAKFAST NOOK (const.) break' fast nook: A small room, usually connected to the kitchen, to serve breakfast in.

BREAK GROUND (const.) break ground: break ground: To start the excavation for a new building.

BREAK JOINTS (const.) break joints: To select and cut boards and materials so that all end joints are not fastened to one supporting member; to arrange joints, such as shingling and siding, so that they are not directly over each other.

BREAK-LINE (graphics) break-line: The last line of a paragraph.

BREAKOFF FEELING (space) break'-off feel' ing: A feeling experienced by some flyers at high altitudes of being suddenly detached from Earth and human society.

BREAST DRILL (const.) breast drill: A tool used to hold and turn a bit or drill for boring holes in wood or metal. Power is transmitted to the drill chuck from a hand-turned crank through bevel gears.

BREEZE (const.) breeze: Furnace ashes.

BREEZEWAY (const.) breeze' way: A covered passageway between two buildings, usually open on the sides.

BREMSSTRAHLUNG (space) brems-trah' lung: Electromagnetic radiation

produced by the rapid change of velocity of an electron.

BREVVIER (graphics) brev' vier: 8 point type size.

BRICK (const.) brick: A block of building material made from clay and then fired or dried. American bricks average 2 1/2 x 4 x 8 inches in size.

BRICK CEMENT (const.) brick cement': A waterproofed masonry cement.

BRICK CONSTRUCTION (const.) brick con struc' tion: Construction with brick and mortar exterior walls which also support the structure.

BRICK COURSE (const.) brick course: A layer of bricks.

BRICK FACING (const.) brick fac' ing: See BRICK VENEER.

BRICK HAMMER (const.) brick ham'-mer: A brick hammer used for cutting and dressing brick.

BRICK SET (const.) brick set: A wide chisel used to cut bricks.

BRICK TROWEL (const.) brick trow' el: A trowel used by the bricklayer for picking up and spreading mortar.

BRICK VENEER (const.) brick ve neer': A single brick wall applied to the exterior of a building for decorative purposes.

BRIDGEBOARD (const.) bridge' board: The string of a stairway consisting of a notched board to support the treads and risers.

BRIDGE CIRCUIT (elec.) bridge cir'-cuit: A circuit with series-parallel groups of components that are connected by a common bridge. The bridge frequently is a meter in measuring devices.

BRIDGE RECTIFIER (elec.) bridge rec'-ti fi er: A full wave rectifier circuit employing four rectifiers in a bridge configuration.

BRIDGE, WHEATSTONE (elec.) bridge, wheat' stone: A bridge circuit for determining the value of an unknown component by comparison to one of known value.

BRIDGING (const.) bridg' ing: Bracing of joists by fitted pairs of diagonal braces between lower edge of one joist to top edge of adjoining joist.

BRIDGING (elec.) bridg' ing: A shunt connection; one circuit connected in parallel with another.

BRIGG'S PIPE THREADS (const.) brigg's pipe threads: The standard pipe thread used in America, for wrought iron and steel pipes.

BRIGHT ANNEALING (metal) bright an-neal' ing: The annealing of metals in a furnace with controlled atmosphere to prevent oxidation.

BRIGHTNESS (elec.) bright' ness: In television. The overall intensity of illumination of the picture.

BRIGHTNESS CONTROL (elec.) bright'-ness con trol': The control on a TV which manually varies the average brightness of the picture.

BRIGHTNESS LEVEL (elec.) bright'-ness lev' el: In television, it is the white level; the zero voltage level of the composite TV signal.

BRIGHTNESS SIGNAL (elec.) bright'-ness sig' nal: See LUMINANCE SIGNAL.

BRILLIANCE (elec.) bril' liance: The degree of clarity and brightness in a reproduced TV picture.

BRILLIANT (graphics) bril' liant: 3 1/2 point type size.

BRILLIANT COLOR (painting and dec.) bril' liant col' or: Very bright.

BRINDLE IRON (const.) brin' dle iron: An iron stirrup for hanging a joist or beam.

BRINE (air cond.) brine: A liquid used in refrigeration for transmission of heat without change in state.

BRINE SYSTEM (air cond.) brine sys'-tem:
CLOSED, a completely enclosed refrigeration system in which the brine does not contact the atmosphere except in the vented expansion tank in the high point of the system.
OPEN, a refrigeration system in which the brine is returned to an open storage tank which serves as a reservoir.

BRINNEL HARDNESS (metal) brin' nel hard' ness: A hardness test for metals based on the penetration of a steel ball 10 millimeters in diameter under a load of 3000 kilograms for a period of ten seconds.

BRIQUETTE (const.) bri' quette: Fuel such as coal or charcoal compressed into small cakes.

BRISTLE (crafts) bris' tle: Coarse stiff hair used in brush making.

BRISTOL BOARD (crafts) bris' tol board: A good quality heavy cardboard supplied in white or colors.

BRITANNIA METAL (crafts.) bri tan ni a met' al: See PEWTER.

BRITISH THERMAL UNIT, Btu (air cond.) Brit'ish ther'mal u'nit, Btu: The amount of heat required to raise one pound of water from 39 deg. to 40 deg. F. One Btu = 778.6 ft. lbs.

BRITTLE (metal) brit'tle: The property of a material which is easily broken.

BROACH (metal) hroach: A metal cutting tool for finishing holes. It is a tapered tool with transverse cutting edges which is forced through a roughly finished hole.

BROACHED WORK (const.) broached work: A finish of broad grooves put on building stone by dressing with a special punch.

BROADCASTING (elec.) broad'cast-ing: The transmitting of radio programs for public entertainment and information.

BROAD TUNED (elec.) broad tuned: A circuit tuned to pass equally well a broad band of frequencies.

BROKEN LINE (draft.) bro'ken line: A line composed of long dashes used to indicate points from which measurements are taken.

BROKEN SECTION (draft.) bro'ken sec'tion: A small part is sectioned, outlined by an irregular line.

BRONZE (metal) bronze: An alloy of copper and tin.

BRONZE WELDING (welding) weld'ing: See BRAZE WELDING.

BRONZING (graphics) bronz'ing: Covering a printed surface with bronze powder.

BRONZING LIQUID (painting and dec.)

bronz'ing liq'uid: A vehicle especially formulated for use as a binder for aluminum or gold bronze powder.

BROWN COAT (const.) brown coat: The second coat of plaster or stucco.

BROWN & SHARPE (elec.) The former name of the American Wire Gauge system of designation of wire sizes.

BROWN AND SHARPE TAPER (metal) Brown and Sharpe ta'per: A taper system used in machine tools, especially milling machine spindles. Sizes are numbered and all have a taper of 1/2 inch per foot except No. 10 which is .5161 inches per foot.

BROWNSTONE (const.) brown'stone: A reddish-brown sandstone used in building construction.

BRUSH (elec.) brush: A sliding contact to make connections to a rotating armature in a generator or motor.

BRUSHABILITY (painting and dec) brush a bil'i ty: The ability or ease with which a paint can be brushed.

BRUSH EFFECT (elec.) brush ef fect': A bluish discharge from sharp points in circuits carrying high voltages.

BRUSH HAND (painting and dec.) brush hand: A painter whose ability lies in his skill in applying material.

B-SUPPLY (elec.) b-sup'ply: Voltages supplied for the plate circuits of electron tubes.

BTU (air cond.) Btu: British thermal unit. The quantity of heat required to raise one pound of water one degree Fahrenheit.

BUCKET TRAP (const.) buck'et trap: A special kind of valve used in a steam heating system for the removal of condensed moisture and air, without allowing steam to escape.

BUCKING BAR (metal) buck' ing bar: A bar held against the head of a rivet while it is being set.

BUCKING COIL (elec.) buck' ing coil: A coil in a loudspeaker in which magnetic fields are produced which oppose the fields of the principal coil.

BUCKLE (const.) buck' le: To bulge upward; warp; lift up.

BUFFER (elec.) buf' fer: An isolation amplifier; an electron tube stage used to prevent interaction between stages.

BUFFER STORAGE (automation) buff'-er stor' age: An intermediate storage between data input and main internal storage.

BUFFET (const.) buf fet' (boo fa'): A small cabinet for holding dishes; a space or counter set aside in a restaurant for serving several kinds of food.

BUFFING COMPOUND (paint. and dec.) buff' ing com' pound: Soft abrasive in stick form, bonded with wax.

BUFFING WHEEL (metal) buff'ing wheel: Polishing wheels made of disks of cotton and felt. They are used with a variety of fine abrasives.

BUG (elec.) bug: A high speed semi-automatic key for transmitting code.

BUILDING BLOCK UNITS (automation) build' ing block u' nits: See MODULAR UNITS.

BUILDING CODE (const.) build' ing code: Local laws and ordinances regulating construction work.

BUILDING LINE (const.) build' ing line: The line between private and public property.

BUILT-IN (const.) built-in: A term used to describe furniture, cabinets and fixtures in a building which are fitted to a special position and usually are a part of the structure.

BUILT-UP (const.) built-up: A term used to describe the use of two or more parts fastened together to serve as a single unit.

BUILDUP (welding) build' up: The amount of weld extending above the surfaces of the base metals being joined.

BUILT-UP ROOF (const.) built-up roof: The application of roofing materials in sealed waterproof layers on a roof which has only a slight slope.

BUILT-UP TIMBER (const.) built-up tim' ber: A beam made by fastening several timbers together and forming a single timber of larger dimension.

BULKHEAD (const.) bulk' head: A structure built over an elevator shaft or stairwell, usually above the roof line.

BULKING VALUE (painting and dec.) bulk' ing val' ue: The ability of a pigment to add volume to a paint.

BULLET CATCH (const.) bul' let catch: A fastener in which a round ball is extended by spring mounted back of ball.

BULL GEAR LOCK (metal) bull gear lock: A pin type lock between the cone pulley and the bull gear in the lathe headstock.

BULL HEADER (const.) bull head' er A brick with one rounded corner used to form window sills and placed around doorways.

BULL LADLE (metal) bull la' dle: A two man ladle for carrying molten metal in a foundry.

BULL NOSE PLANE (const.) bull nose plane: A plane, with its cutting iron placed near the forward end, which permits its use in corners and places difficult to reach.

BULL NOSE STARTING STEP (const.) bull nose start' ing step: A step which is rounded and finished on one end which extends around and beyond the newel post.

BULL PINE (const.) bull pine: California white pine; a highly resinous wood used in building construction.

BULL STRETCHER (const.) bull stretch' er: A brick with one rounded corner and laid with its long face exposed.

BULL WHEEL (metal) bull wheel: A large gear, sometimes called the crank gear, which gives reciprocating motion to arm attached to it by a crankpin.

BULWARK (const.) bul' wark: A wall used for protective purposes; a breakwater.

BUMPER (const.) bump' er: A stop attached to the wall or door to limit the door swing and protect the wall.

BUMPING HAMMER (metal) bump' ing ham' mer: A double faced hammer used to remove dents and bumps from a sheet metal surface. Used by the auto body repairman to reshape body surfaces.

BUNCHING (elec.) bunch' ing: Velocity modulation of an electron stream that produces an alternating current component as a result of differences in electron transit time.

BUNG (crafts.) bung: A quantity of filled fire clay boxes in a kiln.

BUNSEN BURNER (crafts.) bun' sen burn' er: A gas burner, used in the laboratory, that burns a mixture of gas and air.

BuORD (elec.) buord: Abbreviation for Bureau of Ordinance.

BURL (wood.) burl: A protruding lump on a tree resulting from a cluster of buds remaining dormant beneath the bark of a tree. These burls frequently have exquisite grain patterns and are used in furniture making.

BURNED FINISH (painting and decorating) burned fin' ish: A wood finish in which the hard portion of the grain of the wood stands out in relief. The soft portion of the wood grain is burned with a blowtorch and the charred sections removed with a wire brush.

BURNED METAL (welding) burned met'- al: A term applied to metal in which some of the carbon has been changed into carbon dioxide and some iron into iron oxide. Sometimes caused by overheating with an oxyacetylene flame.

BURNETT'S PROCESS (const.) burnett's proc' ess: The treatment of timber with zinc chloride as a preservative.

BURNING (welding) burn' ing: Violent combination of oxygen with any substance which produces heat. This word is sometimes used instead of Flame Cutting.

BURNING IN (painting and dec.) burn'- ing in: Repairing a finish by melting stick shellac into the damaged places by using a heated knife blade or iron.

BURNISH (auto.) bur' nish: To smooth

and polish a surface by rubbing with a special tool under pressure.

BURNISHER (const.) bur'nish er: A hardened steel tool used to finish and polish metal by friction. This tool is used to turn over the edge of a cabinet scraper.

BURNOUT (space) burn'out: The point in time or in the missile trajectory when propellant is exhausted or its flow is cut off.

BURNT SIENNA (painting and decorating) burnt si en'na: Sienna that has been roasted. Reddish brown in color.

BURNT UMBER (painting and decorating) burnt um'ber: Umber that has been roasted. Dark brown in color.

BURIN (graphics) bu'rin: An engraver's tool with an oblique point of tempered steel. Used to engrave lines.

BURR (const.) burr: A ragged edge; a rough edge left by a cutting tool; a washer on the small end of a rivet.

BURR (metal) burr: A small projection or roughness left on metal after machining or cutting.

BURR (plumb.) burr: Roughness and sharp edges on interior wall of a pipe resulting from cutting and improper finishing.

BURST (elec.) burst: See COLOR SYNC BURST.

BUS (elec.) bus: A heavy conductor; busbar.

BUSBAR (elec.) bus'bar: The main circuit to which branch circuits are connected; a heavy solid wire providing a common connection for all points in a circuit of the same voltage. Ex: common ground or AVC BUS.

BUSHING (auto.) bush'ing: A washer type plug used for reducing the size of a hole or to line a hole with bearing or protective materials.

BUSHING (plumb.) bush'ing: A plug which screws into the end of a pipe or fitting. The plug is drilled and tapped to receive a threaded pipe of smaller diameter.

BUTT (const.) butt: To joint end to end without overlap; a door hinge of any type except a strap hinge.

BUTTER (const.) but'ter: To apply mortar to a brick.

BUTTERFLY VALVE (auto.) but'terfly valve: A damper type valve which rotates on a shaft. Used in the automotive carburetor to control air flow into the carburetor.

BUTT GAUGE (wood.) butt gauge: A special marking gauge designed to rapidly mark-out the mortise cuts for a butt hinge.

BUTT HINGE (wood.) butt hinge: A door hinge secured to the edge of the door and the face of the jamb which butts against it.

BUTT-JOINT (const.) butt-joint: The point at which two pieces of timber or lumber butt together.

BUTT JOINT (Wallpaper) (painting and dec.) butt joint: Joint made by trimming both selvedges and butting the edges together.

BUTTON (elec.) but'ton: A metal container filled with carbon granules, used in a carbon microphone.

BUTTONS (metal) but' tons: Steel bushings fastened to work to assist toolmaker in the accurate location of holes.

BUTTRESS (const.) but' tress: A structure built against a wall to increase its strength and stability.

BUTTRESS THREAD (metal) but' tress thread: A thread form triangular in shape with one face perpendicular to the axis of the screw. Used in applications where threads must withstand shock.

BUTT WELDING (metal) butt weld' ing: Welding pieces of metal together without overlapping; to weld directly end to end.

BUTYL ACETATE (painting and dec.) bu' tyl ace' e tate: A lacquer solvent made from butyl alcohol by reaction with acetic acid.

BUTYL ALCOHOL (painting and dec.) bu' tyl al' co hol: An alcohol formed by the combination of hydroxyl with butyl; an alcohol obtained from the fermentation of corn.

BUZZER (elec.) buzz' er: A magnetic device used as a call signal. The buzz is made by a vibrating armature.

BUZZ SAW (const.) buzz saw: A circular saw, power driven.

BX CABLE (elec.) bx cab' le: A flexible armored cable; flexible metallic cover for wires used in electric wiring.

BY-LINE (graphics) by-line: The line over or under a newspaper article identifying the writer.

BYPASS (plumb.) bypass: Any connection which will permit a fluid to flow around a valve, fixture or connection; an alternate path; a secondary pipe which provides an alternate path around an obstruction. The bypass may be valve controlled.

BYPASS CAPACITOR (elec.) bypass capac' i tor: A fixed capacitor which bypasses unwanted a-c currents to ground.

C (elec.) The letter symbol for a capacitor; capacitance; temperature centigrade; symbol for the element carbon.

C and SC (graphics) Letters identifying Capitals and Small Capitals.

CABBAGING PRESS (metal) cab' baging press: A press to compress scrap metal into bundles for easy handling and remelting.

CABINET (graphics) cab' net: A steel or wooden frame containing type cases.

CABINET PROJECTION (draft.) cab' i-net pro jec' tion: An oblique projection in which receding lines of projectors or edges are drawn to half size.

CABINET WORK (const.) cab' i net work: The trade of making fine furniture and cabinets.

CABIN HOOK (const.) cab' in hook: A hook and eye fastener used on cabinet doors.

CABLE (elec.) ca' ble: May be a stranded conductor or a group of single conductors insulated from each other.

CABLE, ENTRANCE (elec.) ca' ble, en' trance: A heavy cable, used for electrical connections between a main line and a building.

CABLE, NONMETALLIC (elec.) ca' ble, non me tal' lic: Two or more insulated wires sheathed in a flexible fabric cover. It is used for interior residential house wiring.

CABLE, SHIELDED (elec.) ca'ble shielded: A conductor or conductors enclosed in a metallic covering which acts as an electromagnetic shield. The shield is usually electrically grounded.

CABOCHON (crafts.) ca bo chon': A smooth rounded stone, without facets.

CABOT'S QUILT (const.) cab'ot's quilt: Insulating material made of dried eel grass and held between sheets of heavy paper. It was used by early pioneer builders in New England.

CABRIOLE (wood.) cab'ri ole: A design of furniture leg which combines a convex and a concave curve and terminates in some type of foot.

CADASTRAL MAP (draft.) ca das'tral map: A map showing the extent, value and ownership of land for purposes of taxation.

CADMIUM (elec.) cad'mi um: A silver-white metal used for plating and as contact and terminals in electronic circuits.

CADMIUM LITHOPONE (painting and dec.) cad'mi um lith'o pone: A series of yellows and reds that are permanent to light and resistant to alkalies.

CADMIUM RED (paint. and dec.) cad'mi um red: Non-fading red pigment made from cadmium and selenium metals.

CADMIUM YELLOW (painting and dec.) cad'mi um yel'low: Pigment prepared by precipitation from acid solution of soluble cadmium salt with hydrogen sulphide gas.

CADUCEUS (const.) ca du'ce us: The staff of Mercury; the symbol of the medical profession.

CAGE (const.) cage: A timber construction which encloses another.

CAISSON (const.) cais'son: A water-tight box or shaft used to surround work and provide working space for underwater construction.

CALCIMINE (painting and decorating) cal'ci mine: Inexpensive paint composed mostly of whiting or chalk, glue and water.

CALCINE (painting and dec.) cal'cine: To change to powder by heat; to burn to ashes or powder; oxidize.

CALCINING (const.) cal'cin ing: Lime burning; making lime by heating limestone to high temperatures.

CALCITE (const.) cal'cite: Limestone; a flux used in the manufacturing of pig iron and steel.

CALCIUM CARBONATE (const.) cal'cium car'bon ate: A white powder or colorless crystalline compound found mainly in limestone, marble and chalk.

CALCIUM CARBONATE (painting and dec.) cal'ci um car'bon ate: Earth product obtained from deposits of chalk, dolomite, etc. Used as extender pigment.

CALCIUM CHLORIDE (const.) cal'ci um chlo'ride: A chemical used to absorb moisture.

CALCIUM DRIERS (painting and dec.) cal'ci um dri'ers: Used widely in combination with other metal driers to convert paint to hard films.

CALCIUM SULPHATE (painting and dec.) cal'ci um sul'phate: White inert pigment which provides very little color or opacity.

CALDRON (metal) cal' dron: A large metal kettle.

CALENDER (painting and dec.) cal' ender: Rolls through which paper is run during manufacturing to produce a smooth glossy finish.

CALENDERED PAPERS (painting and dec.) cal' en dered pa' pers: Wallpapers with hard finish.

CALIBER (plumb.) cal' i ber: Internal diameter or bore measurement.

CALIBRATE (elec.) cal' i brate: To compare and adjust a measuring device to a known standard.

CALIBRATION (air cond.) cal i bra'-tion: The process of dividing and numbering the scale of a measuring instrument. Correction and determination of error in a scale.

CALIFORNIA JOB CASE (graphics) Cal' i for nia job case: A type case containing a complete font of type for hand composition, arranged in a particular manner.

CALIPER (metal) cal' i per: A tool used for measuring outside and inside diameters of work. It is not a direct reading tool. Caliper setting must be measured with scale or micrometer.

CALIPER RULE (wood.) cal' i per rule: A small rule with a sliding extension for measuring inside and outside dimensions. Useful for measuring the thickness of boards, the diameter of a shaft or a hole.

CALKING (plumb.) calk' ing: The plugging of an opening or joint around a pipe with oakum or lead.

CALKING COMPOUND (const.) calk' ing com' pound: A mastic material used in construction to seal joints around doors and windows.

CALORIE (elec.) cal' o rie: The amount of heat energy required to raise one gram of water one degree centigrade.

CALORIFIC VALUE (auto.) cal o rif'-ic val' ue: The heating value of a fuel.

CALORIMETER (air cond.) cal o rim'-e ter: An instrument used to measure the heating value of a fuel.

CAM (metal) cam: A device on a rotating shaft which converts rotary motion into reciprocal motion.

CAM ANGLE (auto.) cam an' gle: The number of degrees of rotation of the distributor shaft during which the breaker points are closed.

CAMBER (auto.) cam' ber: The outward tilt from vertical of the front wheels of an automobile.

CAMBER (const.) cam' ber: The convexity of a beam, during installation, to prevent it from sagging when its load is applied.

CAMBIUM LAYER (wood.) cam' bi um lay' er: A cellular layer between the sapwood and the bark of a tree. This layer forms new sapwood on the inside for each growth period of the tree.

CAMERA BOOM (elec.) cam' er a boom: A versatile mount and base for a camera. The camera may be moved around, up and down and right or left.

CAMERA TUBE (elec.) cam' er a tube: The electronic tube used in a television camera to convert a picture image into electrical signals by a scanning process.

CAM FOLLOWER (auto.) cam fol' lower: A roller or follower which rides on a cam surface and follows the contour of the cam.

CAM GROUND PISTON (auto.) cam ground pis' ton: A piston which is made slightly elliptical in shape, to compensate for heat expansion.

CAMSHAFT (auto.) cam' shaft: A shaft with cams machined at correct intervals to actuate the valve lifting mechanisms.

CAN (space) can: A shield or container for a missile, by which environment can be controlled.

CANDELA (elec.) can del' a: A unit of measurement of light intensity. It is 1.9% smaller than a candle.

CANDELILLA WAX (painting and dec.) can del il' la wax: Wax obtained from small shrub grown in Texas and Mexico.

CANDLE (elec.) can' dle: A unit of luminous intensity.

CANNEL COAL (metal) can' nel coal: A coal which is rich in volatile constituents and burns with a bright flame like wood.

CANOPY (const.) can' o py: An ornamental roof structure usually supported from pillars extending out from a doorway of a building.
(Elec.) A metal cover to protect and improve the appearance of the connection of a light fixture to the ceiling or wall.

CANT (wood.) cant: To tilt; to slant; a molding formed of angles and plain surfaces rather than curves.

CANT HOOK (wood.) cant hook: A tool used to handle logs in the lumbering business. It consists of a stout pointed shaft with a steel pivoted hook attached near the pointed end.

CANTILEVER (const.) can' ti le ver: A structural member supported at one end only and which supports a projecting load.

CANT STRIP (wood.) cant strip: A wooden strip placed under the first course of shingles or siding to give this course the same slant as the other courses.

CAP (const.) cap: A finished cement top on a chimney or a wall.

CAP (plumb.) cap: A fitting to close the end of a threaded pipe.

CAPACITANCE (elec.) cap pac' i tance: The inherent property of an electric circuit that opposes a change in voltage. The property of a circuit whereby energy may be stored in an electrostatic field.

CAPACITANCE, DISTRIBUTED (elec.) ca pac' i tance, dis trib' uted: The capacitance in a circuit resulting from adjacent turns on coils, parallel leads and connections.

CAPACITIVE COUPLING (elec.) ca pac' i tive cou' pling: Coupling resulting from capacitive effect between components or elements in an electron tube.

CAPACITIVE REACTANCE (X_C) (elec.) ca pac' i tive re act' ance: The opposition to an a-c current as a result of capacitance.

CAPACITOR (elec.) ca pac' i tor: A device which possesses capacitance. A simple capacitor consists of two metal plates separated by an insulator.

CAPACITOR (elec.) ca pac' i tor:

AIR, A capacitor which uses air as a dielectric.

BLOCKING, A capacitor used to block d-c but allow a-c to pass.

BYPASS, See BYPASS CAPACITOR.

CERAMIC, A small high voltage capacitor using steatite or titanium dioxide as a dielectric.

DECOUPLING, A capacitor used to prevent a signal from one stage being transferred to another stage.

ELECTROLYTIC, See ELECTRO-LYTIC.

MICA, A fixed or semi-adjustable capacitor using mica as a dielectric.

PADDER, A small semi-variable capacitor connected in series with a main tuning capacitor to adjust the low frequency end of tuning range.

PAPER, A capacitor using metal foil as plates separated by waxed paper.

TRIMMER, A small semi-variable capacitor connected across a main tuning capacitor.

VARIABLE, An adjustable capacitor, usually using air as a dielectric. Its capacity may be changed by moving a set of plates called the rotor which interleave a fixed set of plates called the stator.

CAPACITOR INPUT FILTER (elec.) ca-pac' i tor in' put fil' ter: A filter employing a capacitor as its input.

CAPACITOR MOTOR (elec.) ca pac' i-tor mo' tor: A modified version of the split phase motor, employing a capacitor in series with its starting winding, to produce a phase displacement for starting.

CAPACITOR PICKUP (elec.) ca pac'-i tor pick' up: A phone cartridge which produces an electrical output upon variation of its capacitance.

CAPACITY (elec.) ca pac' i ty: The ability of a battery to produce a current over a given length of time. Capacity is measured in ampere-hours.

CAPE CANAVERAL (space): See Cape Kennedy.

CAPE CHISEL (metal) cape chis' el: A type of cold chisel with a narrow blade for cutting keyways, grooves and slots.

CAPE KENNEDY (space) Cape Ken' ne-dy: A cape on the east coast of Florida used as a laboratory for launching missiles or space vehicles. The Air Force Test Center operates the launching site. Officially known as the Atlantic Missile Range. Formerly named, Cape Canaveral.

CAPILLARITY (air cond.) cap il lar'-i ty: The action of liquids in contact with a solid, such as a slender tube. The liquid is raised or lowered as a result of the combined forces of adhesion, cohesion and surface-tension of the liquid.

CAPILLARY ACTION (welding) cap' il-lar y ac' tion: Property of a liquid to move into small spaces if it has the ability to "wet" these surfaces.

CAPILLARY TUBE (air cond.) cap' il-lar y tube: A small diameter tube used as a flow control for refrigerant between the high and low sides of the system.

CAPITAL (const.) cap' i tal: The upper part of a column; familiar Greek and Roman types are represented as Corinthian, Doric, Ionic, Tuscan and composite types.

CAPITAL LETTER (graphics) cap' i tal let' ter: A large letter of a font of type or of an alphabet.

CAPS (graphics) caps: Capital letters.

CAP SCREW (metal) cap screw: A finished machine screw generally used without a nut.

CAPSTAN (elec.) cap' stan: A wheel or drum used to drive a belt.

CAP STONE (const.) cap stone: A stone used to cap or crown a wall of a structure.

CAPSULE (space) cap' sule: A small, sealed, pressurized cabin with an acceptable environment, usually for containing a man or animal for extremely high altitude flights, oribital space flight, or emergency escape.

CAPTION (graphics) cap' tion: The descriptive material printed under an illustration.

CAPTIVE FIRING (space) cap' tive fir'- ing: Test firing of a complete missile where all or any part of the propulsion system is operated at full or partial thrust while the missile is restrained in the test stand.

CARAT (crafts) car' at: A unit of weight measurement in jewelry equal to about .2 grams or 3.17 grains.

CARBIDE TOOLS (metal) car' bide tools: A machine cutting tool with a carbide tip welded on the cutting edge.

CARBON car' bon: A nonmetallic element found in all organic substances. Symbol C.

CARBON (metal) car' bon: An element which, when combined with iron, forms various kinds of steel.

CARBON ARC WELDING (welding) car'- bon arc weld' ing: An electric welding process in which carbon electrodes are used. A filler rod may or may not be used.

CARBON BLACK (paint. and dec.) car'- bon black: Jet black, nonbleeding pigment, made by burning natural gas in insufficient supply of air.

CARBON DIOXIDE car' bon di ox' ide: The product of complete combustion of carbon fuels. In the solid form it is called "dry ice". In a gaseous state it is used as a fire extinguisher.

CARBON FILAMENT (elec.) car' bon fil' a ment: The filament in an incandescent lamp composed of a carbonized thread or fiber.

CARBON HISS (elec.) car' bon hiss: A noise developed in a carbon microphone when a high d-c current passes through the carbon granules.

CARBONIZATION (air cond.) car bon i- za' tion: Carbon deposits as a result of oxidation of lubricating oils.

CARBON MONOXIDE (auto.) car' bon mon ox' ide: A colorless, tasteless, odorless and very poisonous gas resulting from insufficient oxygen during combustion.

CARBON PILE (elec.) car' bon pile: A variable resistor made of carbon wafers under spring compression. As the wafers are compressed, contact areas between wafers increases and resistance decreases.

CARBON RHEOSTAT (elec.) car' bon rhe' o stat: A variable resistance using carbon as its resistive material.

CARBON STEEL (metal) car' bon steel: A high carbon steel used for making cutting tools.

CARBONIZING (welding) car' bon iz ing: See Carburizing or Reducing Flame.

CARBON TETACHLORIDE (paint. and dec.) car' bon tet ra chlo' ride: A colorless, nonflammable liquid which is used as a solvent and a cleaner. It is used also as a filler in some types of fire extinguishers. Caution: Carbon tetrachloride is dangerous to use. It may be absorbed either through your lungs, or your skin, and the effect is accumulative. If used, be sure excellent ventilation is provided.

CARBOY (elec.) car' boy: A large glass bottle used for shipping and storage of acids and distilled water.

CARBURETOR (auto.) car' bu ret or: A device for mixing and controlling the air and fuel supplied to an engine.

CARBURETOR BARREL (auto.) car 'bu ret or bar' rel: The metal tubular section of a carburetor surrounding the suction air chamber.

CARBURETOR BOWL (auto.) car' bu ret or bowl: A reservoir compartment in a carburetor which holds the liquid fuel or gasoline.

CARBURETOR FLOAT (auto.) car' bu ret or float: A float in the bowl of the carburetor which controls the entry of gasoline to the bowl and maintains it at constant level.

CARBURIZING (metal) car' bu riz ing: The process of adding carbon to the surface of steel by heating the metal while in contact with carbonaceous materials.

CARBURIZING FLAME (metal - welding) car' bu riz ing flame: The flame of an oxacetylene welding torch when improperly adjusted so that there is an excess of acetylene.

CARCASE (wood.) car' case: The frame of a house; the frame of a piece of furniture.

CARDBOARD (graphics) card' board: A stiff, compact pasteboard made in various qualities and thicknesses.

CARD CUT (const.) card cut: Chinese lattice work.

CARDIOID (elec.) car' di oid: A heart shaped response curve in a polar coordinate graph.

CARNAUBA (elec.) car nau' ba: A wax derived from the Brazilian palm seed for insulating components.

CARNAUBA WAX (paint. and dec.) carnau' ba wax: A hard wax obtained from a species of palm grown mostly in Brazil.

CARNOT'S CYCLE carnot's cy' cle: (auto.) A series of operations forming the work cycle of an ideal heat engine of maximum thermal efficiency.

CARPENTER'S SQUARE (wood) car' pen ter's square: See STEEL SQUARE.

CARPET STRIP (wood.) car' pet strip: A strip across a doorway to hold down a carpet.

CARRIAGE (const.) car' riage: The timber which supports the steps of a wooden stairway.

CARRIAGE BOLT (metal) car' riage bolt: An oval head bolt with a square neck which prevents the bolt from turning when the nut is tightened.

CARRIAGES (const.) car' riages: The supports for the treads and risers of a stairway.

CARRIER (automation) car' ri er: The vehicle or carrier signal which can be modulated to transfer information or messages through a machine.

CARRIER (automation) car' ri er: Major part, on the assembly line, to which other parts are fastened or inserted.

CARRIER (elec.) car' ri er: Usually a radio frequency continuous wave to which modulation is applied. The frequency of the transmitting station.

CARRIER (in a semiconductor) (elec.) car' ri er: A conducting hole or electron.

CARRIER SHIFT (elec.) car' ri er shift: A change in average power of a modulated carrier wave.

CARRIER SUPPRESSED (elec.) car' ri er sup pressed': The transmission of radio signals in which the carrier is suppressed and not transmitted.

CARRYING CAPACITY (elec.) car' ry ing ca pac' i ty: The ability of a conductor to carry a current, expressed in amperes. Refer to the National Electric Code.

CARTRIDGE FUSE (elec.) car' tridge fuse: A fuse enclosed in a tubular insulating material. Some types have renewable fusible links.

CARTRIDGE, PHONO (elec.) car' tridge, pho' no: A small device at the end of the phonograph arm which holds the stylus and converts the movement of the stylus into electrical signals. The transducer may be a crystal, ceramic or variable reluctance type.

CASCADE (elec.) cas cade': The arrangement of amplifiers where the output of one stage becomes the input of the next, throughout a series of stages.

CASCADE SYSTEM (air cond.) cas cade' sys' tem: A refrigerating system employing two or more refrigeration circuits, in which the evaporator of one circuit cools the condenser of another circuit.

CASCODE (elec.) cas code': Electron tubes connected so that the second tube acts as a plate load for the first. Used to obtain higher input resistance and retain a low noise factor.

CASE (graphics) case: The printed cover of a book. It has been stamped and made up to proper size to fit book.

CASE (graphics) case: A tray with compartments to hold type from which the compositor works.

CASE BOUND (graphics) case bound: A book bound in stiff board cover.

CASED (const.) cased: Covered or enclosed, usually with finished materials in order to improve appearance.

CASEHARDEN (metal) case' hard en: The process of heating low carbon steel while packed in contact with carbonaceous material, so that its surface will absorb carbon and become high-carbon steel for a depth of several thousandths of an inch.

CASEIN (paint. and dec.) ca' sein: The protein of milk and the principal constituent of cheese. Casein is used extensively in the manufacture of water paints.

CASEMENT (const.) case' ment: Windows which open on hinges.

CASEMENT WINDOW (const.) case' ment win' dow: A window hinged on its vertical edge so that it may be swung inward or outward.

CASE RACK (graphics) case rack: A rack or frame to store cases.

CASING (const.) cas' ing: The finished

trim boards or moldings around a door, window or an exposed timber.

CAST (graphics) cast: A duplicate of a type form obtained from electrotyping or sterotyping.

CAST (paint. and dec.) cast: Inclination of one color to look like another.

CASTELLATED NUT (auto.) cas' tel_lat ed nut: A nut resembling a castle battlement, with holes for locking with a cotter key.

CASTER (auto.) cast' er: The backward tilt of the kingpins in the front wheels of an automobile.

CASTING (metal) cast' ing: Molten metal poured into a mold or container where it solidifies.

CASTING-OFF (graphics) cast' ing_off: Measuring type to determine how it will divide into the page.

CAST IRON (metal) cast iron: One of the common commercial iron forms. It is obtained by remelting pig iron and casting to desired shapes. Cast iron usually contains between 2 and 3.75 percent carbon.

CASTOR OIL (paint. and dec.) cas' tor oil: Oil obtained from the castor bean.

CATALYST cat' a list: A substance which by its presence accelerates velocity of reaction between substances.

CATCH BASIN (plumb.) catch ba' sin: A receptacle or pool to retain liquids for the purpose of settling_out and retaining sediment.

CATCHING THE THREAD (metal) catch' ing the thread: The method of resetting a cutting tool to finish a partially cut thread.

CATCH-LINE (graphics) catch_line: A line in an advertisement consisting of a few words to attract attention, but not necessary to give meaning to the main copy of the advertisement.

CATENARY (elec.) cat' e nar y: The curve formed by the free suspension of a wire between two poles.

CAT HEAD (metal) cat head: An adjustable collar mounted on long slender work in a lathe to provide a true running surface and bearing for a center rest.

CATHODE (elec.) cath' ode: The emitter in an electron tube.

CATHODE FOLLOWER (elec.) cath' ode fol' low er: A single stage Class A amplifier, the output of which is taken from across the unbypassed cathode resistor.

CATHODE RAY TUBE (elec.) cath' ode ray tube: A vacuum tube in which electrons emitted from the cathode are shaped into a narrow beam and accelerated to a high velocity before striking a phosphor-coated viewing screen.

CATION (elec.) cat' i on: A positively charged ion.

CAT-STEP CIRCULAR (graphics) cat-step cir' cu lar: A pull-out circular; a circular printed on two sides of a long strip of paper which is folded over and over.

CAT WALK (const.) cat walk: A narrow walk or bridge over an engine room.

CAT-WHISKER (elec.) cat-whisk' er: A fine wire used to contact a crystal.

CAUL (wood) caul: A tool used to shape veneer to a curved surface.

CAULK (const.) caulk: To fill cracks and seams with caulking material.

CAULKING COMPOUND (const.) caulk'ing compound: A semidrying or slow-drying plastic material used to seal joints or fill crevices around windows, chimneys, etc.

CAVALIER PROJECTION (draft.) cav-a lier' pro jec' tion: An oblique projection with its oblique projectors or edges at an angle of 45 degrees with the plane of projection.

CAVETTO (const.) ca vet' to: A combination concave quarter round and square molding.

CAVIL ca' vil: A heavy sledge hammer used to rough shape stone at the quarry.

CAVITATION (space) cav i ta' tion: The rapid formation and collapse of vapor pockets in a flowing liquid under very low pressure.

CAVITY RESONATOR (elec.) cav' i ty res' o na tor: A metal cavity that acts as a tuned circuit at a specific frequency.

C-BATTERY (elec.) C-bat' ter y: A battery used to supply grid bias voltages.

C CLAMP (wood.) C clamp: A metal screw clamp shaped like the letter C.

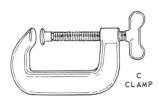

C CLAMP

CEDAR, AROMATIC RED (Juniperus Virginiana) (wood.) ce' dar: A light, soft, fine grained and aromatic wood. Its sapwood is white but the heartwood is reddish-purple.

CEDILLA (graphics) ce dil' la: A mark under the letter c when it occurs before a, o or u to indicate that it has the sound of s.

CEILING (const.) ceil' ing: The material covering which hides the joists of the floor above a room.

CEILING JOISTS (const.) ceil' ing joists: Lumber used to support the ceiling.

CELESTIAL GUIDANCE (space) ce les' tial guid' ance: The guidance of a missile or other vehicle by reference to celestial bodies.

CELESTIAL MECHANICS (space) ce les' tial me chan' ics: The study of the motions of celestial bodies under the influence of gravitational fields.

CELL (elec.) cell: One section of a storage battery; a single electrolytic unit for producing electrical energy.

CELLAR (const.) cel' lar: See BASEMENT.

CELLARET (wood.) cel' lar et: A drawer or compartment in a buffet or sideboard for storing bottles.

CELLULOID (auto.) cel' lu loid: A transparent flexible material made of gun cotton and camphor.

CELLULOSE (paint. and dec.) cel' lulose: An inert substance, the chief component of the cell walls of plants.

CELLULOSE ACETATE (paint. and dec.) cel' lu lose ac' e tate: A binder made by chemical reaction of acetic acid on cellulose.

CELLULOSE NITRATE (paint. and dec.) cel' lu lose ni' trate: A binder made by chemical reaction of nitric acid on cellulose.

CELTIC (graphics) cel' tic: The name of a type face.

CEMENT (const.) ce ment': An adhesive material used to bind objects together.

CEMENT BASE PAINT (paint.and dec.) ce ment' base paint: A paint composed of Portland cement, lime, pigment and other modifying ingredients. Sold as dry powder. Mixed with water for application.

CEMENTED CARBIDES (metal) ce ment' ed car' bides: One of the hardest known substances made from particles of tungsten carbide cemented together with a suitable binder. Carbides from other metals such as tantalum, titanium and others are also used.

CEMENTITE (metal ce ment' ite: Iron carbide, Fe_3C.

CEMENT PLASTER (const.) ce ment' plas' ter: A finish coat of plaster consisting of Portland cement and sand.

CENTER DRILL (metal) cen' ter drill: Usually a combined drill and countersink for drilling center holes in work in preparation for mounting in lathe.

CENTER FREQUENCY (elec.) cen' ter fre' quen cy: The assigned frequency of an FM broadcasting station; the frequency of the unmodulated carrier wave in FM.

CENTER GAUGE (metal) cen' ter gauge: A tool used to check the accuracy of 60 deg. centers.

CENTER GAUGE

CENTER HEAD (metal) cen' ter head: A V-shaped attachment for the blade of a machinest's square, used to locate the center of round stock. See COMBINATION SQUARE.

CENTER HUNG SASH (const.) cen' ter hung sash: A sash hung so that it opens horizontally around a center suspension.

CENTERING (elec.) cen' ter ing: The technical adjustments in a television service to center the picture on the screen.

CENTERING (metal) cen' ter ing: The operation of mounting work between centers in a lathe.

CENTERLESS GRINDING (metal) cen' ter less grind' ing: A grinding machine in which the work rests on supports between a high speed grinding wheel and a regulating wheel moving in the reverse direction.

CENTER LINE (draft.) cen' ter line: A line consisting of alternate short and long dashes, used to designate centers of holes, arcs and symetrical objects.

CENTERLINE OF PERFORMANCE (automation) cen' ter line of perform' ance: The average of a sample of measurements.

CENTER OF GRAVITY (auto.) cen' ter of grav' i ty: The point in a mass around which its weight is evenly balanced or distributed; point of equilibrium.

CENTER OF VISION (draft.) cen' ter of vi' sion: The point on the horizon line directly in front of the observer.

CENTER PUNCH (metal) cen' ter punch: A small round tool with conical point, used for making punch marks. A punch mark is used for starting a drill easily.

CENTER PUNCH

CENTER REST (metal) cen' ter rest: A rest or support for the center of long slender work being turned in a lathe.

CENTERS (metal) cen' ters: Conical points which fit in the hollow spindles of a lathe and are used to support the work being machined.

CENTER-TAP (elec.) cen' ter-tap: A connection made to the center of a coil.

CENTIGRADE (air cond.) cen' ti grade: A temperature measuring system in which 0° equals the freezing point of water and 100° equals the boiling point.

CENTIMETER cen' ti me ter: One hundredth part of a meter; .3937 inches.

CENTRALIZING (automation) cen traliz' ing: The collection of data from all units in a system at one information center.

CENTRIFUGAL FORCE cen trif' u gal force: The force which tends to move a mass from its center of rotation due to inertia.

CENTRIFUGE (air cond.) cen' tri fuge: A device used to separate substances of different densities by centrifugal force.

CENTRIFUGE (space) cen' tri fuge: A large motor-driven apparatus with a long rotating arm at the end of which human and animal subjects or equipment can be revolved at various speeds to simulate very closely the prolonged accelerations encountered in high-performance aircraft, rockets and manned missiles.

CENTRIPETAL FORCE (Auto.) cen trip' e tal force: The force which tends to make a body move towards its center of rotation.

CENTRIPETAL FORCE (space) cen trip' e tal force: A force which is directed away from the center of rotation.

CERAMICS (elec.) ce ram' ics: The art of forming and firing inorganic compounds at high temperatures and changing them into vitreous material.

CERESIN (paint. and dec.) cer' e sin: A hydrocarbon wax which possesses considerable flexibility.

CERMETS (metal) cer' mets: A branch of metallurgy in which ceramics and metals are combined. Used in high temperature applications and when high resistance to wear is required.

CESIUM (elec.) ce' si um: A silver white metallic element used in photoelectric cells.

CESSPOOL (plumb.) cesspool: A pit or hole in the ground for retaining sewage.

CETANE RATING (auto.) ce' tane rat' ing: The rating of ignition qualities of Diesel fuel. It represents the percentage of cetaine in the fuel to produce a specified ignition quality. The higher the number, the better the ignition quality.

CHAD (automation) chad: The pieces of material removed from a tape or card during punching.

CHAIN TONGS (plumb.) chain tongs: A special wrench used to hold or turn a pipe.

CHAIR RAIL (const.) chair rail: A wood

molding, chair back height, around a room, to protect the wall from marring by chairs.

CHALK (crafts) chalk: A soft limestone, composed mainly of small sea shells; a piece of chalk used for marking.

CHALK (paint. and dec.) chalk: A form of natural calcium carbonate.

CHALKING (paint. and dec.) chalk' ing: The decomposition of a paint film into a loose powder on the surface.

CHALK LINE (wood) chalk line: A string used to make a long straight line on a flat surface. The line is coated with colored chalk and fastened taut between two points. A snap of the line produces a chalk line on the surface to be marked.

CHAMFER (wood.) cham' fer: Removing the sharp edge or corner of a board by planing at an angle.

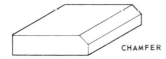

CHAMFER

CHAMOIS (draft.) cham' ois: A soft leather made from sheep, goat or deer skin.

CHAMPLEVE (crafts) cham ple ve': An enameling process where cells or channels are cut in the metal to hold the enamel.

CHANGE GEARS (metal) change gears: An assembly of gears on an engine lathe to produce a variety of carriage speeds in relation to the spindle speed. By this gear box a variety of thread pitches may be cut on the lathe. (auto) The transmission gears of an automobile to provide several forward and reverse speeds.

CHANGE OF STATE (air cond.) change of state: The change from solid, liquid or gas.

CHANNEL (elec.) chan' nel: A division of the radio frequency spectrum such as a band of frequencies allocated to a radio or TV broadcasting station. A TV channel is 6 megacycles wide.

CHAPLET (metal) chap' let: A metal support for a foundry core.

CHAPTER HEADINGS (graphics) chap' ter head' ings: The main title or head at the beginning of a chapter.

CHARACTER (automation) char' ac ter: The necessary marks or holes in a paper tape to identify a number or letter.

CHARACTER (elec.) char' ac ter: The basic pieces of intelligible machine information in a computer, consisting of a group of decimal digits, letters or symbols.

CHARACTERISTIC CURVE (elec.) char ac ter is' tic curve: A graphical representation of the characteristics of a component, circuit or device.

CHARACTERISTIC IMPEDANCE (elec.) char ac ter is' tic im ped' ance: (Symbol Zo) The impedance of a transmission line per unit length determined by the size and separation of the conductors.

CHARGE (air cond.) charge: The amount of refrigerant in a system.

CHARGE (elec.) charge: The process of sending an electric current through a storage battery to renew its chemical action; the acquisition of a charge, either positive or negative by an object.

CHARPY (metal) char' py: An impact

testing machine, where a sample is supported at both ends in a horizontal position and is broken by a hammer or pendulum.

CHASE (graphics) chase: An iron or steel frame, in which forms are locked, so that they may be held firmly on the bed of the press. There are many kinds of chases--cylinder, job, spider, McGreal combination, electrotype, etc.

CHASE (plumb.) chase: A recess in the wall of a building enclosing pipes running between floors.

CHASER (metal) chas' er: Tools used to cut threads by chasing, usually having several teeth of the right pitch; cutting tools used in die heads.

CHASING THREADS (metal) chas' ing threads: Cutting threads by moving a single tool along the work at the right speed to give the proper pitch.

CHASING TOOLS (crafts) chas' ing tools: Steel punch-like tools, carefully forged and shaped on the ends, for making surface decorations and designs on metal.

CHASSIS (auto.) chas' sis: The framework of a vehicle; the metal box on which electronic components are mounted and wired.

CHASSIS GROUND (auto.) chas' sis ground: A term used to describe the condition when the chassis of an electronic device is a common electrical connection at ground potential.

CHATTER (metal) chat' ter: Rapid vibrations of a cutting tool and the work.

CHECKING (paint. and dec.) check' ing: The formation of short narrow cracks in the surface of a paint film.

CHECKING (wood.) check' ing: Cracks in wood due to uneven seasoning.

CHECK VALVE (plumb.) A valve which permits flow in only one direction.

SWING CHECK VALVE

CHEEK (metal) cheek: The middle section of a three part foundry flask.

CHEMICAL FUEL (space) chem' i cal fuel: A fuel that depends upon an oxidizer for combustion or for development of thrust, such as liquid or solid rocket fuel, jet fuel, or internal combustion engine fuel.

CHEMICALLY ACTIVE (paint. and dec.) chem' i cal ly ac' tive: Pigments which react with oil of vehicle to form soaps which influence toughness of film, increase durability, etc. Also pigments such as red lead which react with acids formed at metal surface to prevent rust.

CHEMICALLY PURE (paint. and dec.) chem' i cal ly pure: Of the highest grade but not necessarily 100% pure.

CHEMICAL METALLURGY (metal) chem' i cal met' al lur gy: The study of chemical reactions in the melting, refining and alloying of metals.

CHEMICAL MILLING (automation) chem' i cal mill' ing: Using chemicals for removing metal from rough work.

CHEMOSPHERE (space) chem' o sphere: A region in upper atmosphere in which photochemical reactions take place.

CHERRY (Prunus Serotina) (wood) cher' ry: A beautiful cabinet wood with a rich reddish color and satin lustre. It is moderately heavy, strong, close grained and hard.

CHILL (metal) chill: A metallic mold or section of a mold, which increases the cooling rate of molten iron poured into the mold and increases the hardness of the casting at these points or areas.

CHIMNEY BREAST (const.) chim' ney breast: The part of the wall above a fireplace which projects into the room. It is made wider than necessary for the chimney to improve its outward appearance and to support a mantel.

CHIMNEY EFFECT (air cond.) chim' ney ef fect': The tendency of air to rise in a vertical duct when heated.

CHIMNEY LINING (const.) chim' ney lin' ing: Sections of tile used to line a chimney flue.

CHINA CLAY (crafts) chi' na clay: A very fine white clay used to form the paste of porcelain.

CHINA CLAY (graphics) chi' na clay: A fine white clay used in papermaking.

CHINA CLAY (Aluminate Silicate) (paint. and dec.) chi' na clay: Inert pigment which consists mostly of hydrated aluminum silicate. Imparts to paint quality of easy brushing.

CHINAWOOD OIL (paint. and dec.) chi' na wood oil: See TUNG OIL.

CHINE (wood.) chine: The intersection between the bottom and sides of a boat.

CHINESE BLUE (paint. and dec.) chi nese' blue: A form of iron blue.

CHINESE RED (paint. and dec.) chi nese' red: Chrome orange deep.

CHIP CARVING (wood.) chip car' ving: A general term referring to wood carving done by removing chips of wood by carving chisels.

CHIPLESS METHOD (automation) chip' less meth' od: Manufacturing without chips from cutting tools, by using cold forming electric arc erosion, die casting, chemical milling, powder metallurgy or extrusion.

CHIPPENDALE (wood.) chip' pen dale: A furniture style named after Thomas Chippendale (1718-1779). It is characterized by graceful lines and rococo ornamentation of scrolls, cupids, flowers, leaves and animals.

CHISEL (wood.) chis' el: A flat steel cutting tool, beveled and sharpened on

one end, with a wood or composition handle.

CHOKE (auto.) choke: A device in the automotive carburetor used to limit the flow of air and enrich the air-fuel mixture. It may be manually or automatically controlled.

CHOKE COIL (elec.) choke coil: A high inductance coil used to prevent the passage of pulsating currents, but allows dc to pass.

CHOKE INPUT FILTER (elec.) choke in' put fil' ter: A filter employing a choke as its input.

CHOKE, RF (elec.) choke, rf: A choke coil with a high impedance at radio frequencies.

CHOKE VALVE (auto.) choke valve:

A butterfly valve in the air horn of the carburetor which partially cuts-off the air flow and produces a rich air-fuel mixture for the engine.

CHOPPER (elec.) chop' per: A device which automatically interrupts a circuit. In a dc circuit the chopper changes dc into a pulsating dc.

CHORDAL PITCH (metal) chor' dal pitch: The distance between the centers of two adjacent gear teeth in a straight line.

CHROMA (elec.) chro' ma: The quality of color without reference to its brightness; the quality of light which embraces hue and saturation.

CHROMA (paint. and dec.) chro' ma: Color purity or intensity.

CHROMATICITY (elec.) chro matic' i-ty: The color quality of light.

CHROME GREEN (paint. and dec.) chrome green: Mixture of chrome yellow and Prussian blue.

CHROME ORANGE (paint. and dec.) chrome or' ange: An orange pigment composed principally of basic lead chromate.

CHROME VANADIUM STEEL (metal) chrome va na' di um steel: The alloy steels in the SAE 6100 series containing .8 to 1.1 percent chromium and about .18 percent vanadium. These steels have high strength and exceptional resistance to wear and fatigue.

CHROME YELLOW (paint. and dec.) chrome yel' low: Important inorganic yellow pigment made by mixing solutions of lead acetate and potassium bichromate.

CHROMINANCE (elec.) chro' mi nance: The saturation and hue of color.

CHROMINANCE SIGNAL (elec.) chro' mi nance sig' nal: Color information transmitted to reproduce a colored TV picture.

CHROMINANCE SUBCARRIER (elec.) chro' mi nance sub car' ri er: A subcarrier wave which is modulated by the color information in a televised picture. The sidebands of the subcarrier when added to the monochrome signal produce a colored picture in the color TV.

CHROMIUM OXIDE GREEN (paint. and dec.) chro' mi um ox' ide green: Green pigment which is extremely permanent in color and has good resistance to both alkali and heat.

CHROMODIZING (metal) chro' mo diz-ing: A process of forming a high chromium corrosion resistant case on low carbon steel. The part is packed in chromium dust and aluminum oxide in a retort and heated to about 2400 degrees F. in a hydrogen atmosphere for 3 to 5 hours.

CHRONOMETER (space) chro nom' e-ter: A precision watch; an accurate time-keeping device.

CHRONOMETER (paint. and dec.) chro-nom' e ter: An instrument used to indicate the color of light liquids and oils.

CHUCK (metal) chuck: A work holding device attached to the head stock spindle of a lathe or rotating machine.

CHUCK, COMBINATION (metal) chuck, com bi na' tion: A chuck which may be used either as an independent jaw or universal chuck.

CHUCK, INDEPENDENT (metal) chuck, in de pen' dent: A chuck which has four independently operated jaws.

CHUCK, UNIVERSAL (metal) chuck, u ni ver' sal: A three-jaw chuck in which the jaws move simultaneously and automatically center the work.

CHUFFING (space) chuf' fing: The characteristic of some rockets to burn intermittently and with an irregular puffing noise, called chugging or burping.

CINDER NOTCH (metal) cin' der notch: A hole in the side of the blast furnace for removing molten slag.

CINDERS (const.) cin' ders: Ashes from coal, used as a fill or as an aggregate for cinder blocks.

CINNABAR (metal) cin' na bar: The ore of mercury.

CINQUEFOIL (crafts) cinque' foil: A five leaved rosette or ornament.

CIRCLE CUTTER (wood) cir' cle cut' ter: A tool to cut large round circles from sheet metal, laminated materials, plywood, etc. The cutter is rotated by bit brace or drill press. The circle is cut by a fly cutter tool, which may be adjusted to desired radius by movement along a supporting metal arm.

CIRCLE SHEAR (metal) cir' cle shear: A machine which cuts circles from sheet metal. It is adjustable to selected diameter.

CIRCUIT (elec.) cir' cuit: The various connections and conductors of a specific device; the path of electron flow from the source through components and connections and back to its source.

CIRCUIT BREAKER (elec.) cir' cuit break' er: A protective device, in the form of a relay, which opens the circuit in case of an overload.

CIRCUIT, ETCHED (elec.) cir' cuit, etched: The method of circuit board production in which the actual conduction paths on a copper-clad insulation board are coated with an acid resist. The board is then placed in an acid bath and unprotected parts of the copper-clad are eaten away, leaving the circuit conductors. Components are mounted and soldered between the conductors to form the completed circuit.

CIRCUIT, PLUG-IN (elec.) cir' cuit, plug-in: A total or part of a circuit, usually a printed circuit board, which can be plugged into a piece of equipment. It may be rapidly removed or replaced during service.

CIRCUIT, PRINTED (elec.) cir' cuit, printed: The method of printing circuit conductors on an insulated base. Component parts may also be printed or actual components soldered in place.

CIRCUITRY (space) cir' cuit ry: The system of electric or electronic circuits used in a missile system or sub-system.

CIRCULAR MIL (elec.) cir' cu lar mil: The cross sectional area of a conductor one mil in diameter.

CIRCULAR MIL-FOOT (elec.) cir' cu lar mil-foot: A unit conductor one foot long with a cross sectional area of one circular mil.

CIRCULAR PITCH (metal) cir' cu lar pitch: The distance between similar adjacent teeth in a gear, measured at the pitch line.

CIRCULAR PLANE (wood) cir' cu lar plane: A plane with a flexible bed for planing convex or concave surfaces.

CIRCULAR SAW (wood) cir' cu lar saw: A circular disk saw with its cutting teeth spaced around the edge of the disk. The saw is mounted on an arbor

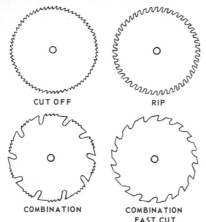

CUT OFF   RIP

COMBINATION   COMBINATION
                 FAST CUT

and turned by power. These saws are made in many types and sizes.

CIRCULATING CURRENT (elec.) cir' cu la ting cur' rent: Inductive and capacitive currents flowing around a parallel circuit.

CIRCUMFERENCE (draft) cir cum' fer-ence: The perimeter of a circle; the line bounding a circle.

CIRCUMFLEX (graphics) cir' cum flex: A curved mark over a vowel to indicate some tone or quality of pronunciation.

CIRCUMLUNAR (space) cir cum lun' ar: Trips or missions in which a vehicle will circle the Moon and return to Earth.

CIRCUMSCRIBE (draft) cir cum scribe': To draw a line around; encircle.

CISELEUR (metal) ci se leur': An engraver; a craftsman who makes metal ornamentation.

CISLUNAR (space) cis lun' ar: In space between the earth and the moon's orbit.

CISSING (wood.) cis' sing: A defect in paint, enamel or varnish work due to poor adhesion.

CITIZENS BAND (elec.) cit' i zens band: A band of frequencies allotted to two-way radio communications by private citizens. Operators are not required to pass technical examinations.

CITRONELLA OIL (paint. and dec.) cit ron el' la oil: An oil with a peculiar odor, obtained from a species of grass grown in Asia.

CLAMP (metal) clamp: A slotted steel strap, used for holding work during machining.

CLAMP DOG (metal) clamp dog: A lathe driving dog which clamps to the work by means of bolts and jaws.

CLAMPING CIRCUIT (elec.) clamp' ing cir' cuit: A circuit used to fix a wave-form at a certain level in reference to a dc reference voltage.

CLAPBOARDS (const.) clap' boards: Wood siding for exterior cover of building.

CLAPPER BOX (metal) clap' per box: A swinging tool holder used on the shaper or planer which permits the tool to ride freely over the work on the return stroke.

CLARENDON (graphics) clar' en don: A name of a type face.

CLASS A, B, C (elec.) See AMPLIFIERS.

CLAW COUPLING (metal) claw

cou' pling: A quick coupling method between the ends of two shafts, in which flanges with mating projections and recesses are caused to mesh and lock together.

CLAW HAMMER (wood.) claw ham' mer: See HAMMER.

CLAY (crafts) clay: Earth used in the manufacture or bricks; a fine grained sedimentary deposit of hydrated silicates of aluminum mixed with other impurities. It is partly colloidal and plastic when wet. It is hard and brittle when dried.

CLEANOUT (plumb.) clean' out: An opening in a drainage line, provided with a screw cover, to permit the removal of stoppages in the line.

CLEAN PROOF (graphic) clean proof: A proof containing few errors.

CLEARANCE (metal) clear' ance: The amount of space between adjacent parts;

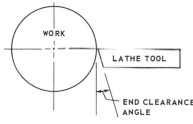

the angle between the cutting edge of a lathe tool and the vertical position of the work.

CLEAVAGE (const.) cleav' age: Split; division; the tendency of a rock to split along a certain line.

CLEVIS (metal) clev' is: A U shaped connector used to connect a rod to a plate or lever.

CLIMB MILLING (metal) climb mill' ing: See DOWN MILLING.

CLINCH (const.) clinch: To bend over, as in clinching a nail.

CLIPPER (elec.) clip' per: A circuit which limits the positive or negative peaks of a wave at a predetermined value.

CLOCKWISE ROTATION (auto) clock' wise ro ta' tion: Rotating in the same direction as the hands of a clock.

CLOISONNE (crafts) cloi son ne' : An enameling process, where the outline of the object consists of wire which encloses the various fields of color.

CLOSED LOOP (automation) closed loop: A feedback control system of a machine in which machine performance is measured and fed back into the process.

CLOSE-GRAIN WOODS (paint and dec.) close-grain woods: Woods such as birch, maple, etc. where the fibers are fine and are held closely together.

CLOSE NIPPLE (plumb.) close nip' ple: A very short piece of pipe, threaded on both ends, used to join two pipes or fittings.

CLOSE STRING (const.) close string: A method of finishing a staircase by building a boxlike curb so that the treads and risers butt against it. The balusters set on the curb.

CLOSURE (const.) clo' sure: A portion of a brick used to close the end of a course of brick in a wall.

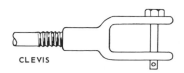

CLEVIS

CLUSTER (space) clus' ter: Two or more engines bound together so as to function as one propulsive unit.

CLUTCH (auto.) clutch: The coupling mechanism between the engine and the transmission of an automobile.

COAGULATE (paint. and dec.) co ag' u-late: To change from a liquid into a dense mass; solidify; curdle.

COAL TAR (crafts) coal tar: A black pitch distilled from bituminous coal.

COAL-TAR PITCH (paint. and dec.) coal-tar pitch: Refined, common pitch obtained as distillation residue from coal tar.

COAL-TAR SOLVENT (paint. and dec.) coal-tar sol' vent: Derived from the distillation of coal tar. Four main products for the paint industry are benzene, toluene, Xylene and solvent naphtha.

COAT (const.) coat: The first application of a material such as paint or plaster.

COATED ELECTRODE (weld.) coated e lec' trode: See COVERED ELEC-TRODE.

COATED PAPER (graphics) coat' ed pa' per: When a highly enamelled paper is desired, a web of paper is first made and then coated and calendered. It comes in glossy and dull finish, and is a prerequisite for high-grade half-tone work.

"COATING IN" (paint. and dec.) "coat' ing in": Applying a coat of paint.

COAT OF PAINT (paint. and dec.) coat of paint: Single layer of paint spread at one time and allowed to harden.

COAXIAL LINE (elec.) co ax' i al line: A concentric transmission line in which the inner conductor is insulated from the tubular outer conductor.

COBALT BLUE (paint. and dec.) co' balt blue: Blue pigment, stable in color.

COBALT DRIER (graphics) co' balt dri'-er: A drying ingredient for ink.

COBALT DRIER (paint. and dec.) co' balt dri' er: Powerful drier which is soluble in all drying oils.

COCHINEAL (paint. and dec.) coch' i-neal: A coloring substance extracted from dried female insects found in Mexico, carminic acid, which is soluble in both water and alcohol.

COCK (plumb.) cock: See BIBB.

COCK AND HENS (graphics) cock and hens: Individual characters that may be joined together to make braces.

COCK-BEAD (const.) cock-bead: A bead molding raised above the surface to which it is applied.

CODE (automation) code: A system of characters to represent information.

CODE (elec.) code: A set of numbers, letters or symbols used to represent information.
Ex: Morse Code

COEFFICIENT OF COUPLING (K) (elec.) co ef fi' cient of cou' pling (K): The percentage of coupling between coils, expressed as a decimal.

COEFFICIENT OF EXPANSION (air cond.) co ef fi' cient of ex pan' sion: The change in length or volume per degree of temperature change.

COEFFICIENT OF FRICTION (auto.) co ef fi' cient of fric' tion: A relationship between the force required to move an object over a surface divided by the pounds of pressure holding the surfaces together.

COERCIVE FORCE (elec.) co er' cive force: The magnetizing force required to reduce residual magnetism to zero.

COFFER (const.) cof' fer: A decorative, sunken panel in the ceiling.

COG (metal) cog: The tooth of a cog-wheel.

COIL (air cond.) coil: A heating or cooling element made of pipe or tubing.

COIL (elec.) coil: A conductor wound on a form or in a spiral helix.

COIL FORM (elec.) coil form: An insulated tube or form on which a coil is wound.

COINING (metal) coin' ing: The process of impressing the image or characters on the die and punch onto a plain metal surface.

COIR (crafts) coir: A fibre from coconut husks used in making rope, matting and brushes.

COKE (metal) coke: A fuel made by baking bituminous coal in a closed oven to drive off gases and other elements. It is about 88 percent carbon.

COLD CHISEL (metal) cold chis' el: A chisel used for cutting metals.

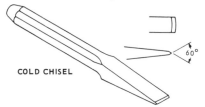

COLD CHISEL

COLD COLOR (painting and dec.) cold col' or: A bluish or greenish color; a color not suggestive of warmth.

COLD COLORS (graphics) cold col' ors: Colors on the blue side of the spectrum.

COLD DRAWN (metal) cold drawn: The shaping of metal by drawing through dies while cold.

COLD-FLOW TEST (space) cold-flow test: A test of a liquid rocket, especially to check or verify the efficiency of a propulsion subsystems that provides for the conditioning and flow of propellants.

COLD FORMING (automation) cold form' ing: Metal shaping processes where the metal is moved or shaped rather than cut. These processes include upsetting, extrusion, swaging, hammering, rolling, bending, drawing and spinning.

COLD-ROLLED (metal) cold-roll' ed: Steel shaped while cold by rolling methods.

COLD SHUTS (metal) cold shuts: A deformation in a metal casting caused by two streams of metal meeting at a temperature insufficient for fusion.

COLD STORAGE (air cond.) cold stor' age: The process of preserving and storing perishable foods on a large scale by refrigeration.

COLD TYPE (graphics) cold type: Type set using no hot metal.

COLD WATER PAINT (paint. and dec.) cold wa' ter paint: The paint in which the binder or vehicle portion is composed of casein, glue or a similar material dissolved in water.

COLD WORKING (metal) cold work' ing: The process of rolling, upsetting, stamping, twisting, forging and drawing metal while cold.

COLLAR (metal) col' lar: A ring formed on a shaft by forging. A ring locked to a shaft by means of a setscrew.

COLLAR BEAM (const.) col' lar beam: Joists placed horizontally across the roof span holding the heels of the rafters in place and forming ceiling joists for the top story of the building; rafter ties.

COLLATE (graphics) col' late: To sort and arrange in proper order; to examine the signatures for a book to ascertain if they are arranged in correct order.

COLLECTOR (elec.) col lec' tor: In a transistor, the semiconductor section which collects the majority carriers. Similar to the plate in a vacuum tube.

COLLECTOR RING (elec.) col lec' tor ring: A circular ring revolving with an armature. Brushes in contact with the ring carry a current from the moving part to the stationary part.

COLLET (metal) col' let: A hollow type holder, which is compressèd against the work, by drawing into the tapered hollow spindle of the lathe.

COLLOIDAL SUSPENSION (paint. and dec.) col loi' dal sus pen' sion: A substance divided into fine particles which remains in permanent suspension in a liquid.

COLLOTYPE (graphics) col' lo type: A photo-planographic method of printing. The printing plate consists of a gelatine film mounted on a heavy plate of glass. The film is made selective of moisture and ink, as in lithography.

COLONNADE (wood) col on nade' : A row of columns.

COLOPHON (graphics) col' o phon: A publisher's trade mark.

COLOR (elec.) col' or: The sensation resulting from stimulation of the retina

of the eye by light waves of certain wave lengths.

COLOR (paint. and dec.) col' or: A property of visible phenomena in which certain impressions or effects are formed on the retina of the eye by light of different wave lengths.

COLOR DECODER (elec.) col' or decod' er: In color television, an apparatus for deriving the signals for the color display from the color signal and color burst.

COLOR-DIFFERENCE SIGNAL (elec.) col' or-dif' fer ence sig' nal: An electrical signal which when added to the monochrome signal in color TV will produce a signal representative of one of the TRISTIMULUS VALUES of a transmitted color.

COLOR FOR TEMPERING (metal) col' or for tem' per ing: An orderly series of colors determined by temperature which appear on steel during tempering processes.

Color	Degrees Fahrenheit
Pale yellow	430
Light Straw	450
Dark Straw	470
Brown	490
Brown & Purple	510
Purple	530
Bright Blue	560
Dark Blue	600

COLORING STRENGTH (paint. and dec.) col' or ing strength: Relative strength or ability of pigments to color base material which is white or light in color.

COLORS-IN-JAPAN (paint and dec.) col' ors-in-ja pan' : Pigment colors ground and mixed with japan drier.

COLOR-IN-OIL (paint. and dec.) col' or-in-oil: A paste formed by mixing a color pigment in linseed or other vegetable oil.

COLOR KILLER (elec.) col' or kill' er: A circuit in a color television which disables the chrominance circuits when monochrome signals are received.

COLOR MAN (paint. and dec.) col' or man: The term applies to the individual — either the journeyman or contractor — who is an expert in tinting and matching colors.

COLOR PICTURE TUBE (elec.) col' or pic' ture tube: A cathode ray tube which will produce a color picture by scanning the raster and by varying the intensity of excitation of phosphors to produce light of chosen primary colors.

COLOR PIGMENTS (paint. and dec.) col' or pig' ments: Pigments such as blue, red, etc. which absorb a portion of the light which falls upon them and reflect or return to the eye certain groups of light bands which enable us to recognize various colors.

COLOR PROOFS (graphics) col' or proofs: Proof of illustration or type pulled in color.

COLOR RETENTION (paint. and dec.) col' or re ten' tion: When a paint product exposed to the elements shows no signs of changing color, it is said to have good color retention.

COLOR SIGNAL (elec.) col' or sig' nal: Any signal in a color television system used to control the chromaticity value of a color television picture.

COLOR-SUBCARRIER (elec.) col' or-sub car' ri er: A carrier frequency of 3.579545 mc which contains the information to place the color side bands in proper place in video frequency spectrum.

COLOR-SYNC BURST (elec.) col' or-sync burst: A 3.58 mc carrier keyed onto the back porch of the TV horizontal-sync pulse. Its purpose is to establish a reference for demodulating the chrominance signal in color TV.

COLOR TRIAD (elec.) col' or tri' ad: A color cell of a three color phosphor-dot screen in a color television tube.

COLOR WORK (graphics) col' or work: That part of the work done in color.

COLPITT'S OSCILLATOR (elec.) col' pitt's os' cil la tor: See OSCILLATORS.

COLUMN (const.) col' umn: A vertical shaft or pillar supporting a structure such as a roof or a floor. A column receives pressure in the direction of its longitudinal axis.

COLUMN RULES (graphics) col' umn rules: Vertical rules or lines used to separate the columns of type matter in newspapers, etc.

COMBINATION CHUCK (metal) com bi na' tion chuck: See CHUCK, UNIVERSAL.

COMBINATION FRAME (const.) combi na' tion frame: A framing system which is a combination of full and balloon framing.

COMBINATION PLATE (graphics) com bi na' tion plate: A printing plate consisting of two kinds of engravings, usually a line and a halftone.

COMBINATION PLIERS (metal) com bi na' tion pli' ers: A common variety of slip-joint pliers with both notched and flat jaws for grasping either round or flat work.

COMBINATION SQUARE (wood)

com bi na' tion square: An adjustable try square with a graduated sliding blade used for marking and gauging. One edge of frame forms a 45° angle for miter work. A level and scriber are usually mounted in frame.

COMBINATION SQUARE SET (metal) com bi na' tion square set: A machinist tool consisting of a square, a bevel protractor and a center head. It is used extensively in layout work.

COMBUSTION (auto.) com bus' tion: The burning of the fuel-air mixture in the cylinder of an engine.

COMBUSTION CHAMBER (auto.) combus' tion cham' ber: The space in an engine cylinder and head above the piston; the space remaining in cylinder and head when piston is at top dead center.

COMET (space) com' et: A loose body of gases and solid matter revolving around the Sun.

COMFORT CHART (air cond.) com' fort chart: A psychrometic chart showing constant comfort lines in terms of temperature, humidity and air movement.

COMMAND (automation) com mand' : A signal which will start a performance or operation.

COMMAND (elec.) com mand' : In a computer, it is one of a set of several signals which occurs as a result of an instruction; an instruction.

COMMINUTE (const.) com' mi nute: To pulverize; to reduce in size by crushing and grinding.

COMMON BASE (elec.) com' mon base: A transistor circuit, in which the base is common to input and output circuits.

COMMON BOARDS (const.) com' mon boards: A grade of lumber; boards one inch thick and up to twelve inches wide.

COMMON BRICK (const.) com' mon brick: Ordinary red bricks of standard size.

COMMON COLLECTOR (elec.) com' mon col lec' tor: A transistor circuit in which the collector is common to input and output circuits.

COMMON EMITTER (elec.) com' mon e mit' ter: A transistor circuit in which the emitter is common to input and output circuits.

COMMON RAFTER (const.) com' mon raft' er: A rafter extending from plate to ridge without a break.

COMMON WALL (const.) com' mon wall: A wall used jointly by two parties, but owned by one.

COMMUTATING FLUX (elec.) com muta' ting flux: The flux necessary to generate the emf that neutralizes the emf of self-induction.

COMMUTATING POLE (elec.) com mutat' ing pole: Small electromagnetic poles placed between the field poles of a generator to reduce commutator arcing due to armature reaction.

COMMUTATION (elec.) com muta' tion: The process of changing the alternating current in a generator armature into direct current in the external circuit by a mechanical switch consisting of commutator bars and brushes.

COMMUTATOR (elec.) com' mu ta tor: A group of bars providing connections between armature coils and brushes. A mechanical switch to maintain current in one direction in external circuit.

COMPARATOR (elec.) com' pa ra tor: A circuit which compares two signals and supplies difference information between the signals.

COMPARATOR (metal) com par' a tor: An optical device by which an enlarged projection of an object may be accurately viewed on a screen.

COMPASS (draft.) com' pass: A drafting instrument consisting of two logs, pivoted together at one end. Used for drawing circles and arcs.

COMPASS SAW (wood.) com' pass saw: A saw with a blade resembling the beak of a swordfish. Used for irregular cuts and cut-outs.

COMPATIBLE (paint. and dec.) compat' i ble: Paint pigments are compatible when they are capable of being used together without harmful chemical reactions.

COMPATIBILITY (elec.) com pat i-bil' i ty: The property of a color television system which permits normal reception in black and white by a monochrome receiver.

COMPENSATOR (elec.) com' pen sa-tor: An auto transformer used for starting large a-c induction motors.

COMPLEMENTARY ANGLES (metal) com ple men' ta ry an' gles: Two angles are complementary when their sum is 90 degrees. Each is a complement of the other.

COMPLEMENTARY COLORS (crafts) com ple men' ta ry col' ors: One of two colors which if combined produce white light.

COMPLETE AUXILIARY (draft.) complete' aux il' ia ry: An auxiliary view of an inclined part of an object, including the remainder of the object in foreshortened dimensions.

COMPLEX NUMBER (elec.) com plex' num' ber: Consisting of a real and an imaginary number connected by a plus or minus sign.

COMPLEX WAVEFORM (elec.) complex' wave' form: A wave form obtained by combining a fundamental frequency and a number of harmonics.

COMPLIANCE (elec.) com pli' ance: The reciprocal of stiffness; the ability to be moved or flexed by an applied force.

COMPOSING ROOM (graphics) com-pos' ing room: A room where type is set and made into forms for printing.

COMPOSING-RULE (graphics) com-pos' ing-rule: A rule used for composing a line of type. It may be made of brass or steel and is usually two points thick.

COMPOSING-STICK (graphics) com-pos' ing-stick: A metal device used by compositors to hold the type while it is being assembled into lines. It has an adjustable knee so that it can be set to different measures. The very latest ones are graduated in ems and half-ems of pica, and are capable of being quickly set to these measures. The composing-stick derived its name from the fact that the first ones were made of wood.

COMPOSITE SIGNAL (elec.) com pos'-ite sig' nal: The television signal including picture information, plus blanking and synchronization signals.

COMPOSITION (graphics) com po si'-tion: That part of printing covering all the necessary operations incident to preparing forms for press.

COMPOSITION ROLLER (graphics) com po si' tion roll' er: A cylinder consisting of a metal core coated with a flexible composition made from a mixture of glue, molasses, glycerine and other materials, and used for inking type forms on printing presses.

COMPOSITION WOOD (const.) com po-si' tion wood: Building materials made by pressing wood fibers into thin sheets.

COMPOUND CIRCUIT (elec.) com' pound cir' cuit: Circuits containing resistors connected in series and in parallel.

COMPOUND GENERATORS, Degree of, (elec.) com' pound gen' er a tors:

FLAT, When the no-load and full-load voltages have the same value.

OVER, The full-load voltage is higher than the no-load voltage.

UNDER, The full-load voltage is less than the no-load voltage.

COMPOUND REST (metal) com' pound rest: A swivelled rest on the cross slide to permit angular adjustment and feed of the cutting tool.

COMPOUND TABLE (metal) com' pound ta' ble: A work-support table for a machine having transverse and longi-tudinal movement.

COMPREGNATED WOOD (wood.) com-preg' nat ed wood: A type of molded plywood where regular plywood is com-pressed during manufacturing forcing the glue through each layer.

COMPRESSED LETTERING (draft.) com pressed' let' ter ing: Drawing letters narrower than normal size.

COMPRESSION (air cond.) com pres'-sion:

COMPOUND, Compression by two or more stages or cylinders.

SINGLE STAGE, Compression by one stage only.

COMPRESSION (auto.) com pres' sion: A reduction in volume; squeezing.

COMPRESSION (elec.) com pres' sion: The reduction in the gain of a signal as a function of the signal magnitude. Ex: The larger magnitude signal would be reduced or compressed to a greater extent than a small signal.

COMPRESSION GAUGE (auto.) com-pres' sion gauge: A meter used to measure cylinder pressure of an auto-motive engine in lbs. per sq. in.

COMPRESSION RATIO (auto.) com-pres' sion ra' tio: The ratio of the volume of the cylinder when piston is at bottom dead center to the volume when piston is at top dead center.

COMPRESSION RING (auto.) com-pres' sion ring: A piston ring used to reduce compression losses as well as an oil seal. It is usually the top ring on the piston.

COMPRESSION STROKE (auto.) com-pres' sion stroke: The upward stroke of the piston during which the air-fuel mixture is compressed.

COMPRESSOR (air cond.) com-pres' sor:

DOUBLE ACTING, A compressor which has two compression strokes for each revolution of the crankshaft.

REFRIGERANT, The part of a re-frigeration system where the low pres-sure refrigerant is compressed into a lower volume at a higher pressure.

SINGLE ACTING, A compressor having one compression stroke per crankshaft revolution.

COMPRESSOR (air cond.) com pres'sor: The pump in a refrigeration unit which forces the warm gaseous refrigerant under pressure to the condenser where it is converted to a liquid state.

COMPUTER (elec.) com put' er: An electronic calculator performing a sequence of computations.

COMPUTER (elec.) com pu' ter:

ANALOG, A computer which substitutes for any given physical quantity, a mechanical, electrical, thermodynamic equivalent quantity that follows, in direct proportion, the same laws of behavior as the original quantity. In general, the analog computer gives a continuous solution to the problem. Ex: Slide rule, automobile speedometer.

DIGITAL, A computer which makes a one-to-one comparison or individual count to calculate. It solves problems in discrete steps, forming a discontinuous solution.

CONCAVE (draft.) con' cave: A curved depression.

CONCAVE WELD FACE (weld.) con'cave weld face: A weld having the center of its face below the weld edges.

CONCENTRIC (auto.) con cen' tric: Two or more circles having a common center.

CONCENTRICITY TOLERANCE (draft.) con cen tric'i ty tol' er ance: Permissible out of roundness of a hole or shaft.

CONCRETE (const.) con' crete: A mixture of portland cement, sand, gravel and water.

CONCRETE BLOCK (const.) con' crete block: A masonry block made of concrete, usually 7 5/8 x 7 5/8 x 15 5/8.

CONDENSATE (paint and dec.) conden' sate: To change a vapor into liquid.

CONDENSATION (auto.) con den sa'tion: The process of changing a vapor to a liquid.

CONDENSATION TRAIL (space) (contrails or vapor trails) con den sa' tion trail: A visible cloud streak, usually brilliantly white in color, which trails behind a missile or other vehicle in flight under certain conditions. It is caused by the formation of water droplets or sometimes ice crystals.

CONDENSED TYPE (graphics) condensed' type: Type narrower than standard size.

CONDENSER (air cond.) con dens' er: An arrangement of tubes or pipes in which the vaporized refrigerant is liquified by the removal of heat.

CONDENSER (elec.) con dens' er: An older name for a capacitor.

CONDUCTANCE (symbol G) (elec.) con duct' ance: The ability of a circuit to conduct current. It is equal to amperes per volt and is measured in mhos.

$$G = \frac{1}{R}$$

CONDUCTANCE, Thermal, called the "C" factor. (air cond.) con duct' ance: The time rate of heat transfer through a body from one bounding surface to another for a unit temperature between the two surfaces.

CONDUCTION (elec.) con duc' tion: The flow of an electric current through a conducting body.

CONDUCTION BAND (elec.) con duc'- tion band: The outermost energy level of an atom.

CONDUCTIVITY (elec.) con duc tiv' i- ty: The ability of a material to conduct an electric current. It is the reciprocal of resistivity.

CONDUCTIVITY, N type (elec.) con duc- tiv' i ty: Conduction by electrons in N type crystal.

CONDUCTIVITY, P type (elec.) con- duc tiv' i ty: Conduction by holes in P type crystal.

CONDUCTIVITY, Thermal, called the "K" factor (air cond.) con duc tiv' i ty: The time rate of heat flow through a unit area of a material when a unit temperature gradient is maintained in a direction perpendicular to the area.

CONDUCTOR (elec.) con duc' tor: A material which permits free motion of a large number of electrons.

CONDUCTOR (plumb.) con duc' tor: A vertical pipe to carry rain water from the roof of a house; downspout.

CONDUCTOR STAKE (metal) con duc'- tor stake: A metal working stake having two long cylindrical ends of different diameters. It is used for working on sheet metal pipes and tubes.

CONDUIT (air cond.) con' duit: A tube or pipe for conveying liquid.

CONDUIT (elec.) con' du it: A metal or fibre pipe or tube used to enclose several electrical conductors; a me- tallic raceway.

CONDUIT BOX (elec.) con' du it box: A metal box used to terminate a conduit.

CONDUIT (elec.) con' du it:

RIGID, thick wall conduit which may be threaded and assembled similar to a pipe.

THIN WALL, a thin wall conduit which is assembled by compression type fit- tings. Easily bent to desired angles.

CONDUIT FITTINGS (elec.) con' du it fit' tings:

BUSHING, a threaded fitting used to attach conduit to an outlet box.

COUPLING, a threaded sleeve used to join the ends of two lengths of conduit.

EMT, electrical mechanical tubing. Another name for thin wall conduit.

ENTRANCE CAP, a weatherproof and insulated cap for terminating the power line connections to a building.

ENTRANCE ELL, a metal box to complete a 90° angle with conduit. A cover allows the electrician to pull wires through conduit in either di- rection.

CONDULET (elec.) con' du let: Special types of conduit fittings manufactured by Crouse-Hinds Co.

CONE (weld.) cone: Inner visible flame shape of neutral or near neutral flame.

CONELRAD (elec.) con' el rad: A radio alert system established by the Federal government in 1951. CONtrol of ELec- tromagnetic RADiation.

CONE OF SILENCE (elec.) cone of si' lence: A conical shaped region above an antenna, in which the radiated field strength is relatively low.

CONE PULLEY (metal) cone pul' ley: A step pulley to provide various speed ratios between motor and headstock spindle.

CONGO GUM (paint. and dec.) con' go gum: A gum resin obtained from the Congo region of Africa.

CONICAL (draft.) con' i cal: CONE shaped.

CONIFER (wood.) co' ni fer: A class of trees, mostly evergreen, which bears cones, such as pine and spruce.

CONNECTING ROD (auto.) con nect' ing rod: The link between the piston and the crankshaft.

CONNECTING ROD BEARING (auto) con nect' ing rod bearing: The bearing at the connection between the rod and the crankshaft.

CONNECTOR (elec.) con nec' tor: Any device on the end of a wire or cable to facilitate connection or disconnection from the equipment.

CONSISTENCY (paint. and dec.) consist' en cy: The fluidity or viscosity of a liquid or paste; resistance of a product to flow.

CONSOLE (space) con' sole: Term applied to a grouping of controls, indicators and similar electrical or mechanical equipment used to monitor readiness of and/or control specific functions of missiles.

CONSOLE MODEL (elec.) con' sole mod' el: A cabinet for a radio or TV which stands on its own legs or base upon the floor. The console contains

the chassis, speaker and all associated equipment.

CONSTANTAN (elec.) con' stan tan: An alloy of copper and nickel used in making precision wire wound resistors.

CONSTANT CURRENT (elec.) con' stant cur' rent: A source which maintains a non-varying current.

CONSTANT-MESH TRANSMISSION (auto) con' stant-mesh trans mis' sion: A transmission in which gears on main shaft and countershaft are in constant mesh.

CONSTANT VOLTAGE OR POTENTIAL (elec.) con' stant volt' age or po ten'- tial: A source which maintains a non-varying voltage as the load varies.

CONSTELLATION (space) con stel la'- tion: Any one of the arbitrary groups of fixed stars, some 90 of which are now recognized.

CONTACT (elec.) con' tact: The points at which metallic contact is made in a relay or switch, thus closing a circuit; to touch.

CONTACT FORMS (elec.) con' tact forms: The arrangement of the switching contacts on a relay.

CONTACTOR (elec.) con' tac tor: A heavy duty magnetic relay used in high current electrical circuits.

CONTACT POTENTIAL (elec.) con' tact po ten' tial: The potential difference existing between the surfaces of metals of different electron affinities that are in contact with each other or connected by an external circuit.

CONTINENTAL CODE (elec.) con' ti- nen tal code: See MORSE CODE.

CONTINUOUS CURRENT (elec.) con-tin' u ous cur' rent: A direct current without pulsations.

CONTINUOUS DUTY (elec.) con tin' u-ous du' ty: The operation of a circuit or a device under a constant load for an indefinite period of time.

CONTINUOUS WASTE (plumb.) con tin'-u ous waste: The drains from two or more fixtures connected to a single trap.

CONTINUOUS WAVE (cw) (elec.) con-tin' u ous wave: An uninterrupted si-nusoidal rf wave radiated into space, with all wave peaks equal in amplitude and evenly spaced along the time axis.

CONTINUOUS WELD (weld.) con tin' u-ous weld: Making the complete weld in one direction.

CONTOUR (crafts) con' tour: A profile; outline.

CONTOURING (automation) con'-tour ing: Three dimensional duplicat-ing.

CONTOUR LINE (draft.) con' tour line: A line on a map drawn through points of the same elevation.

CONTRACTION (auto.) con trac' tion: The compression or reduction in di-mension of an object.

CONTRAST (elec.) con' trast: In tele-vision. The relative difference in in-tensity between blacks and whites in the reproduced picture.

CONTRAST (graphics) con' trast: Dif-ference between white and black shades; comparison of tonal high lights and shadows.

CONTRAST CONTROL (elec.) con' trast

con trol' : A manual control on a TV which varies the picture contrast by varying the gain of the video amplifiers.

CONTROL DIFFERENTIAL (air cond.) con trol' dif fer en' tial: The differ-ence between cut-in and cut-out tem-peratures or pressures.

CONTROL GRID (elec.) con trol' grid: The grid in a vacuum tube closest to the cathode. The grid to which the input signal is fed to the tube.

CONTROLLER (elec.) con trol' ler: A system of switches, relays and in-strumentation used to regulate voltage, current, speed and other predetermined actions of an electrical machine or group of machines.

CONTROLLER RESISTANCE (elec.) con trol' ler re sist' ance: Usually re-fers to the resistance of a motor starter by which the line current is limited until motor reaches rated speed; re-sistance used to vary the speed of a motor.

CONTROL PANEL (automation) con-trol' pan' el: A group of controls which coordinate many power devices and machines used in automation.

CONTROL ROD (elec.) con trol' rod: A rod used to control the power of a nuclear reactor. The absorption of neutrons by the rod reduces the re-actor power output.

CONVECTION (air cond.) con vec' tion: Transfer of heat by air, gas or liquid containing thermal energy.

FORCED, Circulation maintained by a blower, fan or a pump.

NATURAL, Circulation as a result of thermal expansion of the liquid or gas.

CONVECTOR (air cond.) con vec' tor: A surface designed to transfer heat to the surrounding air by convection.

CONVECTOR (plumb.) con vec' tor: A type of heater which depends upon air circulating through and around its heating surface.

CONVENTION (draft.) con ven' tion: A custom; tradition; an agreement as to usage.

CONVERTER (elec.) con vert' er: An electromechanical system for changing alternating current to direct current.

CONVERTER TUBE (elec.) con vert' er tube: A multielement vacuum tube or transistor in which two signals are mixed or heterodyned to produce an intermediate frequency.

CONVEX (draft.) con' vex: Having an outwardly curving surface.

CONVEX WELD (weld.) con' vex weld: A weld with the face above the weld edges.

CONVEYOR (automation) con vey' or: A continuous mechanism for moving products and/or materials from one location to another or from one machine to another. They consist of chain and belt conveyors, transfer machines, chutes and vibratory feeders.

COOLANT (metal) cool' ant: A fluid used in machining operations to cool work and remove chips.

COOL COLORS (paint. and dec.) cool col' ors: Hues or colors in which blue predominates.

COOLING SYSTEM (auto.) cool' ing sys'- tem: All the associated equipment used to cool an automotive engine including

fan, radiator, waterpump, water jackets and connecting pipes and hoses.

COOLING TOWER (air cond.) cool' ing tow' er: A device for cooling water by evaporation as it is showered through a space containing circulating air.

COOPER HEWITT LAMP (elec.) coop' er hew itt lamp: A mercury vapor type lamp used by photographers and engravers.

COORDINATES (automation) co or' dinates: Position of points in the X, Y and Z planes.

COORDINATES (elec.) co-or' di nates: The horizontal and vertical distances to locate a point on a graph.

COPALS (paint. and dec.) co' pals: Group of resinous substances exuding from various tropical trees. Some of copal resins are amber, congo, kauri, manila, Pontianak, West India gum and zanzibar.

COPE (metal) cope: The top section of a flask.

COPED JOINT (const.) coped joint: A fitted joint between moldings when the end of one molding is cut to the profile of the other molding and fitted together.

COPING (const.) cop' ing: A cap or top on a wall to shed moisture.

COPING SAW (wood) cop' ing saw: A metal U shape frame holding a thin flexible blade. Used for cutting round and irregular shapes.

COPOLYMERIZATION (paint. and dec.) co pol y mer i za' tion: Interaction of two or more different molecules to form a new compound having higher molecular weight and different physical properties.

COPPER (metal) cop' per: A soldering iron.

COPPERAS (paint. and dec.) cop' per as: Ferrous sulfate; a green crystalline compound used in dyeing and making ink.

COPPER CLAD (elec.) cop' per clad: Steel wire coated with a layer of copper for increased conductivity.

COPPER ENGRAVING (graphics) cop'-per en grav' ing: The art or process of engraving or etching a design on copper plates, or the taking of impressions or prints from copper plates.

COPPER ETCHING (graphics) cop' per etch' ing: A printing plate reproducing a line drawing, made on copper instead of zinc.

COPPER LOSSES (elec.) cop' per losses: Heat losses in motors, generators and transformers as a result of resistance of wire. Sometimes called the I^2R loss.

COPPER THIN SPACES (graphics) cop' per thin spaces: Pieces of copper, 1/2 point thick usually cut in lengths from 6 points to 48 points.

COPYFLEX (draft.) cop'y flex: A machine which makes exact copies of drawings, without tracings or stencils.

COPY-HOLDER (graphics) cop' y-hold' er: One who reads copy to a proofreader.

CORBEL (const.) cor' bel: A stone or wood bracket projecting out from a wall; a support for an arch or a cornice.

CORBEL OUT (const.) cor' bel out: The building out of one or more courses of stone or brick in order to form a support for beams and timbers; the increase in the exterior size of a brick chimney by successively corbelling out.

CORDIERITE (elec.) cor' di er ite: Insulating material made of magnesium and aluminum silicates.

CORE (elec.) core: The magnetic path through the center of a coil or transformer. It may be air or magnetic materials such as laminated sheets of iron, depending upon application.

CORE BOX (metal) core box: A molding box constructed so that its internal cavity is shaped like the desired core. The box is rammed with sand, then separated and the core removed for drying and baking.

CORE DRILL (metal) core drill: A hollow drill which removes the metal in a solid piece rather than in chips. Used to obtain test samples.

CORE IRON (elec.) core iron: Magnetic materials usually in sheet form, used to form laminated cores for electromagnets and transformers.

CORE LOSSES (elec.) core losses: Losses in a motor, generator or transformer associated with eddy currents and hysteresis in the core.

CORE OVEN (metal) core ov' en: An oven for baking foundry cores.

CORE PRINT (metal) core print: A projection on a pattern which locates the position and forms the impression for a core.

CORE SAND (metal) core sand: Molding sands of relatively clean silica grains with little or no clay.

CORE SATURATION (elec.) core sat u-ra' tion: The tendency of the molecules in an iron core to be oriented in one direction due to direct current.

CORIOLIS EFFECT (space) cor i-ol' is ef fect': The deflection of a body in motion due to the Earth's rotation, diverting horizontal motions to the right in the northern hemisphere and to the left in the southern hemisphere.

CORNER BEAD (const.) cor' ner bead: Thin metal strips with rounded corners, used to protect and support plaster corners and also act as guides for the plasterer.

CORNER BIT BRACE (wood) cor' ner bit brace: A bit brace with a right angle drive so that cranking action can be accomplished in corners and close spaces.

CORNER BLOCK (const.) cor' ner block: A masonry block having one square end.

CORNER JOINT (weld.) cor' ner joint: Junction formed by edges of two pieces of metal touching each other at angle of about 90 deg.

CORNER MARKS (graphics) cor' ner marks: Marks indicating the extreme edges of a job.

CORNER QUADS (graphics) cor' ner quads: Pieces of type metal cast in the form of a right angle, and used around the corners of jobs, the intervening space being filled in with metal of the same thickness.

CORNERSTONE (const.) cor' ner stone: A stone at the corner of a building. It is frequently laid during a ceremony marking the beginning of construction.

CORNER TROWEL (const.) cor' ner trow' el: A V shaped mason's trowel for shaping corners. Made in both inside and outside patterns.

CORNICE (const.) cor' nice: A decorative molding or boards placed at the top of an exterior or interior wall.

CORONA (elec.) co ro' na: The emission of electrons from the surface of electrical conductors at high potentials.

CORROSION (metal) cor ro' sion: The slow oxidation and wasting away of metals.

CORROSIVE (air cond.) cor ro' sive: Having chemically destructive effect on metals.

CORTEX (wood.) cor' tex: The bark of a tree.

CORUNDUM (metal) co run' dum: Aluminum oxide used as an abrasive.

COSMIC RAYS (elec.) cos' mic rays: Highly penetrating radiation waves from outer space, which have extremely short wave length.

COSMOTRON (elec.) cos' mo tron: A proton synchrotron developed by the Brookhaven National Laboratories in 1952.

COTTER PIN (crafts) cot' ter pin: A piece of half round wire bent in the shape of a U.

COULOMB (elec.) cou lomb': A quantity of electrons representing 6.28×10^{18} electrons.

COULOMB, CHARLES AUGUSTIN (1736-1806) (elec.): The renowned French scientist whose work included research in biological energy, friction and the strength of materials. He is best remembered for his contributions to the theory of electrostatic and magnetic forces.

COUMARONE-INDENE RESINS (paint. and dec.) cou m rone'-in' dene res'-ins: Resins derived as by-products in making coke from coal.

COUNTDOWN (space) count' down: The step-by-step process leading to missile launching. It is performed in accordance with a predesigned time schedule.

COUNTER (elec.) coun' ter: An electronic or mechanical device for counting the occurrence or rate of such events as signal pulses, change of state and other distinguishable actions.

COUNTERBALANCE (metal) coun' ter-bal' ance: A weight attached to one side of a moving wheel to offset a weight or force on the opposite side of wheel.

COUNTERBORE (wood) coun' ter bore: To drill a second larger hole using

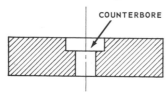

COUNTERBORE

the same center as original hole, to a specified depth.

COUNTERCLOCKWISE ROTATION (auto.) coun' ter clock' wise ro ta'-tion: Rotating in the opposite direction to the hands of a clock.

COUNTER EMF (cemf) (elec.) coun' ter emf: A voltage induced in a conductor moving through a magnetic field which opposes the source voltage.

COUNTER FLASHING (const.) coun' ter flash' ing: Flashing applied over flashing.

COUNTERFLOW (air cond.) coun' ter-flow: Heat exchange between two liquids opposite to the direction of flow.

COUNTER, GEIGER-MUELLER (elec.) coun' ter, Gei' ger-Muel' ler: A radiation counter using a Geiger-Mueller tube and its region of operation. See GEIGER-MUELLER TUBE.

COUNTER, PHOTOELECTRIC (elec.) coun' ter, pho to e lec' tric: A counter which is activated by interrupting a stream of light.

COUNTERPOISE (elec.) coun' ter poise: A system of wires radiating from the base of an antenna and supported above the ground, to act as a ground plane for a Marconi antenna system.

COUNTER, SCINTILLATION (elec.) coun' ter, scin til la' tion: A counter used to detect and measure nuclear radiation by counting flashes of light produced by radiation particles striking a phosphor crystalline target.

COUNTERSHAFT (metal) coun' ter-shaft: A smaller shaft and pulleys over a machine, driven by the main line shaft.

COUNTERSINK (wood.) coun' ter sink: To shape a hole drilled in wood or

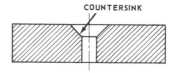

COUNTERSINK

metal with a cone shaped tool, to provide a recess for a flat head screw or bolt.

COUNTERSINK BIT (wood.) coun' ter-sink bit: A bit with a cone shaped cutting head for countersinking.

COUNTERWEIGHTS (auto.) coun' ter-weights: Weights attached to a wheel to obtain rotating balance.

COUPLER (elec.) cou' pler: An electronic device, fixed or variable, used to transfer energy between circuits by means of inductance, capacitance or resistance coupling.

COUPLING (elec.) cou' pling: The percentage of mutual inductance between coils. LINKAGE.

COURSE (const.) course: A layer of stone or brick; a row of shingles or clapboards.

COURSED RUBBLE (const.) coursed rub' ble: Masonry walls composed of roughly shaped stones fitting on level beds or courses.

COVALENT BOND (elec.) co va' lent bond: Atoms joined together, sharing each other's electrons to form a stable molecule.

COVE (const.) cove: A large concave cornice.

COVE CEILING (const.) cove ceil' ing: A ceiling with a sweeping concave curved junction between it and the walls.

COVE MOLDING (wood.) cove mold' ing: A concave molding.

COVER (graphics) cov' er: The outer leaves of a booklet or magazine.

COVERAGE (paint. and dec.) cov' erage: Amount of surface a given quantity of paint will cover; also how well paint conceals surface being painted.

COVERED ELECTRODE (welding) cov' ered e lec' trode: Metal rod used in arc welding which has a covering of materials to aid arc welding process.

COWL (auto) cowl: The part of an auto body which supports the instrument panel and controls.

COWL (plumb.) cowl: A ventilating hood attached to the top of a vent pipe.

COWLING (space) cowl' ing: The metal removable covers around an aircraft engine.

CRACKING (weld.) crack' ing: Term applied to action of opening a valve slightly and then closing the valve immediately.

CRACKLE FINISH (paint and dec.) crack' le fin' ish: A finish in which alligatoring is produced, allowing the undercoat to show through the cracks.

CRADLING (const.) crad' ling: Timbers and boards for supporting lath and plaster in vaulted ceilings.

CRANK (metal.) crank: A lever which has a shaft as its axis.

CRANKING MOTOR (auto.) crank' ing mo' tor: The starter; a motor to initially turn the engine for starting.

CRANKPIN (auto.) crank' pin: The machine surface on the crankshaft crank to which the connecting rod is attached.

CRANKSHAFT (auto.) crank' shaft: The main shaft of an engine, on which offset sections form cranks which swing in a circle as the shaft rotates.

CRATER (weld.) cra' ter: A depression in the face of a weld, usually at the termination of an arc weld.

CRAWLING (paint. and dec.) crawl' ing: Varnish defect in which poor adhesion of varnish to surface in some spots causes it to crawl or gather up into globules instead of covering the surface.

CRAWL SPACE (const.) crawl space: The space beneath a house which is built on piers or a foundation wall.

CRAZING (crafts) craz'ing: Very fine cracks which appear in ceramic ware due to improper firing; fine cracks due to unequal shrinkage between the glaze and body of ceramic ware; fine lines appearing in painted surfaces due to unequal contraction and expansion between coats.

CRAZING (paint. and dec.) craz'ing: Minute, interlacing cracks on the surface of a finish.

CREASING (graphics) creas'ing: The process of creasing cardboard or cover stock before folding to prevent breaking.

CREEP (metal) creep: The slow deformation of steels under constant load at high temperatures.

CREEP (space) creep: The property of a metal which allows it to be permanently deformed when subjected to a stress.

CREEPER (auto.) creep'er: A low platform with casters. A repairman can lie on the creeper and pull himself under a car.

CREOSOTE (const.) cre'o sote: A pungent oily liquid from distilled wood or coal tar, used as a wood preservative.

CREOSOTE OIL (paint. and dec.) cre'o sote oil: A transparent, oily and pungent liquid obtained from the distillation of wood tar or coal tar. It is widely used as a wood preservative and as an antiseptic.

CREST (metal) crest: The top joining surfaces of a thread at the major diameter.

CRICKET (const.) crick'et: A small roof structure placed where two larger surfaces meet at an angle. Its purpose is to improve drainage.

CRIMPING (metal) crimp'ing: The turning or closing down the edge of a piece of sheet metal.

CRIPPLE RAFTER (const.) crip'ple raft'er: A roof rafter that extends between a hip and valley rafter.

CRITERIA (automation) cri ter'i a: The rules by which judgments and decisions are made either by man or by machine.

CRITICAL COUPLING (elec.) crit'i cal cou'pling: The degree of coupling between two resonant circuits which produces maximum transfer of energy.

CRITICAL RANGE (metal) crit'i cal range: The range between critical points on heating and cooling steel within which certain crystalline structure changes take place.

CRITICAL SPEED (auto.) crit'i cal speed: The rotational speed at which vibration will occur.

CRITICAL TEMPERATURE (metal) crit'i cal tem'per a ture: The temperature at which certain chemical changes take place in steel during heating and cooling.

CROCUS (crafts) cro'cus: An iron oxide used for polishing.

CROOKES TUBE (elec.) crookes tube: A tube used to study the conduction of electricity through gasses, such as Xrays.

CROPPING (metal) crop'ping: Shearing or cutting off the ends of a partially rolled ingot.

CREOSOTE STAIN (paint. and dec.) cre' o sote stain: Creosote made mostly from wood and coal tars is mixed with linseed oil, drier and thinned with benzine or kerosene.

CROSS (plumb.) cross: A pipe fitting used to connect four pipes together at right angles.

CROSS CONNECTION (plumb.) cross con nec' tion: Any physical connection of pipes which would directly or indirectly permit the interchange of impure water or waste with pure drinking water.

CROSSCUT SAW (wood.) cross' cut saw: A saw designed to cut across the grain of wood.

CROSSCUT SAW TEETH /15°/ 45°

CROSS FEED (metal) cross feed: A transverse feed; in a lathe it is the feed in a direction at right angles to the axis of the work.

CROSS FILING (metal) cross fil' ing: Using a file against the work and pushing the file endways.

CROSSHATCH GENERATOR (elec.) cross' hatch gen' er a tor: A test instrument used in TV service which produces a cross hatched pattern display on the picture tube. It is also used in color TV to adjust the convergence of beams from the three electron guns.

CROSS HATCHING (draft.) cross hatch'ing: Section lines; the drawing of lines within a sectioned area of an object to designate that it is a section and also the type of material from which the object is made.

CROSSING FILE (metal) cross' ing file: A file shaped like two half round files placed back to back.

CROSSLAP JOINT (wood.) cross'lap: Wood joint assembled as shown.

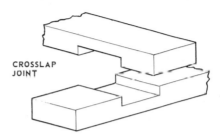

CROSSLAP JOINT

CROSS MODULATION (elec.) cross mod u la' tion: Distortion resulting from undesired signal impressed upon input of radio frequency amplifiers.

CROSS NEUTRALIZATION (elec.) cross neu tral i za' tion: A method of neutralization used with push-pull amplifiers, where a part of the output from each tube is fed back to the grid circuit of each opposite tube through a capacitor.

CROSSOVER (plumb.) cross' o ver: A U shaped fitting permitting a pipe to cross over another pipe when they meet in the same plane.

CROSSOVER FREQUENCY (elec.) cross' o ver fre' quen cy: The frequency in a crossover network at which an equal amount of energy is delivered to each of two loudspeakers.

CROSSOVER NETWORK (elec.) cross'-o ver net' work: A network designed to divide audio frequencies into bands for distribution to loud speakers.

CROSS SECTION (draft.) cross sec' tion: See CROSS HATCHING, a drawing made by imagining that a cut has been made through an entire object at right angles to the longitudinal axis of the work through which the section is taken.

CROSS-SECTION PAPER (draft.) cross-sec' tion pa' per: Special paper ruled out in squares to serve as guide lines when sketching.

CROSS SLIDE (metal) cross slide: The mating dovetail slides on the carriage perpendicular to the lathe bed. The cross slide is controlled by handle and screw for transverse feed. It can also be mechanically linked to the apron for machine cross feed.

CROSS TALK (elec.) cross talk: The leakage from one audio line to another which produces objectional background noise.

CROSS VENTILATION (const.) cross ven ti la' tion: Ventilation by openings in adjacent outside walls.

CROTCH WOOD (wood.) crotch wood: Sections of wood cut from the joint between limbs, branches and trunk of a tree. Exquisite grain patterns of this wood make it valuable in fine furniture construction.

CROWN (weld.) crown: The convex surface of properly finished weld.

CROWNING (const.) crown' ing: To raise the center of a flat surface to improve drainage.

CROWN MOLDING (wood.) crown mold'-ing: A molding with a double curved face.

CRUCIBLE (metal) cru' ci ble: A graphite pot used for melting metals.

CRUCIBLE FURNACE (metal) cru' ci-ble fur' nace: A gas fired furnace for melting nonferrous metals such as aluminum, bronze and copper.

CRUCIBLE STEEL (metal) cru' ci ble steel: A high quality steel produced and prepared in a crucible.

CRUDE OIL (auto.) crude oil: Oil in its natural state.

CRYOGENIC PROPELLANT (space) cryo gen' ic pro pel' lant: A rocket fuel which is liquid only at very low temperatures.

CRYOGENICS (elec.) cryo gen' ics: The use of electronic circuits designed to take advantage of increased efficiency at extremely low temperatures.

CRYOHYDRATE (air cond.) cryo hy'-drate: A frozen mixture of salt and water.

CRYOLITE (metal) cryo' lite: A compound which when fused is a solvent for aluminum oxide, so that metallic aluminum may be recovered in the electrolysis process.

CRYPTOMETER (paint. and dec.) cryp-tom' e ter: An instrument used to measure the opacity of paint.

CRYSTAL CONTROL (elec.) crys' tal con trol' : The control of the frequency of an oscillator by use of a piezoelectric crystal.

CRYSTAL DIODE (elec.) crys' tal di-ode: Diode formed by small semiconductor crystal and a cat whisker.

CRYSTAL FILTER (elec.) crys' tal fil' ter: A sharply tuned filter circuit using quartz crystals.

CRYSTAL LATTICE (elec.) crys' tal lat' tice: The structure of a material when outer electrons are joined in covalent bond.

CRYSTALLIZING LACQUER (paint. and

dec.) crys'tal liz ing lac'quer:
Novelty finish which crystallizes forming unusual crystal and floral patterns
as it dries.

CRYSTAL PICKUP (elec.) crys'tal
pick'up: A phono-cartridge which
produces an electrical output by the
piezoelectric effect of crystals.

C-SUPPLY (elec.) C-sup'ply: Voltages
supplied for the grid bias of electron
tubes, usually a negative voltage.

CUBBY LOCKER (auto.) cub'by lock'er:
The British term for a glove compartment in a car.

CUBIC CONTENT (const.) cu'bic
con'tent: The volume of a building.
Various methods of computing content
are used by different authorities.

CUEING (elec.) cue'ing: A one way
telephone circuit to control program
and direct technical personnel.

CUMULATIVE COMPOUNDING (elec.)
cu'mu la tive com pound'ing: A
compound motor having series windings
connected so that the magnetic fields
aid the fields of the shunt windings.

CUP CENTER (wood.) cup cen'ter: The
dead center in the tailstock of a wood
lathe, which supports the work.

CUP JOINT (plumb.) cup joint: A joint
used in lead pipe work where the end
of one pipe is flared out to receive the
tapered end of the other pipe.

CUPOLA (metal) cu'po la: A furnace
used to remelt and treat pig iron when
used to make castings.

CUPRITE (metal) cu'prite: Red copper
ore found in Arizona.

CUP WHEEL (metal) cup wheel: A
grinding wheel shaped like a cup and
designed to cut on its edge.

CURB (const.) curb: A roof on which
the slope is broken on two or more
sides. A curb is built where the slope
changes; a concrete boundary between
the street and the building lot, which
prevents street drainage water from
running onto lot.

CURB BOX (plumb.) curb box: A cylinder or box placed in the ground over
the curb cock. A rod with attached key
may reach the cock for turning on or
off.

CURB COCK (plumb.) curb cock: The
valve in the service main, usually near
the street.

CURB ROOF (const.) curb roof: See
MANSARD ROOF.

CURIE POINT (elec.) cu'rie point: The
temperature of a ferromagnetic material at which residual magnetism
disappears.

CURRENT (elec.) cur'rent: The transfer of electrical energy in a conductor
by means of electrons moving constantly and changing positions in a
vibrating manner.

CURRENT DENSITY (elec.) cur'rent
den'si ty: Amperes per unit of cross
sectional area of conductor.

CURRENT NODE (elec.) cur'rent node:
The point of zero current on a transmission line which has standing waves.

CURRENT REGULATOR (auto.)
cur'rent reg u la'tor: A circuit relay,
actuated by a series coil in the charging
circuit. Excessive current causes the
relay to insert resistance in the generator field circuit and reduce output
to predetermined value.

CURRENT - VOLTAGE REGULATOR (elec.) cur' rent-volt' age reg'u la tor: A vibrating type relay which regulates the resistance in the field windings of a generator, and consequently provides a steady output voltage under varying loads.

CURTAIN WALL (const.) cur' tain wall: A nonbearing wall between columns which is not supported by girders.

CUT (graphics) cut: Type-high plate used for printing an illustration.

CUT (paint. and dec.) cut: Dispersion of a certain number of pounds of shellac or resin per gallon of volatile liquid. A 4 lb. cut of shellac contains 4 lbs. of dry shellac and 1 gal. of alcohol.

CUT ACID (metal.) cut ac' id: A soldering flux made by dissolving zinc in muriatic acid.

"CUT IN THE SASH" (paint. and dec.): Painting the window sash. This is ordinarily done with a brush, often called a sash tool, which permits the painter to get a clean edge.

CUT NAILS (wood.) cut nails: Machine-cut iron nails rather than round wire nails.

CUTOFF (space) cut' off: The shutting off of a liquid or solid propellant combustion process of a rocket engine, thereby causing a rapid drop toward zero thrust.

CUTOFF BIAS (elec.) cut' off bi' as: The value of a negative voltage applied to the grid of a tube which will cutoff the current flow through the tube.

CUTOUT (elec.) cut' out: A reverse current relay; a disconnect between circuits.

CUTOUT RELAY (auto.) cut' out re'-lay: A reverse current relay which automatically opens if current flows in wrong direction.

CUTTING ANGLE (metal) cut' ting an' gle: The angle between the cutting edge of a tool and the face of the work to be cut.

CUTTING, FLAME (weld.) cut' ting, flame: Cutting metals by a rapid oxidation process at a high temperature produced by a gas flame accompanied by a jet stream of oxygen which blows the oxides away from the cut.

CUTTING FLUID (metal) cut' ting flu'-id: See COOLANT.

CUTTING HEAD (elec.) cut' ting head: A hard steel or diamond stylus controlled by a crystal or electromagnetic device, used for cutting the sound grooves in a phonograph record.

CUTTING MACHINE (graphics) cut' ting ma chine': A mechanical device consisting of a bed, a clamp and a knife, for cutting stock to desired size.

CUTTING PLANE (draft.) cut' ting plane: An imaginary plane used to cut through an object to produce a sectional view.

CUTTING SPEED (metal) cut' ting speed: The rate at which material is cut, measured in feet per minute.

CUTTING TOOLS (metal) cut' ting tools: Single pointed tools for turning, boring, shaping and planing; milling cutters,

ROUND NOSE   FINISHING   ROUGHING   FACING

drills, reamers, taps, dies, broaches, saws and abrasives, each of a great variety of types and sizes.

CUTTLE FISH (crafts) cut' tle fish: A marine molusk having a calcified internal shell. The ground shells are used for polishing.

CW (elec.): Abbreviation for Continuous Wave.

C WASHER (metal) C wash' er: A washer with one side removed so that it is shaped like a letter C. Sometimes called a slip or open washer.

CYANIC (paint. and dec.) cy an' ic: Containing blue, or pertaining to blue color; containing cyanogen.

CYANIDING (metal) cy' a nid ing: Surface hardening low carbon steel by heating in contact with a cyanide salt, and then quenching.

CYBERNETICS (elec.) cy ber net' ics: The study of complex electronic computer systems and their relationship to the human brain.

CYCLE (elec.) cy' cle: A set of events occurring in sequence. One complete reversal of an alternating current from positive to negative and back to starting point.

CYCLOID (draft.) cy' cloid: A curved line generated by a point on the circumference of a circle as the circle rolls along a straight line.

CYCLOTRON (elec.) cy' clo tron: A machine to accelerate charged particles by means of pulsed voltages applied to electrodes. The particles move in a spiral path due to combined force of pulses and a superimposed magnetic field.

CYLINDER (auto.) cyl' in der: A cylindrical shaped enclosure, closed at one end and open at the other.

CYLINDER (draft.) cyl' in der: A geometric figure with a circular cross sectional area; a geometric figure generated by a rectangle rotated around one of its parallel edges as an axis.

CYLINDER (weld.) cyl' in der: A container used to hold gases used in welding.

CYLINDER BANDS (graphics) cyl' in der bands: Strips of thin, flat steel, fastened in position near the cylinder and close to the bed of the press. They keep the rear edge of the sheets from falling on the bed of the press.

CYLINDER BLOCK (auto.) cyl' in der block: The main casting or body of an engine which is bored to fit the pistons.

CYLINDER BORE (auto.) cyl' in der bore: The diameter of the engine cylinder.

CYLINDER GAUGE (metal) cyl' in der gauge: A dial indicator gauge for measuring the inside diameter of a large hole or cylinder. In rebuilding an automobile engine, this gauge is used to measure the diameter, out of roundness and taper of the cylinder bore.

CYLINDER HEAD (auto.) cyl' in der head: The casting which bolts to and closes the engine block. It contains the combustion chambers. The head is sometimes designed to accommodate the valve mechanisms.

CYLINDER PRESS (graphics) cyl' in der press: A printing-press consisting of a cylinder, a flat bed, and an automatic inking device. The type form is locked on the flat bed, and bed moves back and forth beneath the rotating cylinder, the sheet being held on the cylinder while the impression is being taken. If the cylinder makes but one revolution during a forward and backward motion of the bed, it is called a "drum" cylinder; if it makes two revolutions during a forward and backward motion of the bed, it is called a two revolution cylinder. In the latter type of machine, while the bed is moving forward the cylinder is raised so that the bed may pass beneath it; when the bed is moving backward the cylinder is down, taking the impression.

CYMA RECTA (const.) cy' ma rec' ta: A reverse curve molding with the convex curve at the top and concave curve at the bottom.

CYMA REVERSA (const.) cy' ma re ver' sa: A reverse curve molding with the concave curve at the top and the convex curve at the bottom.

CYPRESS (Taxodium Distichum) (wood.) cy' press: Called the "wood eternal." It is extremely resistant to decay and insects. The wood is brown to red in color, fine grained, light, soft and moderately stiff.

DADO (wood.) da' do: A rectangular recess cut in wood across the wood grain. A groove is a rectangular recess which runs with the wood grain. See illustration, page 103.

DADO AND RABBET (wood.) da'do and rab' bet: A wood joint formed by using dado and rabbet cuts. A rabbet is a recess cut along the end or edge of stock. See illustration, page 103.

DADO SAWS (wood.) da' do: A combination of saws and chippers which may be assembled in specified thicknesses. Used to cut dados.

DAIS (const.) da' is: A raised platform at one end of a room.

DAMMAR (paint. and dec.) dam' mar: A natural resin used extensively in the preparation of varnishes and lacquers.

DAMPER (air cond.) damp' er: A valve or plate used to control the flow of air or liquid.

DAMPER (elec.) damp' er: A tube used in a television set as a half-wave rectifier to prevent oscillations in the horizontal output transformer.

DAMPED WAVE (elec.) damped wave: A wave in which successive oscillation decreases in amplitude.

DAMPING (elec.) damp' ing: The gradual decrease in amplitude of oscillations in a tuned circuit, due to energy dissipated in resistance.

DAMP PROOFING (const.) damp' proofing: The treatment of a masonry wall to prevent water seepage through it.

DANDY ROLL (graphics) dan' dy roll: A cylindrical roll used in paper making to produce the watermark and the laid effect on the paper.

DANIELL CELL (elec.) dan' iell cell: A primary cell consisting of a zinc anode in a zinc sulfate solution and a copper cathode in a copper sulfate solution. The electrolytes are separated by a porous pot.

DAPPING DIE (crafts) dap' ping die: A solid metal block with a series of semi-spherical holes of different sizes machined into its surfaces. Used with a dapping punch for forming small semi-spheres in soft metals. Widely used in jewelry making.

DAPPING PUNCH (crafts) dap' ping punch: A metal punch with a ball shaped end. These are made to match the semi-spherical holes in a dapping block.

DARAF (elec.) dar' af: A unit of measurement of elastance; the reciprocal of farad.

DARBY (const.) dar' by: A long flat tool used by plasterers when working on ceilings.

DARDELET THREADS (metal) dar' de let threads: This thread resembles the Acme thread but the thread depth is less. The root of the thread on a bolt and the crest of the thread on a nut are tapered about 6 degrees. Considerable end play is provided so that the tapered surfaces can lock together; a self-locking thread of French design.

DARK CURRENT (elec.) dark cur' rent: The current through a photo tube or semiconductor in the absence of light; the signal output from a television camera tube in the complete absence of light.

D'ARSONVAL METER (elec.) D'ar' sonval me' ter: A stationary-magnet moving coil meter.

DASH (auto.) dash: The dividing partition between the engine and driver in an automobile; the firewall.

DASHES (graphics) dash' es: Plain or ornamental sections of rule used to separate various parts of printed matter.

DASHPOT (auto.) dash' pot: A small cylinder filled with liquid and a piston with a metering orifice. It is used to retard a mechanical action such as the closing rate of the throttle plate in a carburetor as it approaches the idle position.

DASHPOT (elec.) dash' pot: A mechanical device consisting of a piston moving in a cylinder filled with oil or air. It is used to prevent vibration or oscillation of movement or to delay an action.

DATA (automation) da' ta: Specific bits of information to be processed mathematically or logically, or used to control the operation of a machine.

DATAMATION (automation) data ma' tion: Automatic handling of information including computers and office automation.

DATA PROCESSING (automation) da' ta pro' cess ing: The process of handling information; the activity of submitting data to specific operations to make the information more usable for the intended purpose.

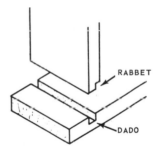

DATA REDUCTION (space) da' ta reduc' tion: The action or process of reducing data to usable form.

DAUBING (metal) daub' ing: Filling cracks in a cupola furnace after a heat; smearing and coating in an unworkmanlike manner.

DBM (elec.): Loss or gain in reference to an arbitrary power level of one milliwatt.

DB METER (elec.) db me' ter: A meter used in audio circuits to measure volume levels in respect to a given reference. Scale is calibrated in DB's.

DC (elec): Direct current.

D–C (elec.): Direct current used as an adjective.

D–C COMPONENT (elec.) d-c compo' nent: The d-c value of an ac wave which has an axis other than zero.

DC GENERATOR (elec.) dc gen' er a- tor: A generator with connections to the armature through a commutator. Its output is a direct current.

D–C INSERTION (elec.) d-c in ser' tion: The insertion of the d-c component of a signal.

DC RESTORATION (elec.) dc res to- ra' tion: Circuits used to reinsert the d-c component of a signal, such as in television, after the d-c component has been removed by RC or trans- former coupling between amplifier stages.

DCWV (elec.): Abbreviation for DI- RECT CURRENT WORKING VOLTAGE. It is a specification of a capacitor.

DEAD AXLE (auto.) dead ax' le: A non- rotating axle.

DEAD CENTER (metal) dead cen' ter: The non-rotating center in the tail- stock.

DEAD END (plumb.) dead end: An ex- tended portion of pipe with a closed end, to which no connections are made.

DEAD FLAT (paint. and dec.) dead flat: No gloss.

DEAD FORM (graphics) dead form: A used form of type that is ready for distribution.

DEAD LINE (graphics) dead line: A line placed on the bed of a cylinder press as a guide for placing the form.

DEADMAN (elec.) dead' man: A log or mass of concrete or steel buried in the ground to which guy wires for towers and poles are attached.

DEAD SPOT (elec.) dead spot: Certain geographical locations in which radio reception of a particular signal is very poor.

DEBUNCHING (elec.) de bunch' ing: Used in velocity modulation. A space charge effect which destroys the bunch- ing of electrons.

DECADE BOX (elec.) dec' ade box: A laboratory instrument in which is as- sembled either resistors or capacitors. A switching arrangement permits the selection of a specific value, in steps of ten.

DECALCOMANIA (crafts) de cal co- ma' ni a: A transfer process; a proc- ess in which a picture insignia or let- ters are transferred from a paper to a smooth surface.

DECALCOMANIA (paint. and dec.) de- cal co ma' ni a: Paint films in the form of pictures or other decorations which can be transferred from a tem- porary paper mounting to other sur- faces.

DECALESCENCE POINT (metal) de ca- les' cence point: The temperature of steel at which a transformation takes place in the structure and there is a distinct change in appearance.

DECALESCENT POINT (elec.) de ca- les' cent point: In heating metal, it is the point at which a sudden decrease in the rate of temperature change occurs, due to the greater heat absorp- tion.

DECARBURIZATION (metal) de car-bur i za' tion: The loss of carbon from the surface of steel during rolling, forging and heat-treating at high temperatures.

DECAY (elec.) de cay' : A term used to express a gradual decrease in values of current and voltage.

DECAY TIME (elec.) de cay' time: The time required for a capacitor to discharge to a specified percentage of its original charge.

DECELERATION (space) de cel er-a' tion: Negative acceleration (slowing down).

DECIBEL (elec.) dec' i bel: One tenth of a BEL. A unit used to express the relative increase or decrease in power. Unit used to express gain or loss in a circuit.

DECIDUOUS (wood.) de cid' u ous: Pertaining to trees which shed their leaves at change of seasons.

DECIMAL CODE (automation) dec' i mal code: A numbering system or code with ten possible states.

DECIMAL EQUIVALENT (metal) dec' i-mal e quiv' a lent: The decimal equivalent to a fraction.

DECKING (const.) deck' ing: Material such as wood, canvas or roofing material used to protect any flat surface from the weather.

DECKLE (graphics) deck' le: A feathery edge produced on paper during manufacturing. It is sometimes left on the printed sheet for artistic effect.

DECLINATION (elec.) dec li na' tion: The angle between true north and magnetic north.

DECOMPRESSION SICKNESS (space) de-com pres' sion sick' ness: A disorder experienced by deep sea divers and aviators caused by reduced barometric pressure and evolved gas bubbles in the body.

DECOUPLE (elec.) de cou' ple: To counteract feedback by shunting signal to ground; to prevent one circuit from affecting another.

DECREMENT (elec.) dec' re ment: A decrease; a loss due to a decrease.

DEDENDUM (metal) de den' dum: The distance from the pitch line to the base of a gear tooth.

DEEMPHASIS (elec.) de em' pha sis: FM receiver circuit to remove pre-emphasis and restore signal to its original form.

DE-ENERGIZE (elec.) de-en' er gize: To remove power from a component or circuit; to turn off a circuit.

DEEP (paint. and dec.) deep: Intense or strong color with no apparent presence of black.

DEFINITION (elec.) def i ni' tion: Sharpness and distinctness in a TV picture; clarity.

DEFLECTION (elec.) de flec' tion: The deviation from zero of a needle in a meter. The movement or bending of an electron beam.

ELECTROMAGNETIC, a method of deflecting the electron beam by means of a varying magnetic field generated in a yoke or coil around the neck of the CRT.

ELECTROSTATIC, a method of deflecting the electron beam by means of varying the voltage on the horizontal and vertical deflection plates in the CRT.

YOKE, a coil positioned around the neck of a CRT which produces deflection of electron beam.

DEFLECTION ANGLE (elec.) deflec'tion an'gle: The maximum angle of deflection of the electron beam in a TV picture tube.

DEFLECTION FACTOR (elec.) deflec'tion fac'tor: The d-c voltage at the deflection plates of a cathode ray tube to produce a beam deflection of one inch on the screen at a given accelerating voltage.

DEFLECTION SENSITIVITY (elec.) deflec'tion sen si tiv'i ty: The amount of deflection of the electron beam in a cathode ray tube per one volt applied to deflection plates.

DEFOREST, LEE (1873-1961): The famous American inventor who perfected the triode vacuum tube, making possible the use of the vacuum tube as an amplifier, a detector or an oscillator. He was a pioneer in the development of radio and sound on film motion pictures.

DEFROSTING CYCLE (air cond.) defrost'ing cy'cle: The operation in a refrigeration unit which permits defrosting during the off period.

DEGASSING (elec.) de gas'sing: A process used to remove gases from a vacuum tube during manufacturing. See GETTER.

DEGENERATIVE FEEDBACK (elec.) degen'er a tive feed'back: Feedback 180° out of phase with input signal so that it subtracts from input.

DEGREE-DAY (air cond.) de gree'-day: A unit based on temperature difference and time, used to specify the normal heating load in winter; Degrees x Days.

DEGREE OF AUTOMATICITY (automation) de gree' of au to ma tic'i ty: The relative intensity of automatic operations in a manufacturing process.

DEHUMIDIFIER (air cond.) de humid'i fi er: A device used to lower the moisture content of the air passing through it.

DEHYDRATED CASTOR OIL (paint. and dec.) de hy drat'ed cas'tor oil: A drying oil prepared from castor oil.

DEHYDRATION (air cond.) de hydra'tion: Removal of moisture from the air by absorption or adsorption materials; the removal of water from stored foods.

DEHYDRATOR (auto.) de hy dra'tor: A device for removing moisture from air or a refrigerant.

DEIONIZATION POTENTIAL (elec.) de i on i za'tion po ten'tial: Voltage across a gas filled tube at which deionization occurs and conduction stops.

DELAYED AGC (elec.) de lay'ed agc: An automatic gain circuit which remains inoperative during weak signal reception. It becomes effective when the input signal passes a predetermined level.

DELAY LINE (elec.) de lay' line: A circuit which may consist of inductors and capacitors which is used to delay a signal pulse. It is used in a color TV receiver to equalize the delay of the luminance and chrominance channels.

DELIQUESCENCE (air cond.) del i ques' scence: The process of becoming liquid by absorption of moisture from the air.

DELTA del' ta: Symbol Δ; the 4th Greek letter; means "a change in" in mathematics.

DELTA CONNECTION (elec.) del' ta con nec' tion: A method of connecting three-phase alternators and transformers so that the start end of one winding is connected to the finish end of the second. The circuit configuration resembles the Greek letter Δ.

DELTA METAL (metal) de;' ta met' al: An alloy of copper and zinc with a small percentage of iron.

DEMAGNETIZATION (elec.) de magnet i za' tion: The removal of magnetism from a magnetized substance.

DEMAND (elec.) de mand' : The amount of power that a power company must supply at a given time or period.

DEMODULATION (elec.) de mod u la'-tion: The process of removing the modulating signal intelligence from the carrier wave in the radio receiver.

DEMODULATOR (elec.) de mod u-la' tor: The section of the radio receiver which rectifies the incoming modulated signal and removes the intelligence; detector.

DEMULSIBILITY (metal) de mul' si-bil i ty: The ability to separate readily from water.

DENATURED ALCOHOL (paint. and dec.) de na' tured al' co hol: Grain or ethyl alcohol made unsuitable for beverage purposes by adding compounds of a poisonous nature.

DENSITY (air cond.) den' si ty: Mass or weight per unit volume.

DENSITY, GASOLINE (auto.) den' si ty, gas' o line: The specific gravity or ratio of the weight of a unit volume of gasoline at 60ºF to the weight of the same volume of water at 39ºF.

DENTILS (const.) den' tils: A series of blocks projecting outward under the cornice of a house.

DEOXIDIZER (metal) de ox' i diz er: Materials which huve a strong affinity for oxygen.

DEPLETION LAYER (in a semiconductor.) (elec.) de ple' tion lay' er: A region in which the mobile carrier charge density is insufficient to neutralize the net fixed charge of donors and acceptors. (IRE)

DEPOLARIZE (auto.) de po' lar ize: To remove polarity; to demagnetize.

DEPOLARIZER (elec.) de po' lar i zer: A chemical agent, rich in oxygen, introduced into a cell to minimize polarization.

DEPTH GAUGE (metal) depth gage: A gauge used to measure the depth of a hole or slot.

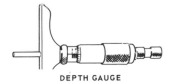

DEPTH GAUGE

VERNIER TYPE, employs the Vernier Scale.

MICROMETER TYPE, screw action, micrometer scale.

DERRICK (const.) der' rick: A type of crane used to move heavy loads. It consists of a vertical post and a boom hinged at the bottom of the post which is raised and lowered by means of cables.

DESCALING (m e t a l) de sca' ling: Process of removing scales which form on metals during exposure to oxidizing atmospheres at relatively high temperatures.

DESCENDER (graphics) de scen' der: The part of a lower case letter that descends below the body of the letter. The letters g, p, q, and y have descenders.

DESICCANT (air cond.) des' ic cant: An absorbent or adsorbent material used to remove water or vapor.

DESTRUCT (space) de struct' : The deliberate action of detonating or otherwise destroying a rocket missile or other vehicle after it has been launched but before it has completed its course.

DESTRUCTIVE DISTILLATION (paint. and dec.) de struc' tive dis til la' tion: Distilling a product at a temperature so high that products obtained are of different chemical composition than existed in the original material.

DETAIL DRAWINGS (d r a f t .) de tail' draw' ings: A drawing of a part of a machine or assembly giving all necessary information to manufacture it.

DETAILS (draft.) de tails': Special enlarged drawings of special features in a house such as the fireplace wall, kitchen cabinets, entrance details and others as needed.

DETAIL SECTION (d r a f t .) de tail' sec' tion: A revolved section, drawn adjacent to the cutting plane, but not on the view of the object.

DETECTION (elec.) de tec' tion: See DEMODULATION.

DETECTOR (elec.) de tec' tor:

CRYSTAL, a type of detection which uses the rectification characteristics of a crystal substance such as galena, silicon, germanium, iron pyrite.

DIODE, a detector using a diode tube or semiconductor as the rectifier of the rf signal.

GRID-LEAK, a detector in which rectification takes place in the grid circuit of a tube.

PLATE, a vacuum tube detector operated at a bias near cut-off so that detection takes place in the plate circuit of tube.

RADIATION, a device used to detect the presence and level of radiation.

RATIO, a detector for FM signals. It is based upon the ratio of output voltages of two diodes which is detected as the intelligence in the signal.

DETERGENT OILS (auto.) de ter' gent oils: Oils with detergents added to improve cleaning ability.

DETONATION (auto.) det o na' tion: A knock in an internal combustion engine due to pre-ignition or too rapid combustion.

DETONATION (s p a c e) det o na' tion: An extremely rapid reaction in which an oxidizer and a fuel combine with large evolution of heat.

DETUNE (elec.) de tune': The changing of the resonant frequency of a tuned circuit so that it is different from the incoming signal frequency.

DEUTERIUM (elec.) deu te' ri um: Heavy hydrogen; hydrogen atoms containing two protons and electrons.

DEUTERON (elec.) deu'ter on: An emitted particle consisting of a proton and a neutron.

DEVELOP (draft.) de vel'op: To draw in detail; to make a pattern of.

DEVELOPED LENGTH (plumb.) de vel'oped length: The center line distances between pipes and fittings.

DEVIATION RATIO (elec.) de vi a'tion ra'tio: A ratio between the maximum frequency deviation in FM to the highest modulating frequency.

DEVIATION SENSITIVITY (elec.) de vi a'tion sen si tiv'i ty: In FM radio, it is the least deviation of frequency which will produce a specified output power.

DEVIL (graphics) dev'il: An apprentice or errand boy around a printing shop.

DEW LINE (DISTANT EARLY WARNING) (space): A defensive line of radar stations at about the 70th parallel on the North American continent.

DIACRITICAL MARKS (graphics) di a crit'i cal marks: Marks used to show the correct pronounciation of a word.

DIAGONAL (draft.) di ag'o nal: A line drawn from corner to corner; slanting; oblique.

DIAGONAL BOND (const.) di ag'o nal bond: Bricks laid obliquely in a wall; often used in colonial architecture.

DIAGONAL SHEATHING (const.) di ag'o nal sheath'ing: Exterior sheathing applied diagonally, rather than horizontally.

DIAL (elec.) di'al: A graduated plate with intervals numbered in desired units. A pointer indicates the value of a setting on the dial, such as a meter dial or a radio dial.

DIAL INDICATOR (metal.) dial in'di ca tor: A dial gauge for checking accuracy of centering. Variations may be visibly recorded by observing the graduations on dial of indicator.

DIAMAGNETIC (elec.) di a mag net'ic: Materials which have a permeability of less than one; the property of being repelled by a magnetic field.

DIAMETER (draft.) di am'e ter: The length of a line drawn through the center of a circle and terminating at the circumference on each end.

DIAMETRAL PITCH (metal) di a met'ral pitch: Number of teeth in a gear divided by the pitch diameter or the number of teeth per inch of pitch diameter.

DIAMOND (metal) di'a mond: The hardest known mineral; crystalline carbon.

DIAMOND (graphics) di'a mond: 4-1/2 point type.

DIAMOND-POINT CHISEL (metal) di'a mond-point chis'el: A type of cold chisel with a diamond shaped cutting edge, for cutting V grooves and square corners.

DIAPER (const.) di'a per: Paving constructed in a checkered pattern, consisting of stone or colored tile.

DIAPHRAGM (elec.) di'a phragm: A thin disk, used in an earphone for producing sound.

DIATHERMY (elec.) di'a ther my: The use of radio frequency currents to produce internal heat in a specified part of the human body, by placing electrodes on opposite sides of area to be heated.

DIE (metal) die: A tool used for shaping, moulding, stamping or cutting metal.

DIE (metal) die: A tool for cutting external threads.

DIE CASTING (metal) die cast' ing: The process of casting where a relatively low melting point metal is forced into a die.

DIE CASTING (metal) die cast' ing: Molten metal forced into a metal mold under pressure.

DIECUT (graphics) die' cut: Using a steel die to cut paper or cardboard to required shape.

DIE FORGING (metal) die forg' ing: The forging of metal into a die. Used in production work.

DIELECTRIC (elec.) di e lec' tric: Insulating material between the plates of a capacitor.

DIELECTRIC CONSTANT (elec.) di e-lec' tric con' stant: A numerical figure representing the ability of a dielectric or insulator to support electric flux. Dry air is assigned the number 1.

DIELECTRIC FIELD OF FORCE (elec.) di e lec' tric field of force: See ELECTROSTATIC FIELD.

DIELECTRIC HEATING (elec.) di e-lec' tric heat' ing: A heating process in a dielectric material by the application of an alternating current field. Heating is the result of molecular friction.

DIELECTRIC STRENGTH (elec.) di e-lec' tric strength: The ability of an

insulator to withstand a potential difference, usually expressed in volts.

DIERESIS (graphics) di er' e sis: Two dots (..) placed over the second of two vowels in a word to show that they are to be pronounced separately.

DIE ROLLING (metal) die roll' ing: The process of passing hot steel through a set of rolls having the developed shape of the part sunk in their surfaces.

DIESEL ENGINE (auto.) die' sel en' gine: An engine operating on the diesel principle. Air is compressed in cylinder on compression stroke and the fuel is injected into the hot compressed air where it is ignited spontaneously.

DIE STAMPING (metal) die stamp' ing: The cutting and forming of sheet metal by a die.

DIFFERENTIAL (auto.) dif fer en' tial: The final drive unit of an automobile which transmits power from propeller shaft to the wheels. It also provides for unequal travel distances between rear wheels as the car turns a corner.

DIFFERENTIAL COMPOUNDING (elec.) dif fer en' tial com pound' ing: A compound motor having series windings connected so that the magnetic fields oppose the fields of the shunt windings.

DIFFERENTIAL INDEXING (metal) dif fer en' tial in' dex ing: A method of indexing work in a milling machine by a combination movement of the index crank and the movement of the index plate. These movements occur at the same time with a differential in their movement relationship. The amount the plate moves for each turn of the index crank is governed by change gears.

DIFFERENTIAL SYNCHRO (elec.) differ en' tial syn' chro: A synchro that has a three-coil distributed winding on its rotor.

DIFFERENTIATOR CIRCUIT (elec.) dif-fer en ti a' tor cir' cuit: A wave forming circuit with a short time con-stant, the output of which is proportional to the rate of change of the input.

DIFFRACTION (elec.) dif frac' tion: The breaking up of radio waves by the earth's surface at the horizon.

DIFFUSER (air cond.) dif fus' er: A grille or grating over the delivery or intake opening of an air passage.

DIFFUSION (elec.) dif fu' sion: The movement of carriers across a semi-conductor junction in the absence of an external force.

DIG (metal) dig: The tendency of a cut-ting tool to dig into the work due to incorrect grinding or setting.

DIGITAL COMPUTER (space) dig'i tal com put' er: A computer in which quantities are represented numerically and which can be used to solve complex problems relating to missile flight path.

DIGITAL SIGNAL (automation) dig'i tal sig' nal: A signal used for computation and control. The digital signal controls by a number of pulses representing the variable or dimension, rather than the pulse width or amplitude.

DILUENT (Lacquer) (paint. and dec.) dil' u ent: Volatile portion of vehicle not capable by itself of dissolving nitrocellulose.

DIMENSION (automation) di men' sion: The dimensions of a process include process factors and measurements of product.

DIMENSION (draft.) di men' sion: Def-inite measurements given on a drawing such as length, width, etc.

DIMENSION LINE (draft.) di men' sion line: A fine continuous line terminating in arrow heads indicating the distance to which the dimension refers. It is usually broken in the center to allow dimension figures.

DIMENSION LUMBER (const.) di-men' sion lum' ber: Lumber two or more inches thick and up to twelve inches wide.

DIMENSIONS, TYPES OF (automation) di men' sions, types of:

CONSTANT, a dimension which can be held at a fixed value and assumed not to change.

CONTIGUOUS, a dimension that can be measured at a number of points, which results in an average or mean dimension.

DISCRETE, a true value dimension measured directly on a definite article.

PARAMETRICAL, a dimension which is set for a particular job to be done. It is assumed not to change during the job.

VARIABLE, dimensions subject to continuous change during duration of job.

DIMETRIC PROJECTION (draft.) di-met' ric pro jec' tion: An object so drawn that two of its principle edges make equal angles with the plane of projection and the third edge makes either a smaller or greater angle, therefore the two axes making equal angles are fore-shortened equally while the third axis is fore-shortened in a different ratio.

DIMMER (auto.) dim' mer: A switch for shifting headlights to low beam to reduce glare from headlights.
(elec.) Any device placed in series with a lamp circuit in order to vary its brilliance.

DIMPLING (metal) dim' pling: Making a small impression in thin metal to house a rivet head; making a small conical impression in metal by a twist drill.

DINGING HAMMER (metal) ding' ing ham' mer: A light double faced hammer with polished faces, used by the metal

worker to remove small dents and irregularities from a sheet metal surface.

DIODE (elec.) di' ode: A two element tube containing a cathode and plate.

DIODE DETECTOR (elec.) di' ode detec' tor: A detector circuit utilizing the unilateral conduction characteristics of a diode.

DIORAMA (draft.) di o ra' ma: A model of a building or scene with foreshortened depth.

DIP (paint. and dec.) dip: To immerse something into a processing liquid or finishing material.

DIP (elec.) dip: The angle which a magnetic needle makes with a horizontal plane, when suspended in a vertical plane.

DIP COATING (paint. and dec.) dip coat' ing: Process of finishing article by immersing it in finishing material.

DIPENTENE (paint. and dec.) di' pentene: Solvent made by destructive distillation of pine stumps.

DIPOLE (elec.) di' pole:

ELECTRIC, a positive and a negative charge separated by a distance.

FOLDED, an antenna where two dipoles are closely spaced and joined together at the ends. One dipole is center-fed.

HALF WAVE, a dipole antenna made up of two one quarter wave length sections; a HERTZ antenna.

MAGNETIC, a magnetic field generated by a current in a closed loop. By convention the dipole is said to have a north and a south pole.

DIPOLE ANTENNA (elec.) di' pole anten' na: A center-fed antenna with two equal radiators usually one quarter wavelength long.

DIPPER (auto.) dip' per: A small cup attached to a bearing on a crankshaft. As bearing revolves the dipper passes through an oil bath and collects a supply of oil for the bearing.

DIRECT CURRENT (dc) (elec.) di rect' cur' rent: The flow of electrons in one direction.

DIRECT DRIVE (metal) di rect' drive: Power transmitted directly without use of shafts or belts.

DIRECT FEEDBACK (elec.) di rect' feed' back: See REGENERATIVE FEEDBACK.

DIRECTIONAL SIGNALS (auto.) di rec'-tion al sig' nals: Right and left flashing lights on both front and rear of an automobile to indicate that the driver intends to turn in that direction. Lights are controlled by lever switch at the steering wheel of the car.

DIRECTOR (elec.) di rec' tor: An element in a beam or directional antenna placed in front of the driven element and usually tuned to a higher frequency than the driven element. It is used to concentrate the antenna field in one direction.

DIRECT POLARITY (weld.) di rect' po-lar' i ty: Direct current flowing from anode (base metal) to cathode (electrode). The electrode is negative and the base metal is positive.

DIRTY (graphics) dir' ty: A case of bad-ly mixed type; a proof with many errors.

DISCOVERER (s p a c e) dis cov' er er: An Air Force research program for the development of advanced space vehicles and systems to perform so-phisticated tasks in space.

DISCRIMINATOR (elec.) dis crim' i na-tor: A type of FM detector.

DISH (elec.) dish: A term used in radar and microwave for a paraboloidal re-flector.

DISH (space) dish: A parabolic type of radio antenna.

DISK SANDER (wood.) disk sand' er: A power driven disk sander with tables and guides for supporting the work.

DISK WHEEL (auto.) disk wheel: A wheel made as one solid stamping; spokeless; the wheel and tire are changed as one unit when needed.

DISPERSIVES (a u t o .) dis per' sives: Additives to oil to prevent contaminants collecting to form sludge.

DISPLACEMENT CURRENT (elec.) dis-place' ment cur' rent: The movement of electrons in a dielectric toward the positive charge.

DISPLAY (automation) dis play': Infor-mation made available to machine op-erator by dials, charts and numerical indicators.

DISPLAY TYPE (g r a p h i c s) dis play' type: A heavy faced type used to set off the words from the regular body of type. Used for headlines and display work.

DISTEMPER (paint. and dec.) dis tem'-per: A water paint in which the vehicle protein is usually casein, egg white or glue. The term, used principally in Great Britain to designate water type paints, is practically obsolete in the United States.

DISTILLATE (paint. and dec.) dis' til-late: A condensed product produced by cooling vapors of a material heated sufficiently to drive off part of the material in the form of vapor.

DISTORTION (elec.) dis tor' tion: The deviations in amplitude, phase and fre-quency between the input and output signals of an amplifier or system.

AMPLITUDE, Distortion resulting from non-linear operation of an electron tube when peaks of input signals are reduced or cut-off by either excessive input signal or incorrect bias.

FREQUENCY, Distortion resulting from signals of some frequencies being amplified more than others or when some frequencies are excluded.

PHASE, Distortion resulting from a shift of phase of some signal fre-quencies.

DISTORTION (weld.) dis tor' tion: Warping of a structure.

DISTRIBUTION (elec.) dis tri bu' tion: A system used to supply electric power to various points; the division of electric currents to various locations.

BOX, a metal box in which connections are made to various circuits.

CENTER, a center of electrical equipment such as boxes, switches and circuit breakers supplied by a main line. Power to other locations is supplied from this center.

LINE, the main power line from which separate circuits are supplied.

PANEL, an assembly of switches, breakers and protective devices from which distribution is made.

DISTRIBUTION (graphics) dis tri-bu' tion: The work of replacing used type back into the cases.

DISTRIBUTOR (air cond.) dis trib' u-tor: A device for dividing the flow of liquid between parallel paths in the evaporator of a refrigerator.

DISTRIBUTOR (elec.) dis trib' u tor: Used in the automotive ignition system. A rotating switch, driven by a gear on the camshaft, which directs the high voltage to the spark plugs at the correct time. The distributor also contains the breaker points and condenser.

DITHERING (automation) dith' er ing: A term used to describe controlled vibration used to overcome unavoidable static friction and backlash effects. It is used by the engineer to fluidize control system behavior.

DITTO LINES (draft.) dit' to lines: Lines used to show a series of identical fea-

tures of an object, to save time and labor.

DIVERGENCE (elec.) di ver' gence: The spreading out from the point of origin, as of light rays or radio waves.

DIVERSIONARY MISSILE (space) di-ver' sion ar y mis' sile: A missile decoy.

DIVERSITY RECEPTION (elec.) di ver'-si ty re cep' tion: A radio reception system using several receivers and antennas to overcome the effect of signal fading.

DIVERTER (elec.) di vert' er: A variable shunt resistance connected across the series field coil of a generator to adjust degree of compounding.

DIVIDER (draft.) di vid' er: A drafting instrument consisting of two pointed legs, pivoted together at one end. Used for layout and transferring measurements.

DIVIDING HEAD (metal) di vid' ing head: A device used to rotate a piece of work through a certain number of degrees, for the purpose of graduating or machining the part.

D LAYER (elec.) D lay' er: An atmospheric layer of low ionization existing 40 to 50 miles from the earth's surface

DOCTOR BLADE (graphics) doc' to blade: A round edge knife used to wip the surplus ink from the surface of th cylinder, during rotogravure printing.

DOG (metal) dog: A driving link betwee the driving plate on a lathe and th work mounted between centers. Se LATHE DOG.

DOG HOUSE (elec.) dog house: A sma

building to house equipment at the base of an antenna.

DOG PLATE (metal) dog plate: A round plate attached to the spindle of a

lathe. The plate is slotted to receive the bent tail of a lathe dog. The plate drives the dog.

DOLLY (elec.) dol' ly: A platform on wheels upon which a TV camera is mounted, so that the camera may be moved easily from one position to another in the studio.

DOMAIN THEORY (elec.) do main' th' o- ry: A theory concerning magnetism, assuming that atomic magnets produced by movement of planetary electrons around the nucleus have a strong tenden- cy to line up together in groups. These groups are called "domains."

DOMESTIC ARCHITECTURE (const.) do mes' tic ar' chi tec ture: Relating to the design, planning and building of homes and private buildings.

DOMINANT COLOR (paint. and dec.) dom' i nant col' or: Color that pre- dominates, or is outstanding.

DONKEY ENGINE (auto.) don' key en'- gine: An auxiliary engine used in log- ging operations.

DONOR IMPURITY (elec.) do' nor im- pu' ri ty: An impurity added to a semi- conductor material which causes nega- tive electron carriers.

DOORBELL (elec.) door' bell: An elec- tric bell for announcing visitors. It is actuated by a push button at an outside door of the home.

DOORBELL TRANSFORMER (elec.) door' bell trans form' er: A step-down transformer from 117 volts ac to usually 6, 12 or 18 volts. Used to operate door- bells, buzzers and door chimes.

DOORFRAME (const.) door' frame: The surrounding case into which a door fits and is hinged.

DOORHEAD (const.) door' head: The upper horizontal part of a door frame.

DOORKNOB TUBE (elec.) door' knob tube: An enlarged version of an acorn tube for higher power applications.

DOORSTOP (const.) door' stop: The strip on the inside face of a door frame against which the door closes; a device which holds a door in any desired position.

DOPE (graphics) dope: A slang expres- sion referring to a pet material of a pressman which is supposed to be the panacea for all pressroom troubles.

DOPE (plumb.) dope: A compound used to lubricate and seal threaded pipe joints.

DOPING (elec.) dop' ing: Adding an im- purity to a semiconductor material.

DOPPLER (space): Christian Doppler (1803-53), an Austrian physicist.

DOPPLER EFFECT (elec.) dop' pler ef fect': The apparent change in fre- quency of sound or light waves, due to the relative velocity of the source and the observer. Effect named after Christian Doppler, the Austrian physi- cist (1803-1853).

DOPPLER EFFECT (space) dop' pler ef fect': The apparent change in fre- quency of vibrations, as of sound, light or radar, when the observed and observer are in motion relative to one another.

DORMER WINDOW (const.) dorm' er win' dow: A window projecting out from the roof of a building. It provides additional interior space and ventilation.

DOSIMETER (elec.) do sim' e ter: An instrument used to measure the exposure to radiation of a material or person.

DOT (graphics) dot: The individual element of a screened printing plate.

DOT GENERATOR (elec.) dot gen' er-a tor: A TV servicing instrument which produces a series of white dots on the television screen. It is used for adjusting convergence in color TV.

DOT-SEQUENTIAL SYSTEM (elec.) dot-se quen' tial sys' tem: The scanning and transmission of TV picture elements one by one in sequence.

DOUBLE BEND (plumb.) dou' ble bend: An S shaped pipe fitting.

DOUBLE-END BOLT (metal) dou' ble-end bolt: A stud bolt; a bolt without a head and threaded on both ends.

DOUBLE HUNG WINDOW (const.) dou' ble hung win' dow: A window consisting of an upper and lower sash hung in one frame.

DOUBLE IONIZATION (elec.) dou' ble i on i za' tion: A condition in a gas filled diode when two electrons are dislodged from each gas molecule.

DOUBLE-LEADED (graphics) dou' ble-leaded: Putting two leads between lines in text matter.

DOUBLE OFFSET (plumb.) dou' ble off' set: Two changes in direction installed in series in a continuous pipe.

DOUBLE POLE (db) (elec.) dou' ble pole: Having two contacts or connections such as a double pole switch.

DOUBLER (elec.) dou' bler: An amplifier circuit in which the output circuit is tuned to two times the input frequency.

DOUBLE SIDE BAND (elec.) dou' ble side band: A method of radio transmission in which the carrier frequency is suppressed and both side bands transmitted.

DOUBLE STUDDING (const.) dou' ble stud' ding: Two studs spiked together to form openings for doors and windows.

DOUBLET (elec.) dou' blet: A half-wave dipole antenna.

DOUBLE—THROW SWITCH (elec.) dou' ble-throw switch: A switch which can be placed in one of two different positions thereby connecting one circuit to either of two other circuits, but not simultaneously.

DOUZIEME dou zieme': A unit of measurement used by watch makers. It equals .0074 inches.

DOVETAIL CUTTER (wood.) dove' tail cut' ter: A woodworking machine which cuts the inner and outer dovetails on the edges of boards to be joined in this manner.

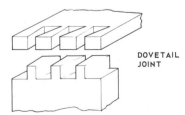

DOVETAIL JOINT

DOVETAILING (const.) dove' tail ing: A woodworkers joint where pieces are

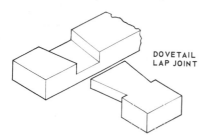

DOVETAIL LAP JOINT

fastened together by letting one piece into another in the form of an extended tail of a dove.

DOVETAIL SAW (wood.) dove' tail saw: A thin blade, fine-toothed backsaw for delicate cutting.

DOWEL (wood.) dow' el: A small round stick of wood.

DOWEL GAUGE (wood.) dow' el gauge: A clamp-on guide for locating position and depth of a dowel hole.

DOWEL JOINT (const.) dow' el joint: A joint reinforced by dowels.

DOWEL MACHINE (wood.) dow' el ma-chine': Machine for making dowels. A square piece of wood is fed into machine and is made round by rotating cutters.

DOWEL SHARPENER (wood.) dow' el sharp' en er: Cone shaped cutting tool, used to chamfer the ends of dowels.

DOWNDRAFT CARBURETOR (auto.) down' draft car' bu re tor: An auto-motive carburetor in which the air enters at the top and is sucked down past the spray nozzle.

DOWNHAND WELDING (weld.) down'-hand weld' ing: See FLAT POSITION WELDING.

DOWN-MILLING (metal) down-mill' ing:

A method of milling, when the work is fed in the same direction as the move-ment of the cutter teeth.

DOWNRANGE (space) down' range: In a direction away from the launch site and along the line of a missile test range.

DOWNSPOUT (const.) down' spout: A pipe or conductor to carry rainwater from the roof to the ground or to a sewer.

DOWNTIME (automation) down' time: Non-operating time to do tool change-over, repair, change of product or process, etc.

DRAFT (metal) draft: The clearance on a pattern to permit easy withdrawal from sand mould.

DRAFTING (draft.) draft' ing: The art of drawing using mechanical instru-ments, rules and squares.

DOWEL MACHINE

DRAFTING MACHINE (draft.) draft' ing: ma chine': A machine used in drawing which combines the T square, triangles and scales. The machine, by means of arms and gears, always maintains the horizontal and vertical scales and rul-ing edges parallel to the predetermined setting. The horizontal and vertical scales are fixed at 90 degree angle to each other. A protractor permits the drawing of accurate lines oblique to the horizontal.

DRAFTSMAN'S SCALE (draft.) drafts'-man's scale: Usually a scale with a triangular cross section. Each of the edges is graduated in a scale, to facilitate drawing at a reduced scale.

DRAG (metal) drag: The bottom section of a flask.

DRAG (space) drag: The aerodynamic force in a direction opposite to that of flight and due to the resistance of the body to motion in air.

DRAG LINK (auto.) drag link: The rod which connects the steering-knuckle arm with the steering gear arm in the steering mechanism of an automobile.

DRAGON'S BLOOD (crafts) drag'on's blood: A coloring agent obtained from a palm tree. It is odorless, tasteless and insoluble in water. In alcohol it forms a red solution.

DRAGON'S BLOOD (paint. and dec.) drag'on's blood: A red gum exuded from the fruit of a species of trees grown in the Malay peninsula.

DRAIN (plumb.) drain: A pipe used for waste drainage.

DRAINAGE FITTING (plumb.) drain' age fit' ting: A threaded cast iron fitting used on drainage pipes.

DRAINAGE PIPE (plumb.) drain' age pipe: A pipe used in a building to remove used water, rain and waste from the building.

DRAIN COCK (plumb.) drain cock: A small valve placed in the low side of a system for drainage.

DRAIN TILE (plumb.) drain tile: Hollow tile pipe, used for draining low lands and places in which water collects.

DRAW (metal - draft.) draw: To bring

the temper of steel from extreme hardness to a desired hardness or temper; to form metal by stretching or pulling through a die; to portray a picture by a system of lines.

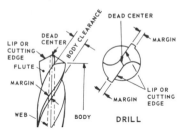

DRAWER SLIP (wood.) draw' er slip: A drawer guide; a strip on which a drawer slides.

DRAWFILING (metal) draw fil' ing: Holding the file by the handle and tip and drawing the file lengthwise with the work.

DRAWING (metal) draw' ing: The process of lengthening material by reducing its cross sectional area.

DRAWING BACK (metal) draw' ing back: The process of reheating hardened steel to some temperature below its critical temperature to change its hardness.

DRAWING BOARD (draft.) draw' ing board: A flat board, usually of soft wood, used as a drawing surface.

DRAWING DIE (metal) draw' ing die: A die used in a press to form a sheet of metal into a cup or depressed shape.

DRAWKNIFE (wood.) draw' knife: A two handled wood cutting tool. The handles are at right angles to the cutting blade. Used for rough work.

DRAWPLATE (crafts.) draw' plate: A steel plate with a series of holes gradually decreasing in size. Used for reduction of size and shaping wires.

DRAW SCREW (metal) draw screw: A small threaded rod used to screw into the threaded hole in the draw plate of a foundry pattern to facilitate withdrawal of pattern from mold.

DRAW SHEET (graphics) draw sheet: The top sheet of a tympan, to which the guides and fenders are attached.

DRAW SPIKE (metal) draw spike: A sharp pointed rod used to remove a wooden foundry pattern from the sand mold.

DRESS (metal) dress: To restore a tool to its original shape by forging and grinding.

DRESSER (plumb.) dress'er: A tool used to straighten leadpipe and sheet metal.

DRESSING (const.) dress'ing: The operation of squaring, planing and smoothing lumber for building.

DRIERS (paint. and dec.) dri'ers: Compounds of certain metals which hasten the drying action of oils when added to paints or varnishes. Most of them are solutions of metallic soaps in oils and volatile solvents. They are known as driers, oil driers, japan driers, liquid driers and japans.

DRIFTBOLT (const.) drift'bolt: A metal rod used to hold heavy timbers in place.

DRIFT ERROR (space) drift er'ror: A change in the output of an instrument over a period of time.

DRIFT KEY (metal) drift key: A tapered piece of flat steel, used as a wedge to remove taper shank tools and drills.

DRIFT PUNCH (metal) drift punch: A tapered metal punch used to bring holes in parts into alignment.

DRILL (metal) drill: An end cutting tool to originate or enlarge a hole in solid material. See illustration, page 118.

DRILL, BREAST (wood.) drill, breast: See BREAST DRILL.

DRILL CHUCK (wood.) drill chuck: A small three jaw chuck to hold drills or

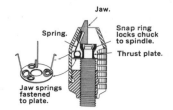

Jaw. — Spring. — Snap ring locks chuck to spindle. — Thrust plate. — Jaw springs fastened to plate.

cutting tools. Used with a hand drill, electric drill motor or drill press.

DRILL MOTOR (wood.) drill mo'tor: A small motor which may be held in the hand, used to turn drills and finishing tools, such as a buffer; sometimes called an Electric Hand Drill.

DRILL POINT GAUGE (metal) drill point gauge: A gauge used in accurately

grinding drills. It determines the correct drill point angle and the length of the drill lips.

DRILL PRESS (metal) drill press: A machine used for drilling holes in material. The work is held fixed on the base or table. The drill is held in a revolving spindle over the work. A feed mechanism is employed to bring the drill in contact with the work.

DRILL ROD (metal) drill rod: Accurately ground and polished tool steel rods.

DRIP (const.) drip: A part of the cornice projecting beyond the other parts for shedding small quantities of rain water.

DRIP LINE (plumb.) drip line: A pipe from a relief valve to conduct the discharge to a floor drain.

DRIP MOLD (const.) drip mold: A projecting mold around the base of a building to prevent rain from running down the face of the foundation walls.

DRIPSTONE (const.) drip' stone: A molding over a window or door to deflect rain.

DRIVE FIT (metal) drive fit: Parts mated with clearances that require driving together. Parts should retain a fixed position indefinitely in relation to each other.

DRIVEN PULLEY (metal) driv'en pul'ley: The pulley that receives power from the driving pulley.

DRIVER (elec.) driv'er: A device, such as a vacuum tube or transistor, which supplies the power to drive another stage, such as a final power amplifier.

DRIVING HOME (metal) driv'ing home: The setting of a part in its final position by a series of hammer blows.

DRIVING PULLEY (metal) driv'ing pul'ley: The pulley which transmits power to the driven pulley by a belt.

DRONE (space) drone: Unmanned self-propelled air vehicle, remotely controlled and specifically designed to be used for reconnaissance, as a target or for other non-destructive purposes.

DROP (elec.) drop: A term used to describe voltage drop.

DROP BLACK (paint. and dec.) drop black: See BONE BLACK.

DROP CLOTH (paint. and dec.) drop cloth: A large piece of fabric used by a painter while painting a room to protect furniture, rugs and other articles from paint damage.

DROP ELL (plumb.) drop ell: An ell with cast lugs on its side for attaching to support.

DROP FORGED (metal) drop forged: A piece of steel, heated on one end, is hammered into impressions formed by steel dies.

DROP FRONT (wood.) drop front: A desk on which the front folds forward to make a flat working surface.

DROP PEN (draft.) drop pen: A pen used for making dots and very small circles.

DROP SIDING (const.) drop sid'ing: Exterior siding, usually 3/4 inch thick, machined into various decorative patterns and is either tongue and grooved or shiplapped together.

DROP TEE (plumb.) drop tee: A T fitting with lugs on its side for attaching to support.

DROSS (metal) dross: The oxides and impurities which form on the surface of molten metal.

DRUM SWITCH (elec.) drum switch: A rotating cylindrical switch.

DRUM WINDING (elec.) drum wind'ing: A method of winding a generator armature where the conductors lie in slots near the surface of the armature.

DRY AIR (air cond.) dry air: Air only without water vapor.

DRY CELL (elec.) dry cell: A non liquid cell, composed of a zinc case, a carbon positive electrode and a paste of ground carbon, manganese dioxide and ammonium chloride as the electrolyte.

DRY FRICTION (auto.) dry fric' tion: The resistance to motion between dry unlubricated surfaces.

DRY FUEL ROCKET (space) dry fuel rock' et: A rocket that uses a mixture of fast-burning powder.

DRY ICE (air cond.) dry ice: Solid carbon dioxide.

DRYING (metal) dry' ing: The process of removing moisture from a mold by injection of hot air or by baking.

DRYING (paint. and dec.) dry' ing: Act of changing from liquid to solid state by evaporation of volatile thinners and by oxidation of oils.

DRYING OILS (paint. and dec.) dry' ing oils: Oils which are converted to solids when exposed to the oxygen in the air.

DRY KILN (wood.) dry kiln: A chamber in which wood is artificially seasoned.

DRY MEASURE dry meas' ure:

2 pints (pt)	= 1 quart (qt)
8 quarts	= 1 peck (pk)
4 pecks	= 1 bushel (bu)
105 quarts	= 1 barrel (bbl)

DRY ROT (const.) dry rot: The rapid decay of lumber in which the rot appears as dry powder similar to worm borings. It is caused by alternate dampness and dryness.

DRY RUBBLE (const.) dry rub' ble: A wall made of rough stone without mortar.

DRY-SAND CORE (metal) dry-sand core: A foundry core which has been baked or dried in an oven. Dry-sand cores are made in core boxes, independent of the mold in which they will be used.

DRY TO HANDLE (paint. and dec.) dry to han' dle: A film of paint is "dry to handle" when it is hardened sufficiently so that it may be handled without being damaged.

DRY TO TOUCH (paint. and ec.) dry to touch: A film of paint is "dry to touch" when it is hardened sufficiently so that it may be touched lightly without any of it adhering to the fingers.

DRY WALL (const.) dry wall: Any materials used for wall coverings that do not need to be mixed with water before application. Various wallboards are an example of dry wall construction.

DRY WEIGHT (space) dry weight: The weight of a rocket vehicle without its fuel.

DRY WELL (const.) dry well: A hole or pit in the ground, filled with stones or gravel, used for the collection of rainwater from downspouts.

DS GLASS (const.) ds glass: Double strength glass, used for glazing large windows.

DUB (graphics) dub: An inexperienced printer.

DUBBING (elec.) dub' bing: The combination of two or more sounds on a recording. One sound must be a recording.

DUCT (air cond.) duct: A sheet metal pipe or passageway used for conveying air.

DUCT (elec.) duct: An enclosed runway for conductors or cables.

DUCTILE (metal) duc' tile: The property of a material capable of being drawn out or hammered thin.

DUCTILITY (metal) duc til' i ty: The characteristic of a material to be drawn to a smaller size.

DULL (paint. and dec.) dull: Term applied to colors that have a neutral or grayed quality.

DULL IRON (metal) dul iron: Molten iron not hot enough for pouring into a mold.

DULL RUBBING (paint. and dec.) dull rub' bing: Act of rubbing a dried film of finishing material to a dull finish, usually with abrasive paper, pumice stone, steel wool and oil or water.

DULL TOOL DETECTION (automation) dull tool de tec' tion: Methods and sensors used to detect the condition of cutting tools in a machine.

DUMMY (graphics) dum' my: General lay-out for a booklet or folder; preliminary sketch.

DUMMY (graphics) dum' my: Unprinted sheets made up into the form in which the finished job will appear.

DUMMY ANTENNA (elec.) dum' my an ten' na: A substitute antenna, usually consisting of resistors, to dissipate transmitter power during test intervals.

DUNCAN PHYFE (wood.) dun' can phyfe: A nineteenth century American furniture designer. His work is designated by a modified Empire and Directoire style.

DUNNAGE (air cond.) dun' nage: Wood packing strips used in stowing cargo to provide air space around packages.

DUOTONE (graphics) du' o tone: A printed reproduction of a black-and-white photograph using two different inks; usually black ink and ink which is a tint of another color, or two closely related hues of the same color. In printing, two halftone printing plates of same screen are used; one is made to emphasize highlights, the other emphasizes shadows of the picture.

DUPLEX CABLE (elec.) du' plex ca' ble: Two wires insulated from each other enclosed in a single insulated covering.

DUPLEX PAPER (paint. and dec.) du' plex pa' per: Wallpaper which consists of two separate papers pasted together, used to create a highly embossed effect.

DUPLEX RECEPTACLE (elec.) du' plex re cep' ta cle: A double outlet receptacle used in house wiring. It provides outlets to connect lamps and appliances. The duplex receptacle is mounted in a metal box in the wall. After connections are made, it is covered with a decorative plate.

DURALUMIN, DURAL (metal) du ral' u-min, du ral': An alloy of aluminum (92%), copper (3-5%) and small percentages of magnesium and manganese which responds to heat treating processes.

DUST BOTTOM (wood.) dust bot' tom: A thin surface of wood placed between drawers in a cabinet.

DUST FREE (paint. and dec.) dust free: A film of paint is "dust free" when dust no longer adheres to it.

DUTCH BOND (const.) Dutch bond: A masonry wall made up of alternate courses of stretchers and headers.

DUTCH DOOR (const.) Dutch door: A two part door designed so that the lower part may be shut while the upper part remains open.

DUTCHMAN (metal) dutch' man: A piece fitted to cover a defect.

DUTCH METAL (paint. and dec.) Dutch metal: Thin leaves of bright brass which are used for overlaying in the same manner in which gold leaf is applied.

DUTY (elec.) du' ty:

CONTINUOUS, constant operation of a device.

CYCLE, operation at specific intervals.

INTERMITTENT, operation at alternate periods of load and no load.

DWELL ANGLE (auto.) dwell an' gle: See CAM ANGLE.

DX (elec.): A distant radio station or communication with a distant radio station.

DYE (paint. and dec.) dye: A material used for dyeing or staining.

DYKEM BLUE (metal.) dy' kem blue: Blue ink used in layout work.

DYNAFLOW (auto.) dy' na flow: A transmission consisting of a hydraulic converter and a set of planetary gears, which gives the driver a choice of several forward speeds and reverse.

DYNAMIC BALANCE (metal) dy nam' ic bal' ance: The balancing of parts so that they will rotate at a specified speed without vibration.

DYNAMIC CHARACTERISTICS (e l e c.)

dy nam' ic char act er is' tics: Characteristics of a tube taking into account the change in plate voltage that occurs with a change in current when a load resistor is connected in series with the plate.

DYNAMIC PICKUP (elec.) dy nam' ic pick' up: A phono-cartridge which produces an electrical output from the motion of a conductor or coil in a magnetic field.

DYNAMIC PLATE RESISTANCE (elec.) dy nam' ic plate re sist' ance: See AC PLATE RESISTANCE.

DYNAMIC SPEAKER (elec.) dy nam' ic speak' er: A loudspeaker which produces sound as the result of the reaction between a fixed magnetic field and a fluctuating field of the voice coil.

DYNAMOMETER (air cond.) dy na-mom' e ter: A device used to measure the power of a motor or engine.

DYNAMOMETER (elec.) dy na mom' e-ter: A measuring instrument based on the opposing torque developed between two sets of current carrying coils.

DYNAMOTOR (elec.) dy' na mo tor: A motor-generator combination using two windings on a single armature. Used to convert ac to dc.

DYNATRON (elec.) dy' na tron: A special type of electron tube containing multiple electrodes so that secondary emission from the plate causes a decrease in plate current with an increase in plate voltage.

DYNE (elec.) dyne: A unit of force in the metric system, identified as that force which will accelerate a mass of one gram at the rate of one centimeter per second for each second during which the force acts.

DYNODE (elec.) dy' node: The electrode in a vacuum tube which performs a useful function by secondary emission.

DYSBARISM (space) dys' bar ism: A term which includes a wide variety of symptoms within the body by changes of ambient pressure.

EARLY WARNING RADAR (space) ear'-ly warn' ing ra' dar: In aircraft control and warning, a radar set or system set up or used near the periphery of a defended area to warn of aircraft approaching the area.

EARPHONES (elec.) ear' phones: A receiver, fitting over the ear, for converting electrical energy at audio frequencies into sound waves.

EARTH OXIDES (elec.) earth ox' ides: Materials, primarily barium and strontium oxide, used as emitters of electrons.

EARTH PIGMENT (paint. and dec.) earth pig' ment: Pigments which occur as deposits in earth and are removed by mining.

EARTH SATELLITE (space) earth sat'-el lite: A body that orbits about the earth.

EASEMENT (const.) ease' ment: Curved part of handrail; private right of way.

EAVES (const.) eaves: The part of the roof which extends beyond and over the walls of a building.

EAVES TROUGH (const.) eaves trough: Metal or wood troughs along the eaves of a building to collect rainwater and conduct it to the downspouts.

EBONITE (elec.) eb' on ite: A hard rubber insulating material.

EBONY (wood.) eb' on y: A heavy, hard and very dark wood; one of a group of persimmon trees native to tropical Africa, Asia and Ceylon.

EBULATOR (air cond.) eb u la' tor: A device inserted in the evaporator tubes of a refrigerator to prevent the refrigerant liquid becoming quiescent at a pressure lower than its boiling point.

EBULLISM (space) eb' ul lism: The formation of bubbles in biological fluids caused by a reduced ambient pressure.

ECCENTRIC (auto.) ec cen' tric: Not having the same center; off center.

ECCENTRIC TURNING (wood) ec-cen' tric turn' ing: Wood turning with the work not mounted on centers; turned work not concentric with the axis of the maintained shaft.

ECCLES-JORDAN TRIGGER (elec.) ec' cles-uor' dan trig' ger: A non-oscillating multivibrator circuit which has two conditions of equilibrium. A pulse will switch conduction from one tube to the other.

ECHINUS-O VOLO (const.) e chi'nus-o' vo lo: A combination convex quarter round and square molding.

ECHO (elec.) ech' o: A wave which has been reflected during transmission and is received at a short interval later.

ECHO BOX (elec.) ech' o box: A hollow or tube like device used in broadcasting to produce artificial echos.

ECLECTIC (draft.) ec lec' tic: A recent architectural trend starting before World War I and continuing to the present. This trend frees the architect from strict adherence to a single architectural form and combines many styles from many periods chosen at random.

ECLIPTIC (space) e clip' tic: Plane of the Earth's orbit around the Sun. It is used as a reference for other inter-planetary orbits.

ECM (automation): Abbreviation for Electro Chemical Milling.

ECONOMIZER (auto.) e con' o miz er: A valve system in a carburetor which enriches the air-fuel mixture at high speeds only.

EDDY CURRENT LOSS (elec.) ed' dy cur' rent loss: Heat loss resulting from eddy currents flowing through resistance of the core.

EDDY CURRENTS (elec.) ed' dy cur'-rents: Induced currents flowing in a core.

EDGE GILDING (graphics) edge gild' ing: Coating the edge of a book with gold leaf.

EDGE JOINT (weld.) edge joint: Joint formed when two pieces of metal are lapped with at least one edge of each at an edge of the other.

EDGE MARBLEIZING (graphics) edge mar' ble iz ing: Marbleizing the edge of a book.

EDGING BOARD (const.) edg' ing board: The first board cut from a log after the slab cut.

EDGING MACHINE (metal) edg' ing ma-chine': A machine used to fold edges of pieces of sheet metal.

EDISON CELL (elec.) ed' i son cell: A cell using positive electrodes of nickel oxide and negative electrodes of pow-dered iron. The electrolyte is a dilute solution of sodium hydroxide.

EDISON EFFECT (elec.) ed' i son ef'-fect: The effect, first noticed by Thomas Edison, that emitted electrons were attracted to a positive plate in a vacuum tube.

EDISON SOCKET (elec.) ed' i son sock'-et: A socket which accepts a light bulb with a screw type base.

EDISWAN (elec.) ed' is wan: A bayonet base socket for a lamp used by the automotive industry.

EDM (automation): Abbreviation for Electric Discharge Machine.

EFFECTIVE HORSEPOWER (auto.) ef-fec' tive horse' pow er: The amount of useful energy that an engine can deliver to a load.

EFFECTIVE RESISTANCE (elec.) ef-fec' tive re sis' tance: The ratio be-tween the true power absorbed in a circuit to the square of the effective current flowing in a circuit.

EFFECTIVE VALUE (elec.) ef fec' tive val' ue: That value of alternating cur-rent of sine wave form that has the equivalent heating effect of a direct current. ($.707 \times E_{peak}$)

EFFECTOR (space) ef fec' tor: The mechanical means of maneuvering a missile during flight.

EFFICIENCY (auto.) ef fi' cien cy: The relationship between actual work pro-duced to the energy expended; power output divided by power input.

EFFICIENCY (elec.) ef fi' cien cy: The ratio between the output power and the input power.

EFFLORESCENCE (const. - paint. and dec.) ef' flo res' cence: A deposit of water soluble salts on the surface of masonry or plaster caused by the dissolving of salts present in the masonry, migration of the solution to the surface and deposition of the salts when the water evaporates.

EFFLUENT (plumb.) ef' flu ent: The liquid discharged from a sewage disposal plant; liquid flowing from a septic tank into the drainage field.

EGGSHELL (graphics) egg' shell: Semi-gloss finish similar to an eggshell; paper having eggshell finish.

EGG SHELL LUSTER (paint. and dec.) egg shell lus' ter: Finish that closely resembles the luster of an egg shell.

EJECTOR (air cond.) e jec' tor: A device used to obtain a lower static pressure by building up a high fluid velocity in a restricted area. The lowered pressure is usually used to draw fluid from another source.

ELASTANCE (elec.) e las' tance: The reciprocal of capacitance; the property of a circuit which opposes retention of an electrostatic charge; it is measured in darafs.

ELASTIC (paint. and dec.) e las' tic: Ability to return to the original volume or shape after distorting force has been removed.

ELASTICITY (metal) e las tic' i ty: The ability of a material to stretch and to return to its original size when the force is removed.

ELASTIC LIMIT (metal) e las' tic lim' it: The greatest stress a material can withstand without permanent deformation.

E LAYER (elec.) e lay' er: A well defined atmospheric layer 50 to 90 miles from earth. Its greatest ion density is at about 70 miles.

ELBOW (plumb.) el' bow: A pipe fitting which joins two pipes at an angle.

ELECTRICAL AXIS (elec.) e lec' tri cal ax' is: See X AXIS.

ELECTRICAL HEIGHT (elec.) e lec'-tri cal height: The height of an antenna expressed as a fraction of the operating wave length.

ELECTRIC DISCHARGE EROSION (automation) e lec' tric dis' charge e ro'-sion: Using the erosive effect of an electric arc to form holes of precise shape.

ELECTRIC FIELD OF FORCE (elec.) e lec' tric field of force: See ELECTROSTATIC FIELD.

ELECTRIC HORSEPOWER (elec.) e-lec' tric horse' pow er: 1 HP = 746 watts.

ELECTRICITY (elec.) e lec tric' i ty: Positive and/or negative charges at rest or in motion; it is a property of the basic particles of all materials consisting of electrons and protons; a form of energy generated by heat, light, friction, chemistry or induction which has chemical, magnetic and radiant effects.

DYNAMIC, electricity moving; current.

STATIC, electricity at rest.

ELECTRIC STEEL (metal) e lec' tric steel: A very high quality steel made in an electric furnace. Most impurities including sulphur and phosphorus can be removed by this process.

ELECTROACOUSTIC (elec.) e lec' tro- a cous' tic: Devices having both acoustical and electrical properties.

ELECTROCARDIOGRAPH (elec.) e lec- tro car' di o graph: An electronic instrument which measures and records the heart beat.

ELECTROCHEMICAL (elec.) e lec' tro- chem' i cal: Chemical action produced by an electric current.

ELECTRODE (elec.) e lec' trode: The elements in a cell; an element in an electron tube which performs one or more functions such as emission, control or collection of electrons; a terminal or connector of an apparatus used in treatment or diagnosis of disease.

ELECTRODE (weld.) e lec' trode: The actual contacting point between the electric welder and the work. The electrodes carry the welding current. In arc welding the electrode is usually melted by the arc and becomes a part of the weld.

ELECTRODYNAMIC (elec.) e lec tro- dy nam' ic: Pertaining to electricity in motion.

ELECTRODYNAMIC SPEAKER (elec.) e lec tro dy nam' ic speak' er: A dynamic speaker that uses an electromagnetic fixed field.

ELECTRODYNAMOMETER TYPE METER (elec.) e lec tro dy na mom' e- ter type me' ter: This meter movement employs electromagnets for both field and moving coils. Stationary fields are connected in series with movable coil.

ELECTROJET (space) e lec' tro jet: Current sheet or stream moving in an ionized layer in the upper atmosphere of a planet.

ELECTROLIER (elec.) e lec' tro lier: A hanging ornamental light fixture with several lamps.

ELECTROLUMINESCENCE (elec.) e- lec tro lum i nes' cence: A more recent method of producing light in which a phosphor-porcelain layer acts as a dielectric to produce light. When a-c voltage is applied to the device, electrons are freed which strike the phosphor atoms which emit light.

ELECTROLYSIS (elec.) e lec trol' y- sis: The separation of materials contained in an electrolyte by means of an electric current passing through the solution.

ELECTROLYTE (auto.) e lec' tro lyte: The active chemical liquid or paste in a battery.

ELECTROLYTIC CAPACITOR (elec.) e lec tro lyt' ic cap ac' i tor: A capacitor with a positive plate of aluminum; a dry paste or liquid forms a negative plate. The dielectric is a thin coat of oxide on the aluminum plate.

ELECTROLYTIC COPPER (metal) e- lec tro lyt' ic cop' per: Copper refined by the electrolytic process. This process produces a metal of high purity (99.94%) and enables precious metals such as gold and silver to be recovered.

ELECTROLYTIC CORROSION (metal) e lec tro lyt' ic cor ro' sion: The eating away of metals by electrolysis when metal in contact with dampness is in the vicinity of an electric current; galvanic or two-metal corrosion.

ELECTROLYTIC IRON (metal) e lec-tro lyt' ic iron: A very pure iron pro_ duced by the electrolysis process. It is used as magnetic cores.

ELECTROLYTIC MACHINING (automa_ tion) e lec tro lyt' ic ma chin' ing: A reverse electroplating operation for removing metal, by using moving elec_ trodes and flowing electrolytes.

ELECTROMAGNET (elec.) e lec tro_ mag' net: A coil wound on a soft iron core. When a current runs through the coil, the core becomes magnetized.

ELECTROMAGNETIC FIELD (elec.) e lec tro mag net' ic field: The area between the poles of a magnet in which exists the magnetic lines of force; the combined electric and magnetic fields produced by a flow of electrons through a wire or coil.

ELECTROMAGNETISM (elec.) e lec_ tro mag' ne tism: A magnetic field set up by current flowing through a coil with an iron core.

ELECTROMETALLURGY (elec.) e lec_ tro met' al lur gy: The electrical processes of refining, welding, anneal_ ing, separating and depositing of metals.

ELECTROMETER (elec.) e lec trom'_ e ter: An instrument used to measure an electric charge. See ELECTRO_ SCOPE.

ELECTROMOTIVE FORCE (emf) (elec.) e lec tro mo' tive force: The force that causes free electrons to move in a conductor. Unit of measurement is the volt.

ELECTRON (elec.) e lec' tron: An ele_ mentary particle with a mass of 9.11×10^{-28} grams and a charge of 1.6×10^{-19} coulombs; negatively charged particle.

ELECTRON (elec.) electron:

BOMBARDMENT, the directing of high speed electrons on a surface to create secondary emission, fluores_ cence, X rays, etc.

BOUND, electrons not free to move within the atoms of certain materials. Such materials are poor conductors.

CONDUCTION, an electron which is free to move under the influence of an electric field.

DRIFT, the movement of electrons through a material.

EMISSION, the ejection of electrons from a material due to heat, light or high electrical potentials.

FLOW, current; the movement of electrons.

FREE, electrons which move easily within an atom. Materials of this na_ ture are good conductors of electricity.

GUN, the part of a cathode_ray tube which emits, controls, focuses and deflects the electron beam.

MULTIPLIER, a special tube in which current amplification is produced by secondary emission.

SECONDARY, electrons emitted from a surface due to bombardment by charged particles.

VOLT, the amount of energy gained or lost as a singly charged particle moves through a potential of one volt. It is equal to 1.602×10^{-12} erg.

ELECTRON BEAM (elec.) e lec' tron: A stream of electrons emitted from a cathode_ray gun which has been shaped and focused into a beam. The beam may be deflected by either electrostatic or electromagnetic forces.

ELECTRON BEAM WELDING (weld.) e lec' tron beam weld' ing: A welding process where heat energy for fusion is produced by a high speed electron beam. Welding is done in a vacuum which eliminates contamination by atmospheric gases.

ELECTRONIC INDUSTRIES ASSOCIATION, EIA (elec.): A national trade organization of electronic manufacturers.

ELECTRONICS (elec.) e lec tron' ics: The field of science dealing with electron devices and their uses.

ELECTRON LENS (elec.) e lec' tron lens: The process of focusing an electron beam into a narrow stream in an electron gun.

ELECTRON MICROSCOPE (elec.) e lec' tron mi' cro scope: A microscope, where the image of a specimen is cast on a fluorescent screen by electrons from an electron gun.

ELECTRON-RAY TUBE (elec.) e lec'- tron-ray tube: A tube containing a triode and a cathode-ray indicator; a tube used as a visual tuning aid, sometimes called a "magic eye."

ELECTRON TUBE (elec.) e lec' tron tube: A highly evacuated metal or glass shell which encloses several elements.

ELECTRON VOLT (elec.) e lec' tron volt: A measure of energy. It represents the energy acquired by an electron while passing through a potential of one volt.

ELECTROPATHY (elec.) e lec trop' a-

thy: The science of electricity and its application to medicine.

ELECTROPHOROUS (elec.) e lec-troph' o rous: An instrument used in the laboratory to produce an electric charge by induction. Ex: Ebonite plate, insulator and metal disc.

ELECTROPISM (elec.) e lec' tro pism: The science of plant growth and electricity.

ELECTROPLATING (elec.) e lec' tro-plat' ing: The process of depositing metal by means of chemical action and electrical current.

ELECTROSCOPE (elec.) e lec' tro-scope: A laboratory device used in the detection of a small electrical charge. It consists of two strips of metal foil suspended in a glass bottle. When charged, the foil strips repel each other.

ELECTROSTATIC FIELD (elec.) e lec-tro stat' ic field: The space around a charged body in which its influence is felt.

ELECTROSTATIC FOCUS (elec.) e lec-tro stat' ic fo' cus: Focusing an electron beam by passing through two anodes with unequal electrostatic fields.

ELECTROSTATIC SPRAYING (paint. and dec.) e lec tro stat' ic spray' ing: By this method the article to be sprayed is attached to one pole of a high voltage electrostatic field. The mist from the spray gun is given an opposite charge and thereby becomes attracted to the article. The mist travels around corners with the result that the article is coated more uniformly on all sides and with very little overspray.

ELECTROSTRICTION (elec.) e lec tro-stric' tion: The piezoelectric property of some elements of undergoing changes in shape and size when a voltage is applied and conversely, of producing a voltage when subjected to pressure or stress.

ELECTROTHERAPY (elec.) e lec tro- ther' a py: The treatment of disease by electricity.

ELECTROTYPE (graphics) e lec' tro- type: A facsimile plate of a type form or another plate, produced by taking an impression in wax, depositing in this mold a thin shell of copper or other metal by an electroplating process, and backing with type metal.

ELECTROVALENCE BOND (e l e c.) e lec' tro va lence bond: See IONIC VALANCE BOND.

ELECTRUM (elec.) e lec' trum: An al- loy of gold and silver; German silver.

ELEMENT (elec.) el' e ment: One of the distinct kinds of substances which either singly or in combination with other elements, makes up all matter in the universe.

ELEVATIONS (d r a ft) el e va' tions: Drawings of the front and sides of a building.

ELIMINATOR (elec.) e lim' i na tor: A power supply used in place of batteries for a radio receiver. Ex: B- Elimi- nator.

ELL (const.) ell: A wing or addition to a building at right angles to the main building.

ELL or ELBOW (plumb.) ell or el' bow: A fitting to join two pipes at an angle.

ELLIPSE (draft.) el lipse': A curve so drawn that at any position the sum of

its distances from two fixed points is constant.

ELONGATION (m e t a l) e lon ga' tion: The amount of permanent extension of a material without rupture.

ELONGATION (w e l d.) e lon ga' tion: Percentage increase in the length of a speciman when stressed to its yield strength.

EM (graphics) em: A square of any type size; the em of pica type is used as a unit of measurement for column width. Six pica ems equal one inch.

EMBOSS (graphics) em boss': To pro- duce a design in relief.

EMBOSSED PAPERS (paint. and dec.) em bossed' pa' pers: Wallpaper run through rollers with raised areas, to provide a light relief effect.

EMBOSSING (c r a f t s) em boss' ing: Decorating metal by raised ornamen- tation.

EMERGENCY BRAKE (auto.) e mer'- gen cy brake: A hand brake on an automobile to be used during parking to prevent the car from rolling.

EMERY (metal) em' er y: Oxides of alumina, iron and silica used as an abrasive; corundum.

EMERY (paint. and dec.) em' er y: A dark hard coarse variety of carbor- undum used for grinding and polishing; a slow-cutting, short-lived abrasive.

EMERY PAPER (c o n s t.) em' er y pa' per: An abrasive paper used on metal.

EMERY WHEEL (metal) em' er y wheel: A grinding wheel made of emery.

EMF (elec.): 'Abbreviation for Electro-motive Force.

EMISSION (elec.) e mis' sion: The es-cape of electrons from a surface.

EMISSION, COLD CATHODE (elec.) e mis' sion, cold cath' ode: The phe-nomena of electrons leaving the surface of a material caused by a high potential field.

EMISSION, Types of (elec.) e mis'-sion:

A0 - Continuous Wave, no modulation.
A1 - Continuous Wave, keyed.
A2 - Telegraphy by keying modulating audio frequency.
A3 - Telephony.
A4 - Facsimile.
A5 - Television.
F0 - Continuous Wave, no FM.
F1 - Telegraphy by frequency shift keying.
F2 - Telegraphy by keying modulating audio frequency.
F3 - Telephony - FM.
F4 - Facsimile.
F5 - Television.

SECONDARY, Emission caused by impact of other electrons striking a surface.

PHOTOELECTRIC, The emission of electrons as a result of light striking the surface of certain materials.

THERMIONIC, The process where heat produces the energy for the re-lease of electrons from the surface of emitter.

EMISSIVITY (air cond.) em is siv' i ty: Characteristic of a surface to give off heat by radiation.

EMISSIVITY (elec.) em is siv' i ty: The rate at which electrons are emit-ted or the capacity to emit.

EMISSIVITY (space) em is siv' i ty: The relative power to emit heat by radiation.

EMITTER (elec.) e mit' ter: The ele-ment in a vacuum tube from which electrons are emitted. The CATHODE.

EMITTER (elec.) e mit' ter:

MAJORITY, in a transistor, the semi-conductor section either P or N type, which emits majority carriers into the interelectrode region.

MINORITY, in a transistor, the semi-conductor section, either P or N type which emits minority carriers into the interelectrode region.

EMPIRICAL (elec.) em pir' i cal: In-formation based upon experience, ob-servation and measurement rather than upon theory.

EMU (elec.): Abbreviation for Electro-magnetic System of Units. A basic system of measurement of electrical quantities, defined by international agreement.

EMULSIFICATION (air cond.) e mul si-fi ca' tion: A mixture of two or more liquids which do not dissolve in each other.

EMULSIFYING AGENTS (paint. and dec.) e mul si fy' ing a' gents: Sub-stances of chemical nature that in-timately mix and disperse dissimilar materials ordinarily immiscible, such as oil and water, to produce a stable emulsion. A substance which when added to a liquid permits suspension of fine particles or globules in the liquid.

EMULSION (paint. and dec.) e mul' sion:

A preparation in which minute particles of one liquid, such as oil, are suspended in another, such as water.

EMULSION PAINT (paint and dec.) e mul' sion paint: A paint made by emulsifying the film-forming portion in a volatile liquid, usually water.

EN (graphics) en: One half an EM.

ENAMEL (paint. and dec.) en am' el: Type of paint made by grinding or mixing pigments with varnishes or lacquers.

ENAMELED BRICK (const.)en am' eled brick: Brick with a glazed finish.

ENAMELED WIRE (elec.) en am' eled wire: Wire coated with an insulating enamel.

ENAMEL FINISH (graphics) en am' el fin' ish: A finish produced on paper by treatment with China clay, satin white and casein. It may be glossy or dull.

ENAMELING (crafts)en am' el ing: The craft of covering metals with enamels and firing in a kiln or furnace.

ENAMELLED (graphics) en am' elled: Coated paper with a high calendered polish.

ENAMELS (crafts) en am' els: A flux combined with oxides of metal.

ENCAPSULATION (elec.) en cap su- la' tion: The process of coating small electronic components or devices in plastic or resin for protection from shock or atmosphere.

ENCLOSURE (elec.) en clo' sure: A special type cabinet for enclosing the speakers of a high fidelity sound system. It is usually decorative and may have certain internal baffles to improve its acoustical properties.

END CLEARANCE (metal) end clear'- ance: The angle a cutting tool is ground sloping down from its end cutting edge to provide relief.

END CUTTING EDGE ANGLE (metal) end cut' ting edge an' gle: The angle showing the amount the nose of the tool has been ground back in reference to the end.

END GRAIN (wood.) end grain: The surface of wood exposed by cutting across the grain of the wood.

ENDLESS SAW (wood.) end' less saw: A bandsaw; a belt saw.

END—MATCH (const.) end—match: Boards having tongue and groove joints on ends as well as edges.

END MILL (metal) end mill: A milling cutter which can cut on both its sides and end.

END PLAY (auto.) end play: The longitudinal movement of a shaft.

END SHEET (graphics) end sheet: The sheet of paper, either plain or decorated, placed between the cover and the body of a book.

END THRUST (metal)end thrust: Longitudinal pressure exerted by a rotating shaft either in a horizontal or vertical position.

ENERGY (auto.)en' er gy: The capacity or ability to do work.

ENERGY GAP (elec.)en' er gy gap: The energy range between the valence band and the conduction band in a semiconductor. See FORBIDDEN REGION.

ENGINEER'S CROSS PEEN HAMMER (wood.) en gi neer's' cross peen ham' mer: See HAMMER.

ENGINEER'S DOUBLE FACE HAMMER (wood.) en gi neer's' dou' ble face ham' mer: See HAMMER.

ENGINE LATHE (metal) en' gine lathe: A machine lathe, larger than a bench lathe, usually mounted on the floor.

ENGLISH (graphics) eng' lish: 14 point type.

ENGLISH CHALK (paint. and dec.) eng' lish chalk: Chalk obtained from the cliffs of England.

ENGOBE (crafts)en gobe' : A thin coating of clay used to cover defects in clay ware.

ENGRAVING (crafts) en grav' ing: The cutting of designs on a metal plate; a picture printed from an engraved plate.

ENGRAVING (graphics) en grav' ing: THE art of producing a design by corrosion or cutting, upon the surface of a plate or block.

ENTABLATURE (const.)en tab' la ture: The uppermost members of a classical order; all portions above a column such as an architrave, a frieze and a cornice.

ENTASIS OF A COLUMN (const.)en' tasis of a col' umn: The purposeful increasing of the diameter of a column near its center, to avoid a hollow appearance if the sides of the column were straight; a slight swelling or bulging of a column.

ENTOURAGE (const.)en tou rage': The surroundings, plot lay-out and landscape of a building.

ENTRANCE SWITCH (elec.) en' trance switch: A disconnect main line switch located at the electrical service entry to a building.

ENTROPY (air cond.) en' tro py: The ratio of the heat added to a substance to the absolute temperature at which it is added.

ENTRY (const.) en' try: A hall or vestibule.

ENVELOPE (elec.) en' ve lope: The enclosed wave form made by outlining the peaks of a modulated r-f wave; the glass or metal enclosure of a vacuum or gas tube.

EPICYCLOID (draft.) ep i cy' cloid: A curved line generated by a point on the circumference of a circle as the circle rolls along on the outside of the circumference of another circle.

EPOCH (space) ep' och: A particular instant in time for which certain data are valid.

EPOXY RESIN (elec.) e pox' y res' in: A plastic material of comparatively high strength used for impregnating and coating electronic components.

EPOXY RESINS (paint. and dec.)e pox' y res' ins: Resins obtained by condensation reaction between phenols and epichlorohydrin.

EQUALIZER (elec.) e' qual iz er: A network of components to change the frequency response in audio circuits.

EQUALIZING PULSE (elec.) e' qual izing pulse: A series of pulses sent by the TV transmitter before and after the serrated vertical pulse.

EQUILATERAL (draft.)e qui lat' er al: Having equal sides.

EQUIPOTENTIAL (elec.) e qui poten'tial: Having the same potential.

ERASE (elec.) e rase': To remove a
recorded signal from a tape; to remove stored information from a computer.

ERASING SHIELD (draft.) e ras'ing
shield: A flat metal plate with an
assortment of holes, to use as a protective device when erasing small parts
of drawings.

ERECTOR LAUNCHER (space) e rec'-
tor launch'er: A mobile piece of equipment that erects a missile to launching position, then serves as a launcher.

ERG (elec.): A unit of work in the
metric system, representing the amount
of work accomplished by a force of one
dyne acting through a distance of one
centimeter.

EROSION (weld.) e ro'sion: Reducing
in size of an object because of a liquid
or gas impact on the object.

ESCALATOR (const.) es'ca la tor: A
moving stairway.

ESCAPE VELOCITY (space) es cape'
vel oc'i ty: The speed a body must
attain to overcome a gravitational field,
such as that of Earth, and thus theoretically travel on to infinity. The velocity
of escape at the Earth's surface is
36,700 feet per second.

ESCUTCHEON (plumb.) es cutch'eon:
A flange around a pipe, to cover the
rough opening where a pipe passes
through the wall or floor.

ESCUTCHEON PIN (crafts) es cutch'-
eon pin: A small pin with a half-round
head used for decorative purposes.

ESSENTIAL OILS (paint. and dec.) es-

sen'tial oils: Oils which have an odor,
such as cedar oil, camphor oil, etc.

ESSEX BOARD MEASURE (const.) es'-
sex board mea'sure: A board measuring scale found on the back of a
steel framing square.

ESSEX TABLE (wood.) es'sex ta'ble:
A table usually found on the body of the

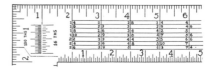

carpenter's square which shows the
board foot measurement for common
widths and lengths of boards.

ESTER (paint. and dec.) es'ter: Organic compound formed from an alcohol
and an organic acid.

ESTER GUM (const.) es'ter gum: A
gum constituent of spar varnish made
from resin and glycerin.

ESTER GUM (paint. and dec.) es'ter
gum: Resin produced synthetically by
rosin reacting with glycerine.

ETCHED CIRCUIT (elec.) etched
cir'cuit: A method of producing a
circuit on a copper clad insulating base.
The circuit is masked out with acid-
resist coating. The board is then etched
in an acid bath, which removes all of
the conducting copper clad except the
circuit.

ETCHING (crafts) etch'ing: The
process of making a decorative design
on metal by submersion in an acid
solution that will eat away unprotected
parts.

ETHYL ACETATE (paint and dec.)
eth'yl ac'e tate: Rapid evaporating

solvent made from ethyl alcohol and acetic acid.

ETHYL ALCOHOL (paint and dec.) eth' yl al' co hol: Alcohol produced by the distillation of fermented grain or from petroleum sources.

ETHYLENE GLYCOL (auto.) eth' yl ene gly' col: A permanent type antifreeze.

ETHYL LACTATE (paint and dec.) eth' yl lac' tate: A solvent made by a reaction between ethyl alcohol and lactic acid.

EUTECTIC (metal) eu tec' tic: Lowest melting point. Maximum fusibility.

EUTECTIC ALLOY (weld.) eu tec' tic al loy': Means the "lowest melting point." A mixture of metals which has a melting point lower than either of the metals or any other mixture of the metals.

EUTECTIC MIXTURE (air cond.) eutec' tic mix' ture: A mixture of substances which melts or freezes at a constant temperature and with a constant composition; the mixture which produces the lowest melting point.

EUTECTOID (metal) eu tec' toid: Steel, containing .9% carbon.

EVAPORATOR (auto.) e vap' o ra tor: The part of a refrigerator unit where the liquid refrigerant is subject to a decrease in pressure and an increase in area so that it will evaporate and absorb heat.

EXCAVATE (const.) ex' ca vate: To dig out; to remove dirt.

EXCELSIOR (wood.) ex cel' si or: Long fine wood shavings used for stuffing and for packing.

EXCITATION (elec.) ex ci ta' tion: To apply a signal to an amplifier circuit; to apply energy to an antenna system; to apply current to energize the field windings of a generator.

EXCITER (elec.) ex cit' er: A small d-c generator used to excite or energize the field windings of a large alternator.

EXCITER LAMP (elec.) ex cit' er lamp: A constant output lamp for exciting the photo electric tube used in a motion picture, sound-on-film, machine.

EXFILTRATION (air cond.) ex fil tra'- tion: Airflow or leakage outward through a wall, joint or leak.

EXHAUST MANIFOLD (auto.) ex haust' man' i fold: A hollow casting on the automotive engine to conduct burned gases from the cylinders. The exhaust pipe is connected to the manifold.

EXHAUST PIPE (auto.) ex haust' pipe: The pipe between the exhaust manifold and the muffler.

EXHAUST STROKE (auto.) ex haust' stroke: The upward stroke of the piston during which the burned gases are forced out of the cylinder.

EXHAUST VALVE (auto.) ex haust' valve: Valve in the exhaust port of cylinder.

EXOSPHERE (space) ex' o sphere: The outermost fringe or layer of the atmosphere.

EXOTIC FUEL (space) ex ot' ic fuel: Unusual fuel combinations for aircraft and rocket use with the purpose of attaining far greater thrust.

EXPANDED (graphics) ex pand' ed: A type face slightly wider than standard.

EXPANDED METAL (metal) ex pand' ed met' al: Sheet metal that has been cut and stamped to a pattern, to permit expansion and shaping to a form; metal used as reinforcement for concrete and plaster.

EXPANDING MANDREL (metal) ex pand' ing man' drel: A mandrel which may be expanded or increased in diameter to hold work placed on it.

EXPANSION BOLT (const.) ex pan' sion bolt: A bolt, which includes a device which expands when tightened. Used to fasten objects to a masonry wall.

EXPANSION COIL (air cond.) ex pan'sion coil: An evaporator constructed of an arrangement of pipes or tubes.

EXPANSION REAMER (metal) ex pan'sion ream' er: An adjustable reamer. By means of a wrench tightened expander, the reamer may be increased in size up to .005 inches.

EXPANSION SHIELD (elec.) ex pan' sion shield: A device used with a machine bolt to fasten the bolt in a masonry wall or surface.

EXPANSIVE BIT (wood.) ex pan' sive bit: An adjustable size auger bit.

EXPANSIVE BIT

EXPONENTIAL HORN (elec.) ex ponen' tial horn: A loudspeaker horn whose cross sectional area increases exponentially with the axial distance.

EXPOSURE (graphics) ex po' sure: The period of time in which a light sensitive material is exposed to light.

EXTENDED (graphics) ex tend' ed: A type face of extreme width.

EXTENDED LETTERING (draft.) extend' ed let' ter ing: Drawing letters wider than normal size.

EXTENDER PIGMENTS (paint. and dec.) ex tend' er pig' ments: Pigments which provide very little hiding power but are useful in stabilizing suspension, improving flow, lowering gloss and providing other desirable qualities.

EXTENSION BIT (wood.) ex ten' sion bit: A long metal rod with chuck to hold a bit at one end. Extends the bit length to drill deep holes or drills holes in inaccessible places.

EXTENSOMETER TEST (metal) ex tensom' e ter test: A measurement to determine the elasticity of a metal.

EXTERNAL THREAD (metal) ex ter' nal thread: The thread on the outside of a part.

EXTINCTION POTENTIAL (elec.) extinc' tion po ten' tial: See DEIONIZATION POTENTIAL.

EXTRADOS (const.) ex' tra dos: The outside curve of an arch.

EXTRAGALACTIC NEBULAE (space) ex tra gal ac' tic neb' u lae: Vast star systems outside our own galaxy.

EXTRINSIC SEMICONDUCTOR (elec.) ex trin' sic sem' i con duc' tor: A semiconductor which depends upon impurities for its electrical properties.

EXTRUDE (air cond.) ex trude': To push out through a die.

EXTRUDED METAL (metal) ex trud'ed met' al: Metal that has been shaped by forcibly pushing through a die.

EXTRUSION (metal) ex tru' sion: The process of forcing either hot or cold metal through a die to shape a long or short part.

EYEBALLS IN, EYEBALLS OUT (space) eye' balls in, eye' balls out: A term used by test pilots to describe the effect of acceleration. "Eyeballs in" would be the effect on the astronaut at lift-off (positive G). During slowdown by retro rockets, the astronaut would experience "Eyeballs out" (negative G).

EYEBOLT (metal) eye' bolt: A bolt with a loop or eye at one end instead of a head.

EZY-OUT (metal) e' zy-out: A tool for removing broken bolts and studs from a hole.

FABRICATION (automation) fab ri ca'- tion: The making of a product from parts and components or assemblies. Also the making of individual parts.

FABRICATION (const.) fab' ri ca' tion: The act of building or putting together; assembly of parts into a whole.

FACADE (const.) fa cade': The front of a building; the part of a building facing the street.

FACE (const.) face: The front of a wall; to cover with a new surface.

FACE (graphics) face: The part of the type face in relief on the end of the type and produces the printing impression.

FACE (metal) face: To machine a flat surface.

FACE (metal) face: Working surface of a gear tooth above the pitch line.

FACE BRICK (const.) face brick: Better quality brick used on exposed surface.

FACE NAILING (const.) face nail' ing: To nail perpendicular to the finished face.

FACE OF WELD (weld.) face of weld: The exposed surface of the weld.

FACEPLATE (metal) face' plate: A plate attached to the live spindle in

the headstock of a machine, to which work may be fastened for machining.

FACING (metal) fac' ing: A lathe operation of finishing ends of work to make ends flat and smooth.

FACSIMILE TRANSMISSION (elec.) facsim' il e trans mis' sion: The transmission of a picture by scanning the picture and converting relative shade values into electrical impulses which are reproduced at the receiver.

FACTOR OF SAFETY (elec.) fac' tor of safe' ty: A specified load on an operating device, component or circuit, usually above normal operating load which the device can handle without damage.

FADE IN (elec.) fade in: This term is used in the television control room to describe the gradual increase of sound and picture signal.

FADE OUT (elec.) fade out: The opposite of fade in.

FADING (elec.) fad' ing: Variations in signal strength that occur at a receiver during the time a signal is being received.

FAGOT (metal) fag' ot: A bundle of iron bars which will be heated, forged and welded into a solid bar.

FAHLUM METAL (crafts) fah' lum met' al: An alloy of tin and lead used in making cheap jewelry.

FAHNSTOCK CLIP (elec.) fahn' stock clip: A spring clip for temporary wire connections.

FAHRENHEIT (air cond.) fahr' en heit: A system of measuring temperature. In this system 32º represents freezing and 212º the boiling temperature of water at atmospheric pressure at sea level (14.696 psi).

FAMILY (graphics) fam' i ly: All type faces of the same design, including all widths and sizes.

FAN BELT (auto.) fan belt: A belt which usually drives the generator and the cooling fan in an automotive engine.

FANNING STRIP (elec.) fan' ning strip: A terminal strip.

FAO (draft.): An abbreviation meaning "Finish All Over."

FARAD (elec.) far' ad: The unit of measurement of capacitance. A capacitor has a capacitance of one farad when a charge of one coulomb raises its potential one volt.

$$C = \frac{Q}{E}$$

FARADAY, MICHAEL (1791-1867) (elec.): English physicist and chemist whose discoveries and inventions included first electric generator, laws of magnetic induction, plane of rotation of polarized light in magnetic field. Unit

of electrical capacity (farad) was named in his honor.

FASCIA (const.) fas' ci a: Flat member of cornice or other trim; usually board to which gutter is fastened.

FAST IDLE (auto.) fast i' dle: A thermostatically operated cam device which maintains a desirable engine speed during warm-up.

FAT (graphics) fat: Copy full of illustrations, blank lines and spaces.

FATHOM fath' om: A unit of measurement equal to 6 ft. or 1.828 meters.

FATTY ACID (paint. and dec.) fat' ty ac' id: Acid which is present in oils or fats in combination with glycerine.

FAUCET (plumb.) fau' cet: A manually controlled valve at the end of a pipe, by which water may be drawn from the pipe.

FAURE PLATE (elec.) faure plate: A plate used in an automotive storage battery consisting of a lead grid structure filled with paste.

FEATHER (metal) feath' er: A sliding key, fitted tightly to the sliding part, but free to move in the spline.

FEATHER EDGE (wood.) feath' er edge: A keen edge, tapering off to nothing.

FEATHERING (paint. and dec.) feath' er ing: A term used to describe the sanding or rubbing down of a surface to a feathery edge, where coating material gradually becomes thinner around the edge until it finally disappears.

FEED (metal) feed: The amount the cutting tool advances into the work per revolution of spindle.

FEED BACK (automation) feed back: The return of information, such as a measurement from the output of a machine to its input so that the machine is self-correcting.

FEEDBACK (elec.) feed' back: Transferring a voltage from the output of a circuit back to its input.

FEEDER (elec.) feed' er: Transmission lines between radio transmitter and antenna; conductors used to distribute power from main distribution to secondary distribution centers.

FEEDER (graphics) feed' er: A mechanism that feeds paper into the press to correct position and holds it in place.

FEED PIPE (plumb.) feed pipe: The main supply line; a pipe which carries a supply directly to the point of use.

"FEEL" (paint. and dec.) feel: The painter's term for the working qualities of a paint.

FEELER (metal) feel' er: Thin, accurately formed metal stock used for gauging; to gauge size by the sense of touch.

FEELER STOCK (auto.) feel' er stock: Thin strips of metal of exact and uniform thickness in thousandths of inches. Used to measure clearances in bearings and mating parts.

FEET (graphics) feet: The sections on the reverse end of type on which it stands.

FELDSPAR feld' spar: A mineral consisting of silicates of aluminum with potassium, sodium or calcium.

FELLING (wood.) fell' ing: The process of cutting down a tree.

FELT (const.) felt: Heavy building paper.

FELT SIDE (graphics) felt side: The felt finish on one side of a paper caused by squeezing the paper through blanket rolls to remove the wire marks made during manufacturing.

FEMALE fe' male: The recessed portion of a piece of work into which another part fits.

FEMALE THREAD (plumb.) fe' male thread: An internal thread.

FENDER (auto.) fend' er: Metal guards over the wheels of a vehicle to prevent throwing of water and dirt. The fender is also decorative and forms a part of the body of the car.

FENDERS (graphics) fend' ers: Pieces of cardboard glued to the tympan to prevent a sheet from slipping over the guides.

FENESTRATION (const.) fen' es tration: The design and arrangement of windows in a building.

FERMI, ENRICO (1901-1954) (elec.): An Italian-U.S. scientist. He was the key figure in the group that achieved the first nuclear chain reaction in 1942. He received the Nobel Prize in 1938.

FERRIC OXIDE (elec.) fer' ric ox' ide: Magnetic iron oxide used to coat recording tapes.

FERRITE (elec.) fer' rite: A magnetic material manufactured from iron and other metals such as nickel, zinc and manganese. Used to make ferrite cores for coils.

FERRITE (metal) fer' rite: Pure iron.

FERRITE CORE (elec.) fer' rite core: A magnetic core made from ferrite.

FERROCHROMIUM (metals) fer' ro-chro' mi um: An alloy of iron and chromium used in the manufacturing of chromium alloy steels.

FERROMAGNETIC (elec.) fer ro mag-net' ic: The property of a material when it has a permeability consider-ably greater than one. Such materials are cobalt, iron, nickel, steel and their alloys.

FERROMANGANESE (metal) fer' ro-man' ga nese: An alloy of 30 to 80 percent manganese and 5 to 8 percent carbon. It is used in powder form and added to molten metal in the ladle before pouring into castings. It is a deoxidizer and counteracts the influ-ence of excessive sulphur in the melt.

FERRONICKEL (metal) fer' ro nick'-el: A nickel-steel alloy used in re-sistance wire in electricity.

FERROPHOSPHOROUS (metal) fer' ro-phos' pho rous:. A high phosphorous content iron used in the making of tin plate.

FERROSILICON (metal) fer' ro sil' i-con: A hard steel containing approxi-mately 97.6 percent iron, .4 percent carbon and 2 percent silicon.

FERROUS (metal) fer' rous: Pertaining to iron compounds.

FERROUS (paint. and dec.) fer' rous: Pertaining to, or derived from iron.

FERROUS SULPHATE (paint. and dec.) fer' rous sul' phate: Product common-ly known as copperas.

FERRULE (const.) fer' rule: The metal part of a screwdriver between the handle and the blade; the metal part of a paint brush between the handle and the bristles.

FETTLE (crafts.) fet' tle: To remove joint lines on a cast or pressed ceramic object.

F HEAD ENGINE (auto.) f head en' gine: An engine which combines the L and I valve arrangement; one valve in block and the other in head.

FIDDLE-BACK (wood.) fid' dle-back: A back of a chair which resembles a fiddle.

FIDELITY (elec.) fi del' i ty: The faithful reproduction and transmission of a signal by a device such as an amplifier without distortion.

FIELD (automation) field: A group of characters treated as a single unit of information.

FIELD (elec.) field: Part of a complete TV picture consisting of either the odd or even lines.

FIELD MAGNETS (elec.) field mag' nets: Electromagnets which make the field of a motor or generator.

FIELD RHEOSTAT (elec.) field rhe' o-stat: A variable resistance connected in the field of a motor or generator.

FIELD STONES (const.) field stones: Rough uncut stones, usually with round-ed surfaces; local stones.

FIELD STRENGTH (elec.) field strength: The measurement of the strength of an electric field in volts per meter at a given distance and direction.

FIERY FINISH (paint. and dec.) fi' er y fin' ish: See BURNED FINISH.

FILAMENT (elec.) fil' a ment: The heating element in a vacuum tube coated with emitting material so that it acts also as the cathode.

FILAMENT VOLTAGE (elec.) fil' a ment volt' age: The voltage required for the heaters or filaments of an electron tube. Value is usually designated by the first number in tube number. Ex: 6BE6 requires 6.3 volt filament voltage.

FILAMENT WINDING (elec.) fil' a ment wind' ing: A winding on a transformer to provide correct filament voltages for vacuum tubes.

FILE (metal) file: A piece of hardened carbon steel having teeth cut into its faces and/or edges in parallel diagonal lines.

FILE CARD (metal) file card: A brush made with short fine wires, used to clean files.

FILE CUTS (metal) file cuts: The type and coarseness of file teeth.

Single Cut: Single series of diagonal cuts on face.

Double Cut: Two courses of cuts on face crossing each other.

Rough, Coarse, Bastard, Second Cut, Smooth, Dead Smooth, refer to the degree of coarseness or the distance apart of the parallel diagonal cuts on the file.

FILE TAPER (metal) file ta' per: The gradual reduction of cross sectional area of a file towards the point.

FILES, TYPES OF (metal) files, types of:

BARRETTE FILE, a flat triangular file with teeth only on the wide face.

CROCHET FILE, a flat file with rounded edges.

CROSSING FILE, similar to a half round file, but with both faces rounded at slightly different curves.

FLAT, a flat rectangular shape with slight taper toward the point.

HALF ROUND FILE, this file has one flat surface and one convex rounded face.

HAND FILE, a flat file with parallel edges. Faces are slightly convex.

KNIFE FILE, a thin knife shaped file.

PILLAR FILE, similar to hand file, only narrower.

RATTAIL FILE, a small round tapered file.

ROUND FILE, round in shape and usually tapered toward the end.

SQUARE FILE, square in shape. Used for filing square holes and bottoms of narrow slots.

WARDING FILE, a very thin flat file.

FILIGREE (crafts) fil' i gree: Delicate ornamental work, used in jewelry making.

FILLER (const.) fill' er: A material used to fill the grain of wood before finishing; gravel, cinders and rocks used as a base for concrete.

FILLER (paint. and dec.) fill' er: Inert material used to fill or level porous surfaces, like open-pore woods such as oak, walnut.

FILLER CAP (elec.) fill' er cap: The cap on each cell of a battery to permit addition of distilled water. Also acts as vent.

FILLER ROD (weld.) fill' er rod: Metal

wire that is melted and added to the welding puddle to produce the necessary increase in bead thickness.

FILLET (draft.) fil' let: A curved or rounded surface between two intersecting surfaces.

FILLET (weld.) fil' let: Weld metal in the internal vertex, or corner, of the angle formed by two pieces of metal, giving the joint additional strength to withstand unusual stresses.

FILMOGENS (paint. and dec.) film' o-gens: Film-forming materials such as linseed oil and varnish resins.

FILTER (air cond.) fil' ter: A device used to remove suspended solids from a liquid; to clean.

FILTER (elec.) fil' ter: A circuit used to attenuate a specific band or bands of frequencies.

FILTER CIRCUITS (elec.) fil' ter cir'-cuits:

BAND PASS, a circuit which passes a specific band of frequencies.

BAND REJECT, a circuit which rejects a specific band of frequencies.

HIGH PASS, a circuit designed to pass the high frequencies and reject the low frequencies.

LOW PASS, a circuit which attenuates the high frequencies.

FILTER PRESS (air cond.) fil' ter press: A press type filter for removing solids from liquid. The residue solids are pressed into cakes or briquettes for easy removal.

FIN (air cond.) fin: A metal projection on a cylinder or radiator to increase its radiation surface for heat removal.

FINAL TRIM (space) fi' nal trim: That action in the flight of a ballistic missile that adjusts it to the exact direction programmed for its flight.

FINDER (elec.) find' er: A viewing device on a TV camera which shows the area covered by the camera.

FINDINGS (crafts) find' ings: Small parts and accessories used in making jewelry.

FINE SILVER (crafts) fine sil' ver: Pure silver.

FINGER JOINT (wood.) fin' ger: Wood joint assembled as shown.

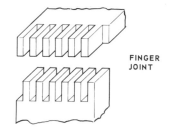

FINGER JOINT

FINISH COAT (paint. and dec.) fin' ish coat: Last coat applied in a paint or wood-finishing job.

FINISH CUT (metal) fin' ish cut: Cuts to bring the material to smooth and accurate dimension.

FINISHING (plumb.) fin' ish ing: The final placement of fixtures installed after completion of flooring and plastering.

FINISH MARK (draft.) fin' ish mark: A symbol indicating a finished surface on a drawing.

FIREBRICK (const.) fire' brick: Special bricks manufactured to stand heat.

FIRECLAY (const.) fireclay: A heat re-sistant cement used to bond firebrick.

FIREDAMP (const.) fire' damp: A gas formed in coal mines which is highly explosive when mixed with proper pro-portions of air.

FIREPLACE (const.) fire' place: A place in a building designed to permit an open fire. It may be free standing or recessed into a wall. It will always have a fire pit and a chimney or flue.

FIRE RESISTANT (const.) fire re sis'-tant: A material which does not burn readily.

FIRE RETARDANT PAINT (paint. and dec.) fire re tar' dant paint: Paint containing substance which slows down rate of combustion of flammable ma-terial or renders material incapable of supporting fire.

FIRE STOP (const.) fire stop: A block or stop in the walls of a building be-tween studs to prevent fire from rising through the air space.

FIRE WALL (auto.) fire wall: The di-viding partition between the engine and operator's seat.

FIRE WALL (const.) fire wall: A ma-sonry or steel wall which subdivides a building to prevent the spreading of a fire from one section to another.

FIRING CHAMBER (space) fir' ing cham' ber: That part of a rocket en-gine or motor that consists of a cham-ber in which the fuel and oxidizer are ignited, and in which pressure of gases is built up to provide an exhaust veloci-ty sufficient for thrust.

FIRING ORDER (auto.) fir' ing or' der: The firing sequence by cylinder number of an engine.

FIRING POINT (elec.) fir' ing point: See IONIZATION POTENTIAL.

FIRST ANGLE PROJECTION (draft.) first an' gle pro jec' tion: An object drawn as if placed in the first quadrant of the intersecting projection planes. The top view appears below the front view.

FIRST—CLASS LEVER first—class le'-ver: A lever with the fulcrum between the power and weight.

FIRST-CLASS LEVER

FIRST DETECTOR (elec.) first de tec'-tor: See MIXER.

FISHING (elec.) fish' ing: A means of pulling wires through an enclosed wall section or conduit by means of a single wire or rope.

FISH JOINT (const.) fish joint: A butt joint secured by side pieces overlapping the joint and fastened to both parts.

FISH OIL (paint. and dec.) fish oil: Only animal oil used to any extent in paint industry. Extracted from fish such as sardine, menhaden and pilchard.

FISH PAPER (elec.) fish pa' per: A strong insulating paper used to wrap conductors and transformer windings.

FISH TAPE (const.) fish tape: A flexi-ble wire that can be pushed through conduits and around bends.

FISSION (space) fis' sion: Splitting an atom with resulting production of nu-clear energy.

FIT (metal) fit: The relationship be-tween two mating parts.

FITS, CLASSIFICATION OF (draft.) fits, classification of:

LOOSE, Class I, Large allowance. Used when accuracy is not required.

FREE, Class II, Liberal allowance. Used as a running fit for speeds at 600 rpm and over.

MEDIUM, Class III, Medium allowance. Used for slow speed machinery and sliding fits.

SNUG, Class IV, Zero allowance. Used when parts are not intended to move freely.

WRINGING, Class V, Zero or negative allowance. Used in semipermanent assembly.

TIGHT, Class VI, Slight negative allowance. Used for fixed gears and pulleys. Requires light pressure to assemble.

MEDIUM FORCE, Class VII, Negative allowance. Used for permanent assembly.

SHRINK, Class VIII, Considerable negative allowance. Used where metals can withstand considerable stress.

FITTINGS (plumb.) fit' tings: Parts used to join pipes together, such as ells, tees, etc.

FIXATIVE (graphics) fix' a tive: A liquid sprayed on a surface or drawing to prevent smearing.

FIXATIVE (paint. and dec.) fix' a tive: A protective coating applied to drawings in crayons, charcoal, etc., usually by spraying to prevent colors from rubbing off.

FIXTURE (metal) fix' ture: A device specially designed to hold a piece of work. Work is accurately located by pins and held by clamps, cam levers or set screws. Used in production work.

FIXTURE JOINT (elec.) fix' ture joint: Connecting a small wire from a lighting fixture to a larger conductor.

FIXTURE SUPPLY (plumb.) fix' ture sup' ply: A supply pipe, sometimes chrome plated for decorative purpose, to a fixture.

FLAG (paint. and dec.) flag: End of hog brush bristle which divides into two or more branches like a tree. Flagging provides brush with ability to hold paint.

FLAGSTONES (const.) flag' stones: Thin slabs of concrete or stone used for terrace floors and walks.

FLAKING (paint. and dec.) flak' ing: Detachment of small pieces of paint film.

FLAME BUCKET (space) flame buck' et: An opening built into the pads of some rockets into which the hot gases of the rocket pour as thrust is built up. The flame bucket is directly under the rocket positioned for launch.

FLAME CUTTING (weld.) flame cut'- ting: See CUTTING.

FLAME GOUGING (metal) flame goug'- ing: The operation of cutting grooves and gouges using a gas welding torch.

FLAME HARDENING (metal) flame hard' en ing: A process of hardening steel by heating with oxy-acetylene torch and quenching.

FLAME PRIMING (metal) flame prim'- ing: A process of preparing iron and steel for painting, by treating with a high velocity oxy-acetylene flame.

FLAMMABLE flam' ma ble: Material which is capable of being easily ignited and of burning with rapidity.

FLANGE (auto.) flange: A rim or collar on an object to hold it in place.

FLANGE UNION (plumb.) flange un' ion: A pair of threaded flanges, which may be screwed onto threaded pipes, and then the pipes may be joined by bolts passing through holes in the flanges.

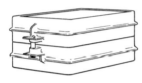

FLASK

FLANK (metal) flank: Working surface of a gear tooth below the pitch line.

FLARE FITTING (air cond.) flare fit'-ting: A type of connection used with soft tubing which involves flaring the ends of the tube for a mechanical seal.

FLASH (weld.) flash: Impact of electric arc rays against the human eye. Also the fin of surplus metal formed at the seam of a resistance weld.

FLASHING (elec.) flash' ing: An electrical discharge around or over an insulating surface.

FLASHING (plumb.) flash' ing: A metal or composition material used on the roof around chimneys and vents to prevent leakage. The metal is so placed that it will shed rain water.

FLASH LINES (metal) flash lines: Marks or ridges formed where excess material flows out around the parting line of a mold.

FLASHOVER (elec.) flash' o ver: A discharge around the surface of an insulator.

FLASH POINT - flash point: The temperature at which fuels and oil may be heated to cause sufficient vaporization so that the vapor can be ignited but insufficient vaporization to sustain combustion.

FLASHTUBE (elec.) flash' tube: An electrical discharge lamp which produces a very brilliant light flash.

FLASK (metal) flask: A two section metal case used in casting.

FLAT BED PRESS (graphics) flat bed press: A press which prints from a flat, plane form.

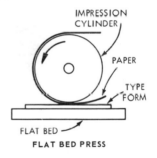

FLAT BED PRESS

FLAT PAD (space) flat pad: A launch pad that is kept or built flat on its surface.

FLAT MILL (paint and dec.) flat mill: A kind of grinding mill used to grind paint pigments. The mill consists of two stones, a lower stone which revolves and an upper stone which is stationary.

FLAT POSITION (weld.) flat po si' tion: A horizontal weld on the upper side of a horizontal surface.

FLATS (graphics) flats: A quantity of sheets of paper, sized 17 x 28 inches or less; unfolded paper; an assembly of photographic negatives in position on goldenrod paper; glass or acetate for exposure in vacuum frame in contact with sensitized metal pressplate; free of gloss; monotonous in hue, shade and color.

FLAT SPOT (auto.) flat spot: A term used to describe a level or momentary lapse in the acceleration of an engine.

FLATTER (metal) flat' ter: A forging tool used for flattening and smoothing work.

FLATTING (paint. and dec.) flat' ting: An ingredient, usually a metallic soap, such as calcium, aluminum or zinc stearate, used in lqcquers and varnishes to reduce the gloss or to give a "rubbed" appearance.

FLATTING OIL (paint. and dec.) flat'ting oil: A varnish-like composition, made of thickened oil dissolved in a thinner, used to reduce paste paint to a flat paint.

FLAT VARNISH (paint. and dec.) flat varn' ish: Varnish which dries with reduced gloss, made by adding such materials as silica, wax, metallic soaps to the varnish.

FLAT WALL PAINT (paint. and dec.) flat wall paint: A type of interior paint which is designed to produce a flat or lusterless finish.

F LAYER (elec.) f lay' er: An atmospheric layer extending from about 90 miles to the upper limits of the ionosphere.

FLEAM (wood) fleam: The angle of bevel of the edge of a saw tooth with respect to the plane of the blade; a surgical knife.

FLEMING, JOHN AMBROSE (1849-1945) (elec.): An English electrical engineer who studied transformers and high-voltage power transmission. He is famous for his invention of the radio tube, called the Fleming valve. He was a professor at University College, London.

FLEMISH BOND (const.) flem' ish bond: A method of laying bricks consisting

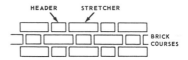

of alternate headers and stretchers in every course. Each header centers on the stretcher above and below.

FLEUR-DE-LIS (const.) fluer de lis': The royal insignia of France. It is widely used as a decorative design.

FLEXIBLE CURVE (draft.) flex' i ble curve: A strip of lead, usually enclosed in rubber, which may be bent into any curve to use as a drawing guide.

FLEXIBLE MATERIAL HANDLING (automation) flex' i ble ma ter' i al hand' ling: The flexibility of handling materials on the production line, when the destination or origin of materials is not fixed.

FLICKER (elec.) flick' er: E r r a t i c movement or jumping or a television picture; erratic change of brightness.

FLIGHT (const.) flight: A run of steps from one landing to another.

FLIGHT BIRD (space) flight bird: A missile awaiting flight test.

FLIGHTBORNE (space) flight' borne: Of an aircraft, missile, or spacecraft. Supported in the aerospace by aero-

dynamic or aerostatic forces, by re_
action to a jet stream or by velocity.

FLINT PAPER (paint. and dec.) flint
pa'per: Abrasive paper which is
grayish-white in color.

FLIP-FLOP (elec.) flip-flop: See
ECCLES-JORDAN TRIGGER.

FLITCH (wood.) flitch: A thin layer or
slice of veneer.

FLOATING (const.) float'ing: The
spreading and equalizing of plaster or
stucco on a wall by means of a board
called a float.

FLOATING AXLE (auto.) float'ing
ax'le: An axle on which the shaft is
relieved of all loads or stresses except
that of the turning wheel.

FLOATING HOLDER (metal) float'ing
hold'er: A holder for a drilling tool
which permits angular or floating move_
ment so that drill will become self
aligning.

FLOATING POWER (auto.) float'ing
pow'er: A term used in automotives
to describe the mounting of the engine
in an auto so that its vibration is ab_
sorbed by rubber cushions.

FLOAT SYSTEM (auto.) float sys'tem:
The part of a carburetor, consisting
of a float and needle valve, which main_
tains the fuel at the correct level.

FLOAT VALVE (plumb.) float valve: A
hollow ball which floats on the surface
of a liquid to which is attached a valve.
It regulates the level of the liquid.

FLOCK (crafts) flock: A decorative fin_
ish produced by throwing soft or fluffy
fibres against a sticky or tacky surface.

FLOCK FINISH (paint. and dec.) flock

fin'ish: Finish obtained by spraying
or sifting flock (short fibers of wool,
silk, rayon) onto a surface to which the
flock fibers will adhere.

FLOCOATING (paint. and dec.) flo coat'_
ing: Process of finishing by flowing
finishing material on article by means
of hose, allowing excess to drain into
tank.

FLOODING (auto.) flood'ing: Feeding
an excessive amount of fuel mixture to
an automotive engine which makes it
difficult to start.

FLOOR DRAIN (plumb.) floor drain: A
receptacle used to receive water to be
drained from floors into the plumbing
system.

FLOOR PLAN (draft.) floor plan: A
drawing which shows the arrangement,
size and shape of rooms of a building,
with location of doors, windows and
other information.

FLOOR VARNISH (paint. and dec.) floor
var'nish: A varnish made specifically
for application to floors.

FLOOR WORK (metal) floor work: Simi_
lar work to bench work, except on large
parts which cannot be lifted to bench.

FLOTATION (air cond.) flo ta'tion:
Treating materials by floating on a
liquid.

FLOTURN PROCESS (metal) flo'turn
pro'cess: See SHEAR SPINNING.

FLOW (automation) flow: The movement
of work from one operation to the
succeeding operation.

FLOW (elec.) flow: The movement of an
electric current through a conductor.

FLOW CHART (draft.) flow chart: A

chart using symbols or blocks showing a sequence of manufacturing events or processes.

FLOWING VARNISH (paint. and dec.) flow' ing var' nish: A varnish which has been designed to produce a smooth lustrous surface without rubbing or polishing.

FLOW OUT (const.) flow out: The ability of some paint to dry without leaving brush marks.

FLUCTUATING CURRENT (elec.) fluc tu a' tion cur' rent: Current which changes value at irregular intervals.

FLUE (const.) flue: A passageway in a chimney for smoke to ascend. Some chimneys have more than one flue.

FLUID COUPLING (auto.) flu' id cou'- pling: A coupling device employing oil as coupling between the driving and driven parts.

FLUID DRIVE (auto.) flu' id drive: A constant torque drive by means of rotors with vanes operating in oil. The driving rotor forces the oil against the driven rotor which results in a fluid transfer of power. Slippage is inversely proportional to speed, which permits smooth starting.

FLUID FRICTION flu' id fric' tion: Friction between layers of the molecules of a fluid; friction between the molecules in a fluid.

FLUIDITY (auto.) flu id' i ty: The property of an oil concerned with the ease with which oil will flow through a hole or spread over bearing surfaces.

FLUORESCENT (elec.) flu o res' cent: The property of a phosphor which indicates that the radiated light will

be extinguished when electron bombardment ceases.

FLUORESCENT PAINT (paint. and dec.) flu o res' cent paint: Luminous paint which glows only during activation by ultraviolet or "black" light.

FLUOROSCOPY (elec.) flu o ros' co py: The techniques used for inspection of opaque objects by means of X ray. The X ray passes through the object and produces an immediate image on a fluorescent screen.

FLUSH (const.) flush: Even; smooth; two continuing surfaces in the same plane.

FLUSHOMETER (plumb.) flush om' e- ter: A special valve which limits the flushing of a fixture with a predetermined quantity of water.

FLUTING (wood.) flut' ing: A decorative process, opposite to reeding, by cutting

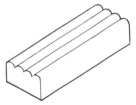

convex channels along the surface of board of table leg.

FLUTTER (elec.) flut' ter: Usually pertains to high frequency distortion in sound reproduction due to variations In speed during recording.

FLUX (elec.) flux: Represented by Greek letter Φ ; total number of lines of magnetic force.

FLUX (weld.) flux: Chemicals used in welding and soldering to promote better fusion of the metals and prevent oxidation.

FLUX DENSITY (symbol B) (elec.) flux den' si ty: The number of lines of flux per cross sectional area of magnetic circuit.

FLUX LEAKAGE (elec.) flux leak' age: The part of the flux which does not link coupled circuit.

FLUX LINKAGE (elec.) flux link' age: The coupling between two circuits by means of magnetic or electric lines of force.

FLY (graphics) fly: A mechanical device used to receive the printed sheets from the cylinder of a press and place them on a pile.

FLYBACK (elec.) fly' back: See RETRACE.

FLY CUTTER (metal) fly cut' ter: A simple formed tool which may be held in an arbor. The arbor is placed in a milling machine spindle and the work to be formed is fed slowly past the revolving cutter; also, a single point tool used in a boring bar.

FLYING BUTTRESS (const.) fly' ing but' tress: A buttress connected with a wall at some distance by an arch or part of an arch. It serves to resist outward pressure, thus distributing the roof thrust. It is used in church construction.

FLYING SPOT CAMERA (elec.) fly' ing spot cam' er a: A camera, so named, because a spot of light is made to scan a picture.

FLYLEAF (graphics) fly' leaf: A blank page at the back or front of a book.

FLYWHEEL (auto.) fly' wheel: A heavy wheel on the end of the crankshaft which absorbs power and causes the engine to run smoothly between power impulses.

FM (elec.): Frequency modulation.

FM TUNER (elec.) FM tu' ner: An FM radio receiver, usually without an audio section, whose detected output is applied directly to the separate audio amplifiers of a high-fidelity sound system.

FOCAL POINT (draft.) fo' cal point: The center of interest in a drawing.

FOCUS (elec.) fo' cus: In the cathode ray tube, it is the point at which all electrons coming from the electron gun will converge.

ELECTROSTATIC, the focusing of the electron beam in a cathode-ray tube by means of accelerating voltages on anodes.

MAGNETIC, the focusing of the electron beam by either permanent or electromagnets placed around the neck of the cathode-ray tube.

FOCUS (graphics) fo' cus: The point at which light passing through the lenses of a camera converges to form a sharp image of the original on the photographic film plate.

FOCUSING COIL (elec.) fo' cus ing coil: A coil producing a magnetic field for focusing, located around the neck of the cathode-ray tube.

FOIL (elec.) foil: Thin sheets of metal such as copper, tin, aluminum, etc. used in the construction of electronic components such as capacitors.

FOLDING MACHINE (graphics) fold' ing ma' chine: A machine which folds paper, ready to be bound in a book.

FOLDOVER (elec.) fold' o ver: A condition in a television picture which appears as if a part of the picture is folded over, either horizontally or vertically.

FOLIO (graphics) fo' li o: A sheet of paper 17 x 22 inches in size; a leaf of a book. A page number.

FOLLOWER REST (metal) fol' low er rest: A back support for long slender work in a lathe so that work will not spring away from cutting tool.

FONT (graphics) font: A complete assortment of any one size and style of type.

FOOT-CANDLE (elec.) foot-can' dle: A unit of measurement of light; the light produced on a surface from a source of one candle at a distance of one foot.

FOOTING (const.) foot' ing: The foundation or support under a wall or column.

FOOT MARGIN (graphics) foot mar' gin: A blank space at the foot of a page.

FOOT-POUND foot-pound: A unit of measurement of work; the energy required to move one pound through a distance of one foot.

"FOOTS" (paint. and dec.) foots: Settlings in vegetable oils.

FORBIDDEN REGION (elec.) forbid' den re' gion: A region between the valence and conduction band of an atom.

FORCE force: That which changes or tends to change the at rest position or motion of a body acted upon. It is measured in foot-pounds. Force may be described as having the characteristics of direction, magnitude and place of application.

FORCE FIT (metal) force fit: Parts mated for permanent assembly by a screw or hydraulic press.

FORECOOLER (air cond.) fore cool' er: A device for precooling water before it is used in refrigeration plant; precooler.

FOREMAN fore' man: A man in charge of a group of workmen.

FORE PLANE (wood.) fore plane: A plane, usually 18" long, used for jointing or planing the edges of long boards.

FORESHORTENED (draft.) fore short'-ened: The appearance of a line inclined to a plane. It does not appear as its true length.

FORESHORTENED LINE (draft.) fore-short' ened line: The length of a line as viewed when the line is oblique to the plane of projection.

FORGE (metal) forge: A furnace for heating metals in preparation for forging.

FORGING (metal) forg' ing: Operations of bending, drawing, spreading and upsetting of metal to form a specified shape and size.

FORM (const.) form: The mold used to shape poured concrete.

FORM (graphics) form: One or more pages of type which have been locked up in a chase, ready to be printed.

FORMING ROLLS (metal.) form' ing rolls: A machine consisting of a series of three rolls adjustable for various gauges of sheet metal. The machine is used to turn and form cylinders of desired diameter.

FORM FACTOR (elec.) form fac' tor:

The ratio of the effective value to the average value of an ac wave. All sine waves have a form factor of 1.11.

FORMING TOOL (metal) form' ing tool: A preformed cutting tool ground to a desired shape.

FORM LACQUER (paint. and dec.) form lac' quer: Thin lacquer or varnish used to coat concrete forms to prevent concrete from adhering to the forms.

FORSTNER BIT (wood.) forst' ner bit: A special type of boring tool without a center spur, used for boring in end grain wood and overlapping holes.

FORWARD WELDING (weld.) for' ward weld' ing: Fusing metal in the same direction as the torch flame points.

FOSSIL RESIN (paint. and dec.) fos' sil res' in: Any of the natural or earth type resins, such as kauri and the Congo copals, which derive their characteristics through aging in the ground.

FOSTER-SEELEY (elec.) fos' ter-see'-ley: A discriminator circuit used in the detection of FM.

FOTOSETTER (graphics) fo' to set ter: A machine made to set type on a film.

FOUCAULT CURRENT (elec.) fou' cault cur' rent: See EDDY CURRENT.

FOULING (auto.) foul' ing: The coating of the part of the spark plug in the combustion chamber with products of combustion, such as carbon.

FOUNDATION (const.) foun da' tion: The supporting base for a structure below grade level; the footings and walls on which a building is constructed.

FOUNDRY (metal) found' ry: A building in which metal castings are made.

FOUNDRY SAND (metal) found' ry sand: Sands, with special properties, used in molding.

FOUNTAIN (graphics) foun' tain: A reservoir for ink or water on a printing press.

FOUR CENTER METHOD (draft.) four cen' ter meth' od: A method of drawing an approximate ellipse.

FOUR COLOR PROCESS (graphics) four col' or pro' cess: A printing process in which all colors may be produced by using the primary colors with the addition of black.

FOUR CYCLE (auto.) four cy' cle: See FOUR STROKE CYCLE.

FOURIER ANALYSIS (elec.) fou rier' a nal' y sis: The series of sine waves which comprise the nonsinusoidal waveform.

FOURIER THEOREM (elec.) fou rier' the' o rem: A nonsinusoidal waveform can be represented by a series of harmonically related sine waves plus a d-c voltage.

FOURNIER, PIÉRE SIMON (graphics) The inventor of the point system of measurement of type.

FOUR POLE (elec.) four pole: Having four contacts as in a switch; having four field poles, as in a generator.

FOUR-STROKE CYCLE (auto.) four-stroke cycle: A cycle of engine operation which requires four strokes for completion.

FOUR-WAY SWITCH (elec.) four-way switch: A switch used in conjunction with three-way switches when control is desired at three or more places.

FOUR-WHEEL DRIVE (auto.) four-wheel drive: A type of automobile in which power is delivered to all four wheels.

FRACTIONAL-PITCH WINDING (elec.) frac'tion al-pitch wind'ing: When the span of an armature coil is less than the pole pitch in a generator.

FRAME (elec.) frame: A complete picture in television consisting of odd and even lines.

FRAME (graphics) frame: A composing stand with slides for holding cases.

FRAME FREQUENCY (elec.) frame fre'quen cy: See PICTURE FREQUENCY.

FRAMEWORK (auto.) frame'work: The rigid steel structure of an automobile for supporting the engine, wheels and body.

FRAMING SQUARE (wood.) fram'ing square: A large L shaped square used by carpenters in building and roof framing.

FREE BEND TEST (weld.) free bend test: Bending a test specimen without using a fixture or guide.

FREE FIT (metal) free fit: A liberal allowance between machine parts; class 2 - running fit.

FREE-FLIGHT ROCKET (space) free-flight rock'et: A rocket without electronic control or guidance.

FREE GYRO (space) free gy'ro: Sometimes referred to as space reference gyro in that the free gyro will maintain its orientation with respect to the stars rather than with respect to the Earth.

FREEHAND (draft.) free'hand: Drawing without the use of guides and devices.

FREE-WHEELING (auto.) free-wheel'ing: An overrunning clutch mechanism in an automobile transmission which disconnects the engine from the rear wheels, if the car speed exceeds the speed of the engine.

FREEZER (air cond.) freez'er: A cold storage room, usually kept below 30° F. A device for freezing perishables.

FREEZING POINT (air cond.) freez'ing point: The temperature at which a given liquid will solidify.

FRENCH CURVE (draft.) french curve: See IRREGULAR CURVE.

FRENCH DOOR (const.) french door: A door in which several panes of glass are substituted for wooden panels.

FRENCH POLISHING (paint. and dec.) french pol'ish ing: High-grade wood finish obtained by applying shellac or French varnish with a cloth pad, and linseed oil as a lubricant to prevent the pad from sticking.

FRENCH PROCESS ZINC OXIDE (paint. and dec.) french proc'ess zinc ox'ide: Zinc oxide pigment made from metallic zinc.

FRENCH WINDOW (const.) french win'dow: A casement window extending down to the floor and serving as a door to a porch or terrace.

FREON 12 (air cond.) fre'on 12: The trade name for dichlorodifluoromethane. Also called F 12.

FREQUENCY (elec.) fre'quen cy: The number of complete cycles per second measured in cycles per second (cps).

FREQUENCY BANDS (elec.) fre' quency bands:

VLF – Very low frequencies 10–30kc.
LF   – Low frequencies 30–300kc.
MF – Medium frequencies
        300–3,000kc.
HF   – High frequencies 3–30mc.
VHF – Very high frequencies
        30–300mc.
UHF – Ultra high frequencies
        300–3,000mc.
SHF – Super high frequencies
        3,000–30,000mc.
EHF – Extremely high frequencies
        30,000–300,000mc.

FREQUENCY DEPARTURE (elec.) fre'-
quen cy de par' ture: The instantaneous change from center frequency in
FM as the result of modulation.

FREQUENCY DEVIATION (elec.) fre'
quen cy de vi a' tion: The maximum
departure from center frequency at the
peak of the modulating signal.

FREQUENCY DOUBLER (elec.) tre'-
quen cy doub' ler: An amplifier stage
in which the plate circuit is tuned to
twice the frequency of the grid tank
circuit.

FREQUENCY METER (elec.) fre' quency me' ter: A meter used to measure
the frequency of an a-c source.

FREQUENCY MODULATION (elec.)
fre' quen cy mod u la' tion (FM): Modulating a transmitter by varying the
frequency of the r-f carrier wave at
an audio rate.

FREQUENCY RESPONSE (elec.) fre'-
quen cy res ponse': A rating of a device indicating its ability to operate over
a specified range of frequencies.

FREQUENCY SWING (elec.) fre' quen-

cy swing: The total frequency swing
from maximum to minimum. It is equal
to twice the deviation.

FREQUENCY TRIPLER (elec.) fre'-
quen cy tri' pler: An amplifier stage
in which the plate circuit is tuned to
three times the frequency (3rd harmonic) of the grid circuit.

FRESCO (const.) fres' co: A method of
painting on wet plaster with water
colors.

FRET (const.) fret: Ornamental work
done in relief, characterized by interlocking and interlacing lines.

FRET SAW (wood.) fret saw: A variation of a coping saw with a deeper throat
or work clearance, used for cutting
ornamental overlays and lattices.

FRIABLE fri' a ble: Easily crumbled
or reduced to powder.

FRICTION (auto.) fric' tion: The resistance to motion between moving parts
or bodies.

FRICTION DRIVE (auto.) fric' tion drive:
Transmission of power by frictional
contact.

FRICTION TAPE (elec.) fric' tion tape:
An insulating tape used in electrical
work to cover and protect a splice
in electrical conductors.

FRIEZE (const.) frieze: A series of
ornamental decorations forming a band
or border around a room; a horizontal
band, usually decorated and ornamental,
between the archtrave and the cornice
of a building.

FRIGORIFIC (air cond.) frig o rif' ic:
Pertaining to cold.

FRINGE HOWL (elec.) fringe howl: A

howl heard in a receiver circuit on the verge of oscillation.

FRISKET (graphics) fris'ket: A sheet of heavy paper stretched across the grippers of a job press and cut out so that only the type can print on the sheet on the tympan. It is used when certain parts of the form mark and spoil the sheet.

FRONT END ALIGNMENT (auto.) front end a lign'ment: Service procedures of checking and adjusting camber, caster, toe-in and turning of the front wheels of an automobile.

FRONT PORCH (elec.) front porch: The part of the pedestal blanking pulse before the sync pulse.

FRONT RAKE (metal) front rake: The same as BACK RAKE.

FRONT SUSPENSION (auto.) front suspen'sion: The frame, supports, shock absorbers, steering mechanism and axles connecting the front wheels of an automobile to the frame and body.

FROST LINE (const.) frost line: The depth to which the earth freezes.

FRUSTUM (draft.) frus'tum: The geometrical figure formed when a cone or a pyramid is cut off with a plane parallel to its base.

FSD (draft.): Abbreviation for FULL-SIZE DETAILS.

FUEL INJECTOR (auto.) fuel in jec'tor: A device used in a diesel engine to meter, atomize and inject fuel at high pressure into a cylinder.

FUEL PUMP (auto.) fu'el pump: A cam actuated diaphragm pump used to pump fuel from tank to carburetor.

FUGITIVE COLORS (paint. and dec.)

fu'gi tive col'ors: Colors which are not permanent; subject to fading.

FULCRUM ful'crum: The point of support for a lever.

FULLER (metal) ful'ler: Forging tools for finishing round corners. Face of tool has convex rounded face.

FULLER FAUCET (plumb.) ful'ler fau'cet: A faucet employing a rubber ball against an opening in a pipe for flow control.

FULL-FLOATING AXLE (auto.) full-float'ing ax'le: The wheel end of the axle is attached to the wheel hub and the wheel is supported by bearings on the outside of the axle housing.

FULL LOAD VOLTAGE (elec.) full load volt'age: The terminal voltage of a battery or supply when full load current is drawn by external circuit.

FULL POINT (graphics) full point: The mark of punctuation called the "period."

FULL SECTION (draft.) full sec'tion: A section made by the cutting plane passing through the entire object.

FULL-WAVE RECTIFIER (elec.) full-wave rec'ti fi er: A rectifier circuit which produces a dc pulse output for each half cycle of applied alternating current.

FUMING (wood.) fum'ing: Aging wood by the use of chemicals.

FUNCTION (automation) func'tion: The function of a machine is the sum of the individual operations accomplished by the machine or station.

FUNCTIONAL VIEWPOINT (automation) func'tion al view'point: The purpose of an action, a product or device.

FUNDAMENTAL (elec.) fund a men' tal: A sine wave that has the same frequency as a complex periodic wave. The component tone of lowest pitch in a complex tone. The reciprocal of the period of a wave.

FURNACE fur' nace: A compartment heated by fuel, such as gas or electricity, for heating water, melting metals or other materials and for heating, drying and baking various kinds of materials.

FURNITURE (graphics) fur' ni ture: Pieces of wood or metal, less than type height and accurately sized, placed around type matter in a chase or inserted in the actual job to produce a blank area.

FURRING (const.) fur' ring: Wood strips fastened to the studs on interior walls and ceilings on which wall materials are attached. Furring is used on masonry walls to provide air space and nailing grounds for finish wall materials.

FUSE (elec.) fuse: A safety protective device which opens an electric circuit if overloaded. A current above rating of the fuse will melt a fusible link and open the circuit.

FUSEL OIL (paint. and dec.) fu' sel oil: Oily liquid produced in small quantities when ethyl alcohol is produced by fermentation of grain.

FUSIBILITY (metal) fu si bil' i ty: The quality or readiness of a metal to pass from solid into liquid form.

FUSIBLE PLUG (air cond.) fu' si ble plug: A type of plug which melts at a predetermined temperature for the relief of pressure.

FUSING POINT (metal) fus' ing point: The temperature at which a metal melts and becomes a liquid.

FUSION (space) fu' sion: The combining (fusing) of atoms to release energy.

FUSION (weld.) fu' sion: Intimate mixing of molten metals.

G OR G-FORCE (space) G or G-force: Force exerted upon an object by gravity or by reaction to acceleration or deceleration, as in a change of direction; One G is the measure of the gravitational pull required to move a body at the rate of about 32.16 feet per second.

GABLE (const.) ga' ble: The triangular portion of a building contained between the slopes of a double-sloped roof.

GADGET gad' get: A small, handy device.

GAUGE (air cond.) gauge: An instrument for measuring pressure or level of gas or liquid; a scale of measurement for wire size, drill sizes and sheet metal thickness.

GAUGE BLOCKS (metal) gauge blocks: A set of accurately machined rectangular blocks of tool steel, carefully hardened and finished. Each block is accurate to a few millionths of an inch.

GAGGERS (metal) gag' gers: Metal supports used in sand casting to reinforce the sand in the cope.

GAIN (const.) gain: A notch or mortise into which another part is fitted.

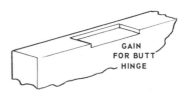

GAIN
FOR BUTT
HINGE

GAIN (elec.) gain: The ratio between the output power, current or voltage to the input power, current or voltage.

GAIN (wood.) gain: Cutting an inset on edge of door and frame so that the butt hinges will fit flush with edge.

GALAXY (space) gal' ax y: The group of several billion suns, stars, star clusters, nebulae, etc. to which the Earth's Sun belongs. Also called the Milky Way.

GALENA (elec.) ga le' na: A crystal compound of lead and sulphur used as a detector in a crystal radio receiver.

GALLEY (graphics) gal' ley: A shallow oblong tray of brass or steel used to hold composed type.

GALLEY PRESS (graphics) gal' ley press: A proof press for galleys consisting of a base and a heavy roller running on tracks.

GALLEY RACK (graphics) gal' ley rack: A sectional rack with inclined slides for holding galleys.

GALLING (metal) gall' ing: The tendency of some metals to seize or freeze when brought into contact with each other under pressure and with no lubricant.

GALVANIC CORROSION (metal) galvan' ic cor ro' sion: The wasting away of two dissimular metals in contact, due to generation of an electric current.

GALVANIZED IRON (paint. and dec.) gal' va nized iron: Sheet metal coated by dipping in hot zinc.

GALVANIZING (metal) gal' va ni zing: A protective coating for steel by dipping in molten zinc.

GALVANNOMETER (elec.) gal vannom' e ter: A meter which indicates very small amounts of current and voltage.

GAMBREL ROOF (const.) gam' brel roof: See MANSARD ROOF.

GAMMA (elec.) gam' ma: Greek letter ∂, represents the current gain of a common-collector connected transistor. It is equal to the ratio of a change in emitter current to a change in base current while the collector voltage is constant.

GAMMA (elec.) gam' ma: In television. A numerical factor indicating the degree of expansion or compression of light values in a picture.

GAMMA RAYS (elec.) gam' ma rays: Electromagnetic radiation from an excited atomic nucleus; radioactive radiation of very short wave length.

GANG DRILL (metal) gang drill: An assembly, including several drill presses, working on one worktable with a common base.

GANGED (elec.) ganged': Two or more variable components, such as capacitors or potentiometers, operated by a single shaft.

GANG SWITCH (elec.) gang switch: Two or more switches mounted together in a single box at a single location.

GANG TOOLS (metal) gang tools: Several tools set in one holder so that each will do its proportional amount of cutting.

GANTRY (space) gan' try: Crane-type structure, with platforms on different levels, used to erect, assemble and service large missiles.

GAP (elec.) gap: The space between the coil and the armature in a relay; the portion of a magnetic circuit which contains no core material, such as an air gap.

GARBAGE (space) gar' bage: Miscellaneous objects in orbit, including pieces of other satellites.

GARNET gar' net: A semiprecious gem stone used for watch bearings and as an abrasive.

GARNET PAPER (paint and dec.) gar' net pa' per: Abrasive which is reddish in color, hard and sharp; comes from the same source as semi-precious jewel by that name.

GAS COCK (plumb.) gas cock: Small valves for controlling the flow of gas.

GAS COCK

GAS-FILLED TUBE (elec.) gas-filled tube: Tubes designed to contain a specific gas in place of air, usually nitrogen, neon, argon or mercury vapor.

GASHING (metal) gash' ing: The rough cutting of machine parts.

GASKET (auto.) gas' ket: A flat piece of rubber, asbestos, metal or paper material placed between mating parts to prevent leakage.

GAS MAIN (plumb.) gas main: The main gas supply pipe serving a building.

GAS METAL-ARC WELDING (weld.) gas met' al-arc weld' ing: Welding using a continuously fed consumable electrode and a shielding gas.

GAS POCKETS (weld.) gas pock' ets: Cavities in weld metal caused by entrapped gas.

GAS REFRIGERATOR (air cond.) gas re frig' er a tor: A refrigerator operating on thermal energy of a burning gas.

GASSY TUBE (elec.) gas' sy tube: An electron tube containing enough gas to adversely affect its performance as an amplifier.

GAS TUNGSTEN-ARC WELDING (weld.) gas tung' sten-arc weld' ing: Welding using a tungsten electrode and a shielding gas.

GATE (elec.) gate: A circuit which permits an output only when a predetermined set of input conditions are met.

GATE (metal) gate: A hole made through the molding sand in the cope, through which molten metal may be poured.

GATE-LEG TABLE (wood.) gate-leg ta'-ble: A dropleaf table whose leaves, when raised, are supported by swinging legs.

GATE VALVE (plumb.) gate valve: A valve in which the flow is controlled by a moving gate or disk sliding in machined grooves at right angles to the water flow. The gate is moved by action of the threaded stem of the control handle.

GAUGE (const.) gauge: The mixing of plaster of paris with plaster to cause it to set quickly.

GAUGE (crafts.) gauge: The thickness of sheet metal by number.

GAUGE PIN (graphics) gauge pin: A paper guide on the tympan of a platen-press.

GAUSS (elec.) gauss: A measurement of flux density in lines per square centi-meter.

GAUSS, KARL FRIEDRICH (1777-1855) (elec.): The mathematical genius of Germany. For most of his life he was the director of the observatory at the University of Göttingen. His studies were devoted to mathematics, astron-omy and physics.

GEAR (metal) gear: A toothed wheel; a system of wheels, valve motions, bolts; equipment required for a desired oper-ation or activity such as "radio gear."

GEAR CLUSTER (metal) gear clus' ter: Several gears mounted together to op-erate as a unit.

GEAR RATIO (metal) gear ra' tio: The ratio between the number of teeth on the driving gear to the number of teeth on the driven gear.

GEAR SHIFTING (auto.) gear shift' ing: The intermeshing of selected gears in order to vary the speed ratio and power between engine and final drive assembly.

GEAR TRAIN (auto.) gear train: An ar-rangement of two or more gears con-necting driving and driven parts.

GEIGER-MULLER TUBE (elec.) Gei'-ger-Mul' ler tube: A tube used in radi-ation detecting and counting devices. When nuclear particles enter tube through window, the gas in the tube is temporarily ionized and a pulse dis-charge takes place. The pulse is col-lected by center electrode.

GEISSLER TUBE (elec.) geiss' ler tube: A gas filled tube which glows a par-ticular color depending on the charac-teristic of the gas used.

GENELITE (metal) gen' e lite: A bronze bearing metal containing a large percentage of graphite which permits absorption of lubricant.

GENERATOR (air cond.) gen' er a tor: A part of the absorption system of a refrigerator; the section of a refrig-erator used to convert liquid refrig-erant to its gaseous state by means of heating.

GENERATOR (auto.) gen er a' tor: A device to convert mechanical energy in-to electrical energy. The generator, in the automobile, supplies the electrical needs of the car and maintains the storage battery at the proper charge.

GENERATOR (elec.) gen' er a tor: A rotating electric machine to provide a large source of electrical energy. A generator converts mechanical energy to electric energy.

GENERATORS, TYPES OF (elec.) gen' er a tors, types of:

COMPOUND, Uses both series and shunt windings.

INDEPENDENTLY EXCITED, The field windings are excited by a separate d-c source.

SERIES, The field windings are con-nected in series with the armature and the load.

SHUNT, The field windings are con-nected across the armature in shunt with the load.

GENEVA MOTION (metal) ge ne' va mo' tion: A mechanical power trans-mission device which gives positive

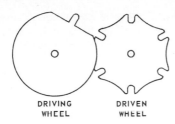

DRIVING   DRIVEN
WHEEL   WHEEL

but intermittent motion to the driven wheel, but prevents movement of the driven wheel in either direction without the driver.

GEOCENTRIC (space) ge o cen' tric: Relating to or measured from the center of the Earth.

GEODETIC (space) ge o det' ic: The science which deals with the size and shape of the earth.

GEOMETRIC PROGRESSION (metal) ge- o met' ric pro gres' sion: A series of numbers when any number of the series equals the preceding number multiplied by a given constant.

GEOPHYSICS (space) ge o phy' sics: The physics of the earth and its environment.

GERMANIUM (elec.) ger ma' ni um: A rare grayish-white metallic chemical element. Symbol GE; Atomic Wg't, 72.60; Atomic Number, 32.

GERMAN SIDING (const.) ger' man sid'- ing: Exterior wall finish boards with a hollow curve along the outside of the top edge and rabbeted along the inside of the lower edge.

GERMAN SILVER (crafts) Ger' man sil' ver: An alloy of copper, nickel and zinc.

GETTER (elec.) get' ter: A material used in an electron tube which is ignited after tube is evacuated and removes any residual gases.

GHOST (elec.) ghost: In TV. A duplicate image of a reproduced picture, caused by multipath reception of reflected signals.

"GHOSTING" (paint. and dec.) ghost' ing: A coating with a skippy appearance.

GIB (metal) gib: A metal shim, usually adjustable, to compensate for wear between sliding machine parts.

GILBERT (elec.) gil' bert: A unit of measurement of magneto-motive force. It represents the force required to establish one maxwell in a circuit with one Rel of reluctance.

GILBERT, WILLIAM (1540-1603) (elec.): An English physician to Queen Elizabeth I. He first recognized the "earth as a magnet" and explained the action of the compass. He is remembered as the father of the studies of terrestrial magnetism.

GILDING (paint and dec.) gild' ing: Process of obtaining a finish by using metal leaf (metal hammered into very thin sheets).

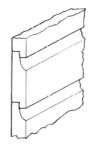

GERMAN SIDING

GILSONITE (paint. and dec.) gil' son ite: A pure asphalt found mainly in Utah. Used in making black asphaltum varnish.

GIMBAL (space) gim' bal: Mechanical frame containing two mutually perpendicular intersecting axes of rotation.

GIMBALS (metal) gim' bals: A device which permits the supported object to remain level regardless of the motion of adjacent parts; self-aligning bearings.

GIMLET (wood.) gim' let: A small wood boring tool with a T handle.

GINGERBREAD (const.) gin' ger bread: Useless decorations; meaningless ornamentation.

GINGERBREAD (graphics) gin' ger-bread: Useless decoations; meaningless ornamentation.

GIRDER (const.) gird' er: A large solid or built-up timber or steel beam used to support a concentrated load.

GIRDLED (wood.) gir' dled: A practice of cutting away the cambrium layer around the circumference of a tree which causes it to die.

GLASS BLOCKS (const.) glass blocks: Translucent blocks of glass used in building.

GLASS BOX (draft.) glass box: A method of visualizing multiview projection by placing an object in a glass box and observing surfaces as they would project to the glass picture planes or sides of the box.

GLAZED (crafts) glazed: With a smooth shiny surface.

GLAZED BRICKS (const.) glazed bricks: Bricks with a hard shiny glazed finish.

GLAZING (air cond.) glaz' ing: The food preserving process of freezing a coat of ice on frozen food by dipping in water.

GLAZING (const.) glaz' ing: The operation of putting glass in a sash.

GLAZING (metal) glaz' ing: The wearing away and dulling of the abrasive particles in a grinding wheel.

GLAZING (paint. and dec.) glaz' ing: A process of applying transparent or translucent coatings over a painted surface to produce blended effects; the work of a glazier in fitting a window with glass.

GLOBE VALVE (plumb.) globe valve: A valve employing a circular disk against a metal seat which surrounds the flow opening. The disk is forced onto or withdrawn by screw action as control handle is turned.

GLOSS (paint. and dec.) gloss: A term used to indicate the shine, luster or sheen of a dried film.

GLOSS OIL (paint. and dec.) gloss oil: A varnish composed primarily of limed rosin and petroleum thinner.

GLOST (crafts) glost: Glazed ware in the process of firing in the kiln.

GLOWCOIL (elec.) glow' coil: A resistance wire wound on a ceramic cone-shaped form. The coil screws into a lamp base. It is used as a heating element.

GLOW-TUBE (elec.) glow-tube: A glow-discharge tube, such as a neon glow tube, used in voltage regulation.

GLUE (wood.) glue: An adhesive; adhesives obtained from bones, gelatin, starch and resins.

GLYCERINE (GLYCEROL) (paint. and dec.) glyc' er ine: A type of alcohol which is sweet tasting, clear, almost colorless and odorless. Glycerine is used extensively in the production of alkyd resins and ester gum.

GLYPTAL (elec.) glyp' tal: A tradename of General Electric for alkyd
resin varnishes and cements. It is
transparent, waterproof and very adhesive. It is used as a protective coat
for wiring and as insulation.

GNOTOBIOTICS (space) gnot o bi-
ot' ics: The study of germ-free
animals.

GOBO (elec.) go' bo: A light shield for
the lens of a TV camera; a sound shield
for a microphone.

GODROON (wood.) go droon': An oval
ornamentation used on moldings.

GO-GAUGE (metal) go-gauge: An external or internal gauge which closely
fits a machined part for which it was
intended.

GOLDENROD FLAT (graphics) gold' en-
rod flat: Method of assembly of lithographic negatives into a complete layout form. Goldenrod paper is ruled to
required layout, windows are cut to
fit the work and negatives are fastened
into position.

GOLD PAINT (paint. and dec.) gold paint:
Mixture of bronze powder and bronzing
liquid.

GONIOMETER (elec.) go ni om' e ter:
A device used to measure the angle or
direction of a received radio signal.

GOOSENECK (elec.) goose' neck: A
flexible support for a microphone or
lamp.

GOOSENECK (plumb.) goose' neck: A
"U" shaped piece of small pipe used as
a faucet on some sinks and lavatories.

GOTHIC (graphics) goth' ic: A style of
type devoid of serifs and characterized
by straight lines of even width.

GOTHIC LETTERS (draft.) goth' ic
let' ters: A simplified single stroke
letter used in drawing.

GOUGE (wood.) gouge: A type of chisel
with a curved blade.

GOUGING (weld.) goug' ing: Cutting of
a groove in the surface of a metal
using a gas cutting torch.

GOULD BATTERY (elec.) gould battery: A lead-acid cell using glass wool
separators.

GOVERNOR (auto.) gov' er nor: A device to limit the speed of an engine.

GOX (space) gox: Gaseous oxygen.

GRADATION (graphics) gra da' tion:
The range of tones from highlights to
deep shadow.

GRADE (const.) grade: The level of the
ground around a building.

GRADE (plumb.) grade: The pitch of a
drain pipe in inches per foot.

GRADIENT (elec.) gra' di ent: The rate
of change of a physical quantity.

GRADING (const.) grad' ing: The leveling and sloping of the ground around a
building for drainage and landscaping
purposes.

GRAIN (space) grain: The body of a
solid propellant used in a rocket, fashioned to a particular size and shape
so as to burn smoothly without severe
surges or detonations.

GRAIN (wood.) grain: Texture, pattern
and arrangement of the fibers of wood.

GRAIN ALCOHOL (paint. and dec.) grain
al' co hol: Ethyl alcohol made from
grain by distillation.

GRAININESS (paint. and dec.) grain'i-
ness: Roughness of a protective film
resembling grains of sand.

GRAINING (wood.) grain'ing: Making
an imitational grain pattern on wood
by using paint and a special comb-like
tool.

GRAIN RAISING (paint. and dec.) grain
rais'ing: Causing short fibers on surface of bare wood to stand up by applying water.

GRAMME-RING (elec.) gramme-ring:
A method of winding a generator armature.

GRAPHIC ARTS (graphics) graph'ic
arts: A name that embraces every
form of printing that has for its object
the production of text or illustration.

GRAPHITE (paint. and dec.) graph'ite:
Black pigment consisting mostly of
carbon obtained from natural deposits,
or produced from coke in electric
furnace.

GRAPHITE (graphics) graph'ite: A fine
carbon dust used as a release in
electrotyping.

GRAVE (graphics) grave: An accent
mark used to show that a letter is not
strongly accented.

GRAVEL (const.) grav'el: Small stones.

GRAVER (crafts) grav'er: Sharp chisel
like tools used for cutting metal such
as in engraving.

GRAVISPHERE (space) grav'i sphere:
The spherical extent in which the force
of a given celestial body's gravity is
predominant in relation to that of other
celestial bodies.

GRAVITY (auto.) grav'i ty: The attractive force that tends to draw an
object toward the center of the earth.

GRAVITY WELL (space) grav'i ty well:
Analogy in which the gravitational field
is considered as a deep pit out of
which a space vehicle has to climb to
escape from a planetary body.

GRAY IRON (metal) gray iron: Cast iron
which shows a gray crystalline structure. The iron contains considerable
graphite. It is composed of a steel-
like matrix, the continuity of which is
interrupted by numerous particles of
graphite.

GRAYISH (paint. and dec.) gray'ish:
Lacking in intensity of color.

GREASE (auto.) grease: A semi-solid
lubricant composed of emulsified mineral oils and soda or lime soap.

GREASE GUN (auto.) grease gun: A gun
type device for forcing lubricants into
a bearing.

GREASE TRAP (plumb.) grease trap: A
catch basin interceptor with a clean out
for preventing the passage of soaps and
greases in the sewer system.

GREASY FRICTION (auto.) greas'y
fric'tion: A resistance to motion between moving parts which have been
coated with oil or grease.

GREAT PRIMER (graphics) great
prim'er: 18 point type size.

GREEN CORE (metal) green core: A
foundry core that has not been baked.

GREENFIELD (elec.) green'field: A
flexible metallic conduit used in the
connection of electrical power to machinery and in applications which require bends of the conduit at various
angles.

GREEN GOLD (crafts) green gold: An alloy of 25 percent silver and 75 percent gold.

GREEN LAKE (paint. and dec.) green lake: Mixture of Prussian blue and yellow lake, sold under various trade names.

GREEN LUMBER (const.) green lum'ber: Lumber not seasoned properly.

GREEN SAND (metal) green sand: Foundry sand which has been dampened with water.

GRID (elec.) grid: A grid of fine wire placed between the cathode and plate of an electron tube.

GRID BIAS (elec.) grid bi'as: The voltage between the grid and the cathode, usually negative.

GRID CURRENT (elec.) grid cur'rent: Current flowing in the grid circuit of an electron tube, when grid is driven positive.

GRID DIP METER (elec.) grid dip me'ter: A test instrument for measuring resonant frequencies, detecting harmonics and checking relative field strength of signals.

GRID LEAK DETECTOR (elec.) grid leak de tec'tor: A triode amplifier connected so that it functions like a diode detector and an amplifier. Detection takes place in the grid circuit.

GRID MODULATION (elec.) grid mod u-la'tion: A modulation circuit where the modulating signal is fed to the grid of the modulated stage.

GRID VOLTAGE (elec.) grid vol'tage: The bias or C voltage applied to the grid of a vacuum tube.

GRILLE (air cond.) grille: See DIFFUSER.

GRILLE (const.) grille: An ornamental iron protective and decorative grating, used as a screen or cover for windows and doors.

GRILLE (elec.) grille: An ornamental arrangement of wood and/or metal across the face of a loudspeaker.

GRIND (metal) grind: To sharpen; to reduce the size of or remove material by contact with an abrasive wheel.

GRINDING MACHINE (metal) grind'ing ma chine': A machine which employs a rotating abrasive wheel instead of a cutting tool.

GRINDSTONE (metal) grind'stone: A natural sandstone wheel used for sharpening tools.

GRIPPER EDGE (graphics) grip'per edge: The edge of the paper which is taken by the grippers on a cylinder press; guide edge of paper.

GRIPPERS (graphics) grip'pers: The small fingers on a cylinder press that hold the sheet firmly against the cylinder while the impression is being taken. On a job press the grippers are simply flat pieces of steel that press against the sheet and hold it firmly against the tympan.

GRIPPERS (metal) grip'pers: Thin triangular cross section pieces of metal about six inches long, used to hold down thin pieces of work in a vise.

GRIT (metal) grit: The abrasive particles used in the manufacturing of grinding wheels. The size of these particles are graded by a grit number.

GROMMET (elec.) grom'met: A rubber

insulating washer, used to protect wires running through a hole in a metal chassis or panel.

GROOVE (wood.) groove: A square or rectangular channel cut in wood in the same direction as the grain of the wood.

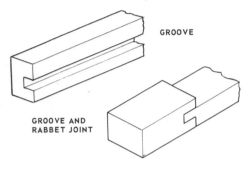

GROOVE

GROOVE AND
RABBET JOINT

GROOVE WELD (weld.) groove weld: A welding rod fused into a joint which has the base metal removed to form a V, U, or J trough at the edge of the metals to be joined.

GROUND (elec.) ground: The common return circuit in electronic equipment whose potential is zero; a connection to earth by means of plates or rods.

GROUND CLAMP (elec.) ground clamp: A mechanical clamping device to connect a wire or conduit to ground, such as a ground rod or water pipe.

GROUND COAT (paint. and dec.) ground coat: The coating material which is applied before the graining colors or glazing coat.

GROUND JOINT (plumb.) ground joint: A precision machined joint which does not require a gasket.

GROUND KEY VALVE (plumb.) ground key valve: A valve consisting of a conical shaped plug which fits into a machined hole. The plug has a hole through it. Flow is controlled by turn-

ing the plug so that a part of the hole forms a passageway for the liquid.

GROUND LINE (draft.) ground line: In perspective drawing, it is the intersection of the ground plane and the picture plane.

GROUND PAPER (paint. and dec.) ground pa' per: Wallpaper coated with an overall background color.

GROUND RETURN (auto.) ground re'-turn: The body and chassis of an automobile in which one side of all electrical devices is attached. This forms a common path and completes the electrical circuit back to the battery.

GROUNDS (const.) grounds: Pieces of wood placed within a wall to provide a base for fastening other work; square strips of wood around windows and doors as a plaster stop.

GROUND WATER (plumb.) ground wa'-ter: Water in or flowing in the ground.

GROUND WAVES (elec.) ground waves: The part of a transmitted radio wave which follows the surface of the earth.

GROUND WAVES (space) ground waves: The waves formed in the ground by an explosion.

GROUT (const.) grout: A thin mortar used for pointing-up and finishing mortar joints.

GROWLER (elec.) growl' er: A magnetic device used for testing armatures.

GROWTH (elec.) growth: A term used to express a gradual increase in values of current and voltage.

GUANINE CRYSTALS (paint. and dec.) gua' nine crys' tals: Multi—faceted crystals found in the skin attached to scales of sardine herring that thrive in cold water.

GUARD BAND (elec.) guard band: A narrow band of frequencies at the high end of each TV channel to prevent interference between adjacent channels.

GUDGEONS (graphics) gudg' eons: Metal wheels that are slipped over the ends of the rollerstocks on a job press.

GUIDED AIRCRAFT MISSILE (space) guid' ed air' craft mis' sile: A type of self-propelled missile, normally carried by a parent aircraft, which after launching can be guided to surface targets.

GUIDED AIRCRAFT ROCKET (space) guid' ed air' craft rock' et: A type of self-propelled armament carried by aircraft for attack on airborn targets, and which after launching can be guided to the target.

GUIDED BEND TEST (weld.) guid' ed bend test: Bending a specimen in a definite way by using a fixture.

GUIDED MISSILE (space) guid' ed mis' sile: An unmanned vehicle, moving in aerospace, whose trajectory or flight path is capable of being altered by an external or internal mechanism.

GUIDES (graphics) guides: Pins or quads fastened to the tympan of a press so placed that the printing comes into proper position on the sheet.

GUM (paint. and dec.) gum: A natural mucilaginous vegetable secretion that hardens but, unlike a resin, is water-soluble.

GUM (wood.) gum: A fine textured hardwood. It varies in color from a pinkish cast to a deep reddish brown. It has

an even texture and is easy to work. It is easily stained to resemble other hardwoods.

GUM ARABIC (paint. and dec.) gum ar' a bic: The dry gummy exudation of Acacia Senegal. This white powdered resin is sometimes used in cold water paint and in show card colors.

GUMMING UP (graphics) gum' ming up: Apply a gum arabic solution to a lithographic plate to prevent oxidation of non-printing area.

GUM TURPENTINE (paint. and dec.) gum tur' pen tine: Oleoresinous material obtained from living pine trees.

GUN COTTON (const.) gun cot' ton: A high explosive made by treating cotton with nitric and sulphuric acids.

GUN METAL gun met' al: An alloy of copper and tin.

GUTENBERG, JOHANN, · (1398—1468) (graphics): A German printer credited with the invention of movable type.

GUNTER'S CHAIN gun' ter's chain: A measuring chain used by the surveyor. It is 66 ft. in length. It has 100 links. Each link being 7.92 inches long.

GUSSET (const.) gus' set: An angle brace or plate used to stiffen a corner of a piece of work.

GUTTA-PERCHA (elec.) gut' ta-per'-cha: Gum obtained from milk juice of several East Indian trees. It is especially valuable for electrical insulation.

GUTTER (const.) gut' ter: A wood or metal trough around the eave of a building to collect and conduct rain water.

GUY (elec.) guy: A wire or rope support for a pole or tower.

GYPSUM (const.) gyp' sum: Hydrous sulphate of calcium ($CaSO_4 2H_2O$). When heated and the water removed, the resulting product is plaster of paris.

GYPSUM (paint. and dec.) gyp' sum: A common mineral composed of hydrous calcium sulphate. Gypsum, when heated, forms plaster of paris. Fabricated gypsum products used in building include wallboards, plasterboards, etc.

GYROSCOPE (space) gy' ro scope: Device consisting of a wheel so mounted that its spinning axis is free to rotate about either of two other axes perpendicular to itself and to each other; once set in rotation, its axle will maintain a constant direction.

G-Y SIGNAL (elec.) G-Y sig' nal: In color TV, it is one of the three color difference signals.

HACK SAW (metal) hack saw: A metal U-shaped frame with a handle attached

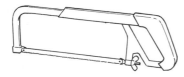

to one end. Saw blades fastened to frame are designed to cut metal.

HAFT (wood.) haft: A handle for a knife, a dagger or an awl.

HAIR LINES (paint. and dec.) hair lines: Very narrow cracks in a paint or varnish film.

HAIR SPACES (graphics) hair spaces: Spaces thinner than 5 em.

HAIRSPRING (elec.) hair' spring: A spring on the moving-coil of a meter to return indicator to zero position. Springs also act as electrical connections to coil.

HALF CENTER (metal) half cen' ter: A lathe center with one side of the conical face partially cut away. Used in facing operations.

HALF-LIFE (elec.) half-life: The time required for any radioisotope to reduce to one half its original value.

HALF NUT (metal) half nut: A half nut used to engage the lead screw in a lathe when cutting threads.

HALF SECTION (draft.) half sec' tion: View in which cutting plane passes only half way through an object, and one quarter of object is removed.

HALF STORY (const.) half sto' ry: Upper floor of a house, directly under roof. It may or may not have some side wall.

HALF S TRAP (plumb.) half s trap: A trap shaped like one half the letter S.

HALFTONE (graphics) half' tone: A photomechanical printing surface in which detail and tone values are shown by a series of spaced dots of varying size and shape. The dot area varies in direct proportion to the intensity of tones represented.

HALF VIEW (draft.) half view: The half view of a symetrical object. Used when insufficient space is available to represent the total object in proper scale.

HALF-WAVE RECTIFIER (elec.) half-wave rec' ti fi er: A rectifier which permits one half of an alternating current cycle to pass and rejects the reverse current of the remaining half cycle. Its output is pulsating dc.

HALL (const.) hall: The entranceway to a house; a long room which provides a passageway to a group of rooms.

HALVED PATTERN (metal) halved pat'

tern: A foundry pattern made in two parts to permit easy removal from the sand molding.

HALVING (const.) halv' ing: Joining two pieces of wood by cutting each to one half its thickness and lapping the pieces together.

HAM (elec.) ham: The slang name for a radio amateur or experimenter.

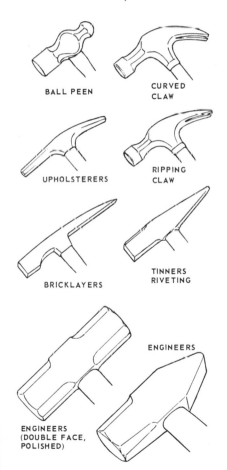

BALL PEEN

CURVED CLAW

UPHOLSTERERS

RIPPING CLAW

BRICKLAYERS

TINNERS RIVETING

ENGINEERS

ENGINEERS (DOUBLE FACE, POLISHED)

HAMMER (wood) ham' mer: A tool for pounding, usually consisting of a metal head with a handle.

BALL PEEN, a hammer used in metal working. It has one flat face for

pounding and the other a hemi-spherical shaped head for forming metal and peening rivets.

BRICKLAYER'S, a hammer specially adapted to the mason's trade, with one face for hammering and the other a long chisel face for cutting bricks and stone.

CLAW, a hammer with curved claws for pulling nails.

ENGINEER'S CROSS PEEN, a small sledge hammer with a short handle. One face is wedge shaped.

ENGINEER'S, DOUBLE FACE, a heavy hammer with two faces for pounding.

RIPPING, a hammer with straight claws for prying and ripping boards.

RIVETING, a small hammer with one square flat face and a wedge shaped face. Used by the tinsmith in sheet metal work.

UPHOLSTERER'S, a light hammer with a long round head, to be able to hammer in close spaces. Frequently one head is magnetized to hold a tack.

HAMMERED EFFECT FINISH (paint. and dec.) ham' mered ef fect' fin' ish: So called because of its resemblance to hammered metal. Produced by incorporating aluminum powder in vehicle which controls leafing and non-leafing effect to create unique designs.

HAM SLANGUAGE (elec.) ham slan'-guage: A contraction meaning "slang language" used by amateur radio operators for clarity and abbreviation in code communications.

HAND DRILL (wood.) hand drill: A gear type tool, fashioned after the household eggbeater. It holds and turns small twist drills.

HAND MILLER (metal) hand mill' er: A small milling machine with hand operated feed system.

HAND PRINTS (paint. and dec.) hand prints: Wallpapers printed by hand, usually with the silk screen process.

HAND PROOF (graphics) hand proof: A proof of a printing plate where the inking and printing is done by hand.

HANDRAIL (const.) hand' rail: A rail along a stairway or at the edge of a balcony or gallery placed for convenient grasping by the hand.

HANDSAW (wood.) hand' saw: The ordinary one hand saw used by wood-workers and carpenters. It may be either a rip or crosscut saw.

HAND SHIELD (weld.) hand shield: See SHIELD.

HAND VISE (metal) hand vise: A clamping device for holding small objects in the hand while working on them.

HANGER (const.) hang' er: An iron support of a beam or pipe.

HANSA YELLOW (paint. and dec.) han' sa yel' low: A family of organic yellow pigments.

HARDEN (metal) hard' en: To harden metals by heating and cooling at pre-determined rates. In tool steel the metal is heated to 1400-1500° and rapidly cooled or quenched in water or oil.

HARDENABILITY (metal) har den a-bil' i ty: The ability of steel to achieve a desired hardness.

HARDENING (metal) hard' en ing: The process of heating and quenching cer-tain iron alloys to produce a superior hardness.

HARD FACING (metal) hard fac' ing: The process of welding a layer of wear-resisting alloy to surfaces subjected to severe abrasive wear.

HARDNESS (elec.) hard' ness: A term used to describe the degree of evacua-tion in an electron tube.

HARDNESS (metal) hard' ness: The property of metal to resist permanent deformation when a load is applied.

HARDNESS IN WATER (plumb.) hard'-ness in wa' ter: The amount of car-bonates and sulfates of calcium and magnesium in the water solution.

HARD OIL FINISH (paint. and dec.) hard oil fin' ish: A varnish giving the effect of a rubbed-in-oil finish but producing, a hard surface.

HARDPAN (const.) hard' pan: A layer of rock under soft soil.

HARD RUBBER (elec.) hard rub' ber: A vulcanized rubber insulating ma-terial.

HARD SOLDER (metal) hard sol' der: See SPELTER and SILVER SOLDER.

HARDWARE (const.) hard' ware: The metal parts of a house such as locks, hinges, nails, etc.

HARDWARE (space) hard' ware: The physical object, as distinguished from its capability or function. The actual engines, case, pumps, guidance system, or other components of the missile.

HARDY (metal) har' dy: A square shank chisel which fits into a square hole in an anvil. Used for cutting metals.

HARMONIC ANALYSIS (elec.) har mon'-ic a nal' y sis: The study of complex waveforms in terms of their harmonic content.

HARMONIC DISTORTION (elec.) har-mon' ic dis tor' tion: Distortion due to non-linear characteristics of a device so that harmonics other than the funda-mental frequency appear in the output when the input is sinusoidal.

HARMONIC FREQUENCY (elec.) har-mon' ic fre' quen cy: A frequency which is a multiple of a fundamental frequency. Example: If the fundamental frequency is 1000 kc, then the second harmonic is 2 x 1000 kc or 2000 kc; the third harmonic is 3 x 1000 kc or 3000 kc, and so on.

HARNESS (elec.) har' ness: A group of connection wires or cables bundled together and installed as a group.

HARTLEY OSCILLATOR (elec.) hart' ley os cil la' tor: See OSCIL-LATORS.

HASH (elec.) hash: Interference to a radio signal resulting from sparking of motor or generator brushes or vibrat-ing contact points.

HATCHET (wood.) hatch' et: A small special purpose hand axe.

CLAW HATCHET, A general purpose hatchet used for cutting, ripping and prying.

HALF HATCHET, A hatchet with a cutting head that is straight on one edge and curved on the other. Opposite head is a hammer. See illustration.

LATHING HATCHET, A type of half hatchet with a narrower blade. It was originally designed for work of cutting and splitting wood laths.

HATCHING (draft.) hatch' ing: The drawing of equally spaced diagonal lines indicating a sectional view of an object.

HAWK (const.) hawk: A small square board with a handle underneath. Used to hold mortar or plaster.

H BEAM (const.) h beam: A steel beam whose cross section is shaped like the letter H.

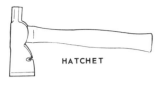

HATCHET

HEAD (auto.) head: See CYLINDER HEAD.

HEAD (const.) head: The top part of a door or window opening.

HEAD (elec.) head:

ERASING, A device on a recorder for removing previously magnetically re-corded information.

MAGNETIC RECORDING, A device for converting signal variations pro-duced by sound into magnetic variations for storage on magnetic tape or other media.

MAGNETIC REPRODUCING, A de-vice to convert magnetic variations in the storage media into electrical sound signals.

HEAD (graphics) head: The top line of a page.

HEAD, DYNAMIC (air cond.) head, dy-nam' ic: The sum of the static and velocity pressures in a flowing liquid, at the point of measurement.

HEADER (metal) head' er: A cold form-ing machine for upsetting metal. So named because it originally was used to head nails.

HEADER (const.) head' er: Stones or bricks extending beyond the thickness of the wall; a beam placed between two long beams, and making T joints with the long beams; a short beam placed between two other structural members at right angles.

HEADER (plumb.) head' er: A pipe with many outlets. See MANIFOLD.

HEADPHONE (elec.) head' phone: See EARPHONES.

HEAD, PRESSURE (air cond.) head, pres' sure: The operating pressure measured at the discharge outlet of a compressor.

HEAD ROOM (const.) head room: The vertical space clearance between a stairway and the ceiling above.

HEAD, STATIC (air cond.) head, sta' tic: The pressure of a fluid expressed in terms of inches of mercury or other manometric device.

HEADSTOCK (metal) head' stock: The driving mechanism of a lathe including stock casting and spindles. Back gears may also be a part of the headstock in addition to gears for operating the lead screw.

HEAD TORQUE SEQUENCE (auto.) head torque se' quence: The pattern or order in which to tighten the head bolts of an engine.

HEADWAY (const.) head' way: The clear head space in a stairway or arch.

HEARTH (const.) hearth: The floor of a fireplace and the portion in front of the fireplace extending into the room.

HEARTWOOD (wood.) heart' wood: The layers of wood developed around the pith of a tree as it grows.

HEAT (air cond.) heat: Energy trans-ferred by a difference in temperature.

HEAT (metal) heat: In the foundry, the reduction of a charge in a cupola fur-nace to a fluid state.

HEAT (weld.) heat: That which raises or lowers the temperature of a body; molecular energy in motion.

HEAT-AFFECTED ZONE (weld.) heat-af fect' ed zone: That part of the base metal which has been altered by the heat from the welding, brazing or cutting operation.

HEAT CONDUCTIVITY (weld.) heat con-duc tiv' i ty: Speed and efficiency of heat energy movement through a sub-stance.

HEATER (elec.) heat' er: A resistance heating element used to heat the cathode in a vacuum tube.

HEAT EXCHANGE (air cond) heat ex-change': A device or manifold system by which heat is transferred from one system to another.

HEATING, DIELECTRIC (elec.) heat'-ing, di e lec' tric: See DIELECTRIC HEATING.

HEATING, INDUCTION (elec.) heat' ing, in duc' tion: See INDUCTION HEAT-ING.

HEAT, LATENT (air cond.) heat, la'-tent: Heat associated with the change of state of a substance. Ex: Heat of vaporization.

HEAT LOSS (elec.) heat loss: Energy lost due to resistance.

HEAT OF CONDENSATION (air cond.) heat of con den sa' tion: The latent heat energy given up when a gas changes to a liquid.

HEAT PUMP (air cond.) heat pump: A dual function heating and cooling machine; a machine designed to deliver heat to an area or working space, and by a change-over system the same machine may be used to remove heat from an area or space.

HEAT, SENSIBLE (air cond.) heat, sen'si ble: Heat associated with a change In temperature.

HEAT SINK (elec. - space) heat sink: A contrivance for the absorption or transfer of heat away from a critical part or parts.

HEAT, SPECIFIC (air cond.) heat, specif' ic: The energy required to produce one degree temperature rise per unit of mass. Usually measured in btu per lb. per degree F.

HEAT TRANSMISSION (air cond.) heat trans mis' sion: The conduction, convection and radiation of heat.

HEAT TREATING (metal) heat treat' ing: The process of varying characteristics of metals by heating to predetermine temperatures and cooling at specified rates.

HEAT TREATING FURNACE (metal) heat treat' ing fur' nace: A gas fired furnace in which metal parts are heat treated. Industrial types have accurate control of both temperature and atmosphere.

HEAT VALUE (auto.) heat val' ue: The power obtained from burning a unit amount of fuel in an excess of oxygen. It is measured in btu.

HEAT WAVE (elec.) heat wave: An electromagnetic wave in the infrared region of the spectrum.

HEAVISIDE-KENNELLY LAYER (space) heav' i side-ken nel' ly lay' er: Region of the ionosphere that reflects certain radio waves back to earth.

HEAVISIDE LAYER (elec.) heav' i side lay' er: A layer of ionized gas above the earth's surface which reflects radio sky waves back to earth.

HEAVY BODIED OIL (paint. and dec.) heav' y bod' ied oil: A high viscosity oil.

HECTOGRAPH (draft.) hec' to graph: A duplicating process using a gelatin pad which has been imprinted with a drawing or typed material in aniline materials.

HEEL (const.) heel: The end cut on a rafter; the end of the rafter which rests on the top plate.

HEIGHT GAUGE (metal) height gauge: A tool used for measuring and layout of points from a plane or base surface. The upright is graduated for direct reading.

HELIARC WELDING (metal) he' li arc weld' ing: A method of welding in which the electrode is enclosed in a tube through which pure helium gas is blown to surround the arc and exclude the air.

HELIX (draft.) he' lix: A space curve generated by a point moving uniformly around the surface of a cylinder.

HELIX (elec.) he' lix: A coil; a solenoid.

HELMET (weld.) hel' met: A protecting

hood which fits over the arc welder's head, provided with a lens of safety glass through which the operator may safely observe the electric arc.

HEMATITE (metal) hem' a tite: A rich iron ore.

HEMLOCK (wood.) hem' lock: An inexpensive wood used extensively for framing buildings.

HEMPSEED OIL (paint. and dec.) hemp'- seed oil: An oil obtained from the hemp plant. It is used in paints and varnishes.

HENRY (h) (elec.) hen' ry: Unit of measurement of inductance. A coil has one henry of inductance if an emf of one volt is induced when the current through the inductor is changing at a rate of one ampere per second.

HENRY, JOSEPH (1797-1878) (elec.): An American scientist who discovered the principle of magnetic induction. However his work was not published and brought later fame when also discovered by Faraday. He was a professor at Princeton University. He is credited with the creation of the U.S. Weather Bureau.

HENRY TANK PEN (draft.) hen' ry tank pen: A pen which contains an ink reservoir just above its point.

HEPPLEWHITE (wood.) hep' ple white: A furniture style named after George Hepplewhite of London (died 1786). It is characterized by inlaid mahogany, classic motifs and graceful curves from the influence of Chippendale and the French. Shield, heart-shaped and oval chair backs were used extensively by Hepplewhite.

HEPTAGON (draft.) hep' ta gon: A plane figure having seven sides and seven angles.

HEPTODE (elec.) hep' tode: An electron tube with seven elements, usually a cathode, plate and five grids.

HERMAPHRODITE CALIPER (metal) her maph' ro dite cal' i per: A spe-

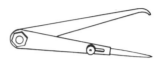

cial caliper with one sharp pointed leg, used for layout work.

HERMETICALLY-SEALED UNIT (air cond) her met'i cal ly-sealed u' nit: The sealed unit in a refrigerator, in which the condenser unit is enclosed with the motor and compressor. Usually no access is provided for servicing and the complete unit is replaced if inoperative.

HERRINGBONE (const.) her' ring bone: Bricks, stone and other materials applied diagonally in a building for decorative purposes.

HERTZ ANTENNA (elec.) hertz an ten'- na: An antenna which does not depend upon ground for its operation.

HERTZ, HEINRICH RUDOLPH (1857-1894) (elec.): The German scientist who first discovered the existence of electromagnetic waves.

HERTZIAN WAVE (elec.) hertz' i an wave: A radio wave.

HESSELMAN ENGINE (auto.) hes' sel man en' gine: A low compression diesel engine using electric spark ignition.

HETERODYNE (elec.) het' er o dyne: The process of combining two signals of different frequencies to obtain the difference frequency.

HEWING (wood.) hew' ing: The rough dressing of timber by an axe.

HEXAGON (draft.) hex' a gon: A six sided plane geometric figure.

HEXODE (elec.) hex' ode: An electron tube with six elements, usually a cathode, plate and four grids.

HICKEY (elec.) hick' ey: A tool used for bending metal conduit and pipe.

HICKORY (wood.) hick' o ry: A hard tough wood, used extensively for work which requires bending.

HIDDEN LINE (draft.) hid' den line: See INVISIBLE LINE.

HIDING POWER (paint. and dec.) hid' ing pow' er: Capacity of a paint to hide or obscure the surface on which it is applied; degree of opacity of a pigment or paint.

HIGH BOY (wood.) high boy: A tall chest of drawers mounted on legs.

HIGH BRASS (metal) high brass: Commercial brass containing about 65 percent copper and 35 percent zinc.

HIGH COMPRESSION (auto.) high compres' sion: The compression of the air fuel mixture in the cylinder head on the upward stroke of the piston.

HIGH FIDELITY (elec.) high fi del' i-ty: Abbreviation, Hi-Fi; a term used to describe high quality sound systems; a sound system which faithfully reproduces the original sound.

HIGH FLASH POINT (auto.) high flash point: Flashpoint refers to the ignition temperature of lubricating oils. A high flash point means it will only ignite at a very high temperature.

HIGH LEVEL MODULATION (elec.) high lev' el mod u la' tion: The modulation takes place in the final amplifier at a high level of plate voltage.

HIGHLIGHTING (paint. and dec.) high'-light ing: Making certain parts of a finished project appear lighter than other parts.

HIGHLIGHTS (crafts) high' lights: Raised portions of a figure or design.

HIGH MU TUBE (elec.) high mu tube: An electron tube with a high amplification factor.

HIGH PASS FILTER (elec.) high pass fil' ter: See FILTER, HIGH PASS.

HIGH POTENTIAL (elec.) high po ten'-tial: A dangerously high voltage usually over 500 volts.

HIGH SIDE (air cond.) high side: The part of a refrigeration system operating at condenser pressures.

HIGH SPEED CIRCUIT (auto.) high speed cir' cuit: The carburetor circuit consisting of the venturi, the main fuel nozzle and other passages which supply the air-fuel mixture to the engine when the throttle is opened from the idle or low speed position.

HIGH SPEED STEEL (metal) high speed steel: A steel made to withstand considerable heat and still retain its hardness.

HIGH TENSION (elec.) high ten' sion: Refers to wires carrying extremely high voltages; power transmission lines.

HIP RAFTER (const.) hip raft' er: The supporting rafter at an external roof angle intersection.

HIP ROOF (const.) hip roof: A roof

that rises from all four sides of a building with equal pitches.

HIPS (const.) hips: The inclined timbers which support the intersections in a hip roof.

HOB (metal) hob: A worm shaped milling cutter with cutting teeth produced by milling gashes across the thread.

HOBBING (metal) hob' bing: A machine process for generating gear teeth.

HOGGING (metal) hog' ging: Very heavy cuts taken by metal machine tools.

HOLD CONTROL (elec.) hold con trol': Manually operated controls on a TV receiver for adjusting the horizontal and vertical sweep frequencies.

HOLE (elec.) hole: A positive charge. A space left by a removed electron.

HOLE GAUGE (metal) hole gauge: A small spring loaded gauge which is permitted to expand to maximum in a small hole. It is then locked, removed from hole and measured with a micrometer.

HOLE INJECTION (elec.) hole in jec'-tion: The creation of holes in a semi-conductor material by removal of electrons by a strong electric field around a point contact.

HOLE SAW (metal) hole saw: A circular saw used to cut large holes in metal, wood or fibre. The saw is held on

center by a pilot drill. The size of the hole is determined by the diameter of the hole saw.

HOLIDAYS (paint. and dec.) hol' i days: Areas of a surface missed by the painter.

HOLLOWING (crafts) hol' low ing: The process of making a bowl like depression in metal by using a ball peen hammer to force the metal into a prepared mold.

HOLLOW TILE (const.) hol' low tile: Hollow burnt-clay or terra-cotta blocks, used extensively for building both interior and exterior walls.

HOME (space) home: Of a guided missile: to direct itself toward a target by guiding on heat waves, radar, echoes, radio waves or other radiation emanating from the target.

HONE (metal) hone: An abrasive device designed for finishing internal cylindrical surfaces. A fine abrasive stone used for sharpening tools.

HONING (auto.) hon' ing: An abrasive process of cleaning up and resurfacing the interior of cylinders by a rotating hone.

HOOD (auto.) hood: The part of the automobile body which covers the engine.

HOOKED SCALE (metal) hooked scale: A scale with a small hook on one end to allow user to make measurements when he cannot see if the rule is even with the measuring edge.

HOOK-ON METER (elec.) hook-on me'-ter: A meter employing a current transformer with a split core so that it may be hooked around a current carrying conductor and measure the current without disconnecting the wire.

HOOK UP (elec.) hook up: The connections between components in an electrical circuit or device.

HOP (elec.) hop: See SKIP.

HORIZON DISTANCE (elec.) ho ri' zon dis' tance: The line of sight distance from a transmitting antenna to the horizon.

HORIZON LINE (draft.) ho ri' zon line: In perspective drawing, it is the intersection of the plane of the observer's eye with the picture plane.

HORIZONTAL (draft.) hor i zon' tal: Parallel to the horizon.

HORIZONTAL HOLD CONTROL (elec.) hor i zon' tal hold con' trol: A control on a television set to adjust the frequency of the horizontal sweep oscillator so that it will synchronize with the received picture signal.

HORIZONTAL POLARIZATION (elec.) hor i zon' tal po lar i za' tion: An antenna positioned horizontally, so that its electric field is parallel to the earth's surface.

HORIZONTAL POSITION (weld.) hor i zon' tal po' si tion: A weld performed on a horizontal seam.

HORNBLENDE horn' blende: A greenish black mineral containing iron and silicates of magnesium, calcium and aluminum.

HOROLOGY ho rol' o gy: The science of time measurement; the construction and repair of clocks and watches.

HORSE, also **SAWHORSE** (wood.) horse, also saw' horse: A trestle or four legged support for work; a temporary staging support.

HORSEPOWER (elec.) horse' pow er:

33,000 ft. lbs. of work per minute or 550 ft. lbs. of work per second equals one horsepower. Also 746 watts = 1 hp.

HORSEPOWER HOUR (elec.) horse' pow er hour: The power performed by one horsepower (746 watts) expended continuously for one hour.

HOSE (weld.) hose: Flexible conductor to carry gases from welding regulator to the torch. It is made of fabric and rubber.

HOT (elec.) hot: Carrying a current; danger of shock; high temperature.

HOT (elec.) hot: Abbreviation for Horizontal Oscillator Transformer.

HOT BOX (metal) hot box: An overheated bearing, due to improper fit or poor lubrication.

HOT CATHODE (elec.) hot cath' ode: Emission of electrons from a cathode as a result of heat.

HOTCHKISS DRIVE (auto.) hotch' kiss drive: The drive system in which rear end torque is absorbed by the rear springs.

HOT DIPPING (metal) hot dip' ping: Either cleaning or coating a material by dipping in a hot solution.

HOT LACQUER PROCESS (paint. and dec.) hot lac' quer pro' cess: Process where heat is used instead of volatile thinner to reduce the consistency of lacquer. Hot lacquer can be applied with a higher percentage of solids than room-temperature lacquer.

HOT PLUG (auto.) hot plug: A spark plug which runs warmer than others in an engine. Certain plugs are designed to run at higher heat ranges.

HOT-ROLLED (m e t a l) hot-roll' ed: Steel shaped at high temperatures by running through forming rollers.

HOT TYPE (graphics) hot type: Type cast from molten metal.

HOT WIRE METER (e l e c.) hot wire me' ter: A meter which uses the thermal contraction and expansion of a wire to indicate the magnitude of a current or voltage.

HOT WORKING (metal) hot work' ing: The processes of hammering, pressing, rolling, upsetting or bending metal while it is at high temperature.

HOUND DOG (GAM-77) (space) hound dog: An Air Force air-to-surface guided missile whose range is over 500 miles.

HOUSE PAINT, OUTSIDE (p a i n t. and dec.) house paint, out' side: Paint designed for use on the exterior of buildings, fences and other surfaces exposed to the weather.

HOUSE TRAP (plumb.) house trap: A trap in the sewer line immediately inside the foundation of the building to serve as a barrier and prevent gases in the public sewer from entering the house system.

HOWLER (elec.) howl' er: A device used by the telephone company to make a loud varying sound to tell customer that phone is off the hook.

H-PLANE (draft.) H-plane: The horizontal picture plane in orthographic projection which shows the top or plan view.

HUB (plumb.) hub: See BELL.

HUE (paint. and dec.) hue: A general term used to distinguish one color from another, like a red hue, yellow hue, etc.

HUM (elec.) hum: A form of distortion introduced in an amplifier as a result of coupling to stray electromagnetic and electrostatic fields or insufficient filtering.

HUMAN ENGINEERING (a u t o m a t i o n) hu' man eng i neer' ing: The measuring of man's capabilities and limitations and designing machines or processes to accomodate man rather than the machine.

HUMIDIFY (air cond.) hu mid' i fy: The process of adding water vapor to the air or other substances.

HUMIDIFIER (air cond.) hu mid' i fi er: A device to add moisture to the air.

HUMIDISTAT (air cond.) hu mid' i stat: A control device sensitive to humidity.

HUMIDITY (air cond.) hu mid' i ty: The water vapor contained in a given space; the amount of moisture in the air.

HUMIDITY, RELATIVE (air cond.) hu-mid' i ty, rel' a tive: The amount of moisture in the air at a given temperature to the amount it could contain.

HUNDREDTHS SCALE (wood.) hun' dredths scale: A scale used to convert inches into decimal values. It is found on the carpenter's steel square.

HUNTING (elec.) hunt' ing: The tendency of a mechanical or electrical system to oscillate about its normal position or frequency.

HUNTING LINK (metal) hunt' ing link: A link in a chain drive which can be opened to permit addition of or removal of a link to adjust length of chain.

HYDRANT (plumb.) hy' drant: A faucet or outlet, usually used for a relatively large supply of water on the outside of the house, for irrigation or fire protection.

HYDRATOR (air cond.) hy' dra tor: A special covered dish or container in a refrigerator which is maintained at a higher relative humidity than the balance of the refrigerator.

HYDRAULIC JACK (auto.) hy drau' lic jack: A hydraulic operated jack. The jack is raised by movement of a lever on a small force pump which is a part of the mechanism.

HYDRAULIC PRESS (metal) hy drau' lic press: A larger adaptation of the hand arbor press. Pressure is applied by hydraulics rather than mechanical leverage.

HYDROELECTRIC (elec.) hy dro elec' tric: Pertaining to the generation of electric power by waterpower.

HYDROLYSIS (air cond.) hy drol' y sis: The reaction of a material or substance with water.

HYDRAZONE (space) hy' dra zone: An exotic fuel formed by the action of hydrazine or one of its derivatives on a compound containing the carbonyl group CO.

HYDROCARBON (paint. and dec.) hy-dro car' bon: Compound consisting of hydrogen and carbon.

HYDROCARBON FUEL (space) hy dro-car' bon fuel: Gasoline or kerosene.

HYDROCARBON RESINS (paint. and dec.) hy dro car' bon res' ins: Obtained by catalytic polymerization of petroleum fractions.

HYDROFORMING (metal) hy dro form'-ing: A forming operation in which hydraulic fluid under pressure is used to force metal over a die.

HYDROGEN (weld.) hy' dro gen: A gas formed of the single element hydrogen. It is considered one of the most active gases. When combined with oxygen, it forms a very clean flame.

HYDROLYTE (air cond.) hy' dro lyte: A substance undergoing hydrolysis.

HYDROMETER (elec.) hy drom' e ter: A bulb type instrument used to measure specific gravity of a liquid.

HYDRONICS (plumb.) hy dron' ics: A word used to describe the practice of heating and cooling with water.

HYDROPHONE (elec.) hy' dro phone: A type of electroacoustic transducer to convert water-borne sound waves into electrical signals. Used in SONAR.

HYDROSPINNING (metal) hy' dro spin-ning: A metal forming operation of spinning using hydraulic force and control of forming rollers which shape the metal over a mandrel. Used to shape missile nose cones and aircraft sections.

HYDROSTATIC PRESSURE (air cond.) hy dro stat' ic pres' sure: The force per unit area exerted upon a small body immersed in and moving with the flow of a fluid.

HYDROSTATICS hy dro stat' ics: A branch of physics which is concerned with pressure and the equilibrium of a liquid.

HYDROUS (paint. and dec.) hy' drous: Containing water.

HYGROMETER (elec.) hy grom' e ter:

A device for measuring humidity of the air.

HYGROSCOPIC (air cond.) hy gro-scop' ic: Absorbing moisture from the air.

HYGROSTAT (air cond.) hy' gro stat: See HUMIDISTAT.

HYPERACOUSTIC ZONE (space) hy-per a cous' tic zone: The region in the upper atmosphere between 60 and 100 miles where the distance between the rarefied air molecules roughly equals the wave length of sound, so that sound is transmitted with less volume than at lower levels.

HYPERBOLA (draft.) hy per' bo la: A curve generated by a point moving so that its locus in any position is constantly equal to the difference from two fixed points (foci).

HYPEREUTECTOID (metal) hy per eu-tec' toid: Steel containing over .9% carbon.

HYPOID (auto.) hy' poid: System of gearing where pinion gear meshes with

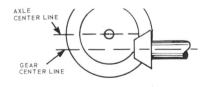

ring gear below center line of ring gear. Allows lower drive thus removing large hump in floor of car.

HYPOTENUSE hy pot' e nuse: The diagonal which joins the sides of a right triangle; the side opposite the right angle of a right triangle.

HYPOXIA (space) hy pox' i a: Oxygen deficiency in the blood, cells or tissue of the body.

HYSTERESIS (elec.) hys ter e' sis: The property of a magnetic substance that causes the magnetization to lag behind the force that produces it.

HYSTERESIS LOOP (elec.) hys ter e'-sis loop: A graph showing the density of a magnetic field as the magnetizing force is varied uniformly through one cycle of alternating current.

HYSTERESIS LOSS (elec.) hys ter e' sis loss: The energy loss in a substance as molecules or domains move through a cycle of magnetization. Loss due to molecular friction.

I-BEAM (const.) I - beam: A steel beam shaped like the letter I.

ICE BOX (air cond.) ice box: A refrigerator using ice as a cooling mechanism.

ICE POINT (air cond.) ice point: The temperature at which water freezes under normal pressure.

ICING (auto.) ic' ing: Ice formed in the carburetor as a result of rapid vaporization of fuel, which lowers the temperature sufficiently to cause the moisture in the air to freeze.

ICONOSCOPE (elec.) i con' o scope: A camera tube used in television in which the scene is focused on a mosaic plate of photo sensitive cells. An electron gun scans the mosaic with an electron beam and converts picture information into electrical signals.

I DEMODULATOR (elec.) I de mod' u-la tor: In color TV, it is the demodulator which converts one of the two quadrature chrominance carriers into an I subcarrier.

IDLE CIRCUIT (auto.) i' dle cir' cuit: The passages and valves in a carburetor which supply air-fuel mixture to the engine when the throttle is closed.

IDLER GEAR (metal) i' dler gear: A gear placed between the driving and driven gear in a gear chain. The idler changes the direction of rotation of the driven gear.

IDLING JET (auto.) i' dling jet: A jet in the carburetor which controls the gasoline to the engine during idle speeds.

IF AMPLIFIER (elec.) IF am' pli fi er: An intermediate frequency amplifier.

IFF (elec.) iff: Identification Friend or Foe. Used in radar. System of identifying approaching targets.

IGNITER (space) ig ni' ter: A device used to start combustion or ignite the fuel in a rocket.

IGNITION COIL (elec.) ig ni' tion coil: An induction coil used in the automotive ignition system to produce high voltages required for spark plugs.

IGNITION DISTRIBUTOR (elec.) ig ni'- tion dis trib' u tor: A rotating switch device to connect the high voltage to the correct spark plug at the proper time in the automotive engine.

IGNITION POINTS (elec.) ig ni' tion points: The points in the breaker which open the primary circuit of the ignition coil at the proper instant to produce a high voltage for ignition.

IGNITION SYSTEM (elec.) ig ni' tion sys' tem: The complete group of components making up the high tension ignition in an automotive engine. Components include the battery, ignition coil, breaker points, distributor, spark plugs and connecting wires.

IGNITRON (elec.) ig ni' tron: A heavy duty mercury arc rectifier tube.

I-HEAD ENGINE (auto.) I-head en' gine: Commonly called the overhead valve engine. Valves are located in line in the engine head and operated by push rods and rocker arms.

IMAGE (elec.) im' age: The electronically reproduced picture produced on the TV screen.

IMAGE FREQUENCY (elec.) im' age fre' quen cy: In the superheterodyne receiver, it is the undesired incoming signal which will beat with the local oscillator and produce the same IF as the desired signal. The image frequency is equal to the desired incoming signal plus two times the IF frequency.

IMAGE ORTHICON (elec.) im' age or' thi con: A TV camera tube, employing an image section, a scanning section and an electron multiplier. The optical image is converted into an electrical charge on a target plate which is scanned by an electron beam.

IMPACT AREA (space) im pact' ar'- ea: The area in which a rocket strikes the Earth's surface.

IMPASTO (paint. and dec.) im pas' to: Thick application of pigment to canvas or other surface, which makes the painting stand out in bold relief.

IMPEDANCE (Z) (elec.) im ped' ance: The total resistance to the flow of an a-c current as a result of resistance and reactance.

IMPEDANCE MATCHING (elec.) im- ped' ance match' ing: Sometimes called Z match; the matching of two different impedances to obtain maximum transfer of power.

IMPERIAL GALLON (paint. and dec.) im pe 'ri al gal' lon: Unit of volume measure used in Great Britain and Canada. It contains 277.42 cubic inches and weighs 10 pounds; compared with U.S. gallon of 231 cubic inches and 8.33 pounds in weight.

IMPOSING STONE (graphics) im pos' ing stone: The stone on which compositors impose type matter and lock it up in chases.

IMPOSITION (graphics) im po si' tion: The arrangement of forms in proper order on the stone, and the locking them in the chase, ready for the press.

IMPRESSED VOLTAGE (elec.) im pressed' volt' age: Any voltage applied to a device.

IMPRESSION (graphics) im pres' sion: The ink image, impressed upon the paper as it runs through the press.

IMPRINT (graphics) im' print: The name or trademark of a publisher.

IMPULSE (elec.) im' pulse: A sudden change in voltage or current.

IMPURITY (elec.) im pur' i ty: Atoms within a crystalline solid which are foreign to the crystal. See DONOR and ACCEPTOR IMPURITY.

INCANDESCENT (elec.) in can des' cent: Glowing due to heat.

INCANDESCENT LAMP (elec.) in can des' cent lamp: A lamp which gives light due to a filament glowing at a white heat.

INCISE (const.) in cise': To cut in; engrave; carve.

INCISE CUTTING (wood.) in cise' cut' ting: Cutting out spaces and curved

shapes inside the edge area of a piece of wood.

INCLINED (draft.) in clined': A line or plane at an angle to a horizontal line or plane.

INCLINOMETER (elec.) in cli nom' e-ter: A magnetic compass which rotates in a vertical plane, used to indicate the direction of the Earth's magnetic field.

INCLUSIONS (metal) in clu' sions: Slag and other foreign matter retained in finished steel.

INCREASER (plumb.) in creas' er: A pipe coupling used between pipes of different sizes.

INCREMENT (elec.) in' cre ment: A small change in a variable quantity.

INCREMENTAL INDUCTANCE (elec.) in cre men' tal in duct' ance: The net effective inductance of a coil with the d-c core saturation effect present.

INDENTATION (wood.) in den ta' tion: A zigzag furniture molding.

INDENTED (const.) in dent' ed: Toothed; notched.

INDEX (automation) in' dex: The point at which a specific action is desired.

INDEX (metal) in' dex: The process of moving work any desired amount on its axis.

INDEXING CENTER (metal) in' dex ing cen' ter: See DIVIDING HEAD.

INDIA INK (draft.) in' di a ink: A free flowing waterproof black ink used in drafting.

INDIAN RED (paint. and dec.) in' di an red: Red pigment made artificially by calcining copperas. Has excellent permanency, is non-bleeding, alkali and acid fast.

INDICATED HORSEPOWER (auto.) in' di ca ted horse' power: The power developed inside the internal combustion engine as a result of the combustion of fuel and air.

INDIRECT LIGHTING (elec.) in di rect' light' ing: Light directed toward a wall or ceiling having a light colored surface. It is reflected and diffused into the room area to be lighted.

INDIRECTLY HEATED (elec.) in directly heat' ed: An electron tube employing a separate heater for its cathode.

INDIUM (elec.) in' di um: A rare, lustrous, white, soft and ductile metal. Used in doping semi-conductors materials.

INDUCED CURRENT (elec.) in duced' cur' rent: The current that flows as the result of an induced emf.

INDUCED EMF (elec.) in duced' emf: Voltage induced in a conductor as it moves through a magnetic field.

INDUCTANCE (elec.) in duct' ance: The inherent property of an electric circuit that opposes a change in current. The property of a circuit whereby energy may be stored in a magnetic field.

INDUCTANCE, MUTUAL (elec.) in duct' ance, mu' tu al: See MUTUAL INDUCTANCE.

INDUCTION BAKING (paint. and dec.) in duc' tion bak' ing: Using heat induced by electrostatic and electromagnetic means for baking of finishes.

INDUCTION HEATING (metal) in-

duc' tion heat' ing: The process of heating steel by electric induction. Heat is produced by high frequency currents within the metal.

INDUCTION MOTOR (elec.) in duc' tion mo' tor: An a-c motor operating on the principle of a rotating magnetic field produced by out-of-phase currents. The rotor has no electrical connections, but receives energy by transformer action from the field windings. Motor torque is developed by the interaction of rotor current and the rotating field.

INDUCTIVE CIRCUIT (elec.) in duc' tive cir' cuit: A circuit in which an appreciable emf is induced while the current is changing.

INDUCTIVE COUPLING (elec.) in duc' tive cou' pling: The coupling between two circuits by means of induction.

INDUCTIVE LOAD (elec.) in duc' tive load: A load connected to an alternating current source which causes the current to lag behind the voltage.

INDUCTIVE REACTANCE (X_L) (elec.) in duc' tive re act' ance: The opposition to an a-c current as a result of inductance.

INDUCTOR (elec.) in duc' tor: A coil; a component with the properties of inductance.

INDUSTRIAL AUTOMATION (automation) in dus' tri al au to ma' tion: The automatic manufacturing of goods and products.

INDUSTRIAL CONTROLLER (automation) in dus' tri al con trol' ler: A manually operated control device.

INERT (paint. and dec.) in ert': Chemically inactive.

INERT GAS (air cond.) in ert' gas: A gas which undergoes no change when mixed with a volatile refrigerant.

INERT GAS ARC WELDING (weld.) in-ert' gas arc weld' ing: Surrounding the arc with a gas which does not react with the electrode and base metal and keeps the atmosphere away from the arc.

INERTIA (auto.) in er' tia: The property of all bodies to resist movement, change of speed or direction.

INERTIAL FORCE (space) in er' tial force: The force produced by the re-action of a body to an accelerating force, equal in magnitude and opposite in direction to the accelerating force. Inertial force endures only so long as the accelerating force endures.

INERTIAL GUIDANCE (space) in er' tial guid' ance: An automatic navigation system using gyroscopic devices, etc. for high speed aircraft, missiles, and spacecraft which absorbs and interprets such data as speed, position, etc. and automatically adjusts the vehicle to a predetermined flight path.

INFILTRATION (air cond.) in fil-tra' tion: The inward flow of air through a porous wall, crack or leak.

INFINITE IMPEDANCE (elec.) in' fi-nite im ped' ance: An extremely high impedance; in the order of several million megohms.

INFINITE IMPEDANCE DETECTOR (elec.) in' fi nite im ped' ance de tec'-tor: A detector, usually biased near cutoff, whose output is taken from across the cathode resistor, like a cathode follower circuit. It has a high input impedance, since the grid is never driven positive.

INFORMATION (elec.) in for ma' tion: The intelligence in a radio or TV signal, such as picture information.

INFRARED (elec.) in fra red': Invisible part of spectrum between radio waves and red portion of visible spectrum.

INFRARED GUIDANCE (space) in fra-red' guid' ance: A system for recon-naissance of targets and navigation using infrared heat sources.

INFRARED HEATING in fra red' heat'-ing: Heating by a focused high intensity infrared heat. Used for baking and drying.

INFRARED RAYS (weld.) in fra red' rays: Heat rays which emanate from both the arc and the welding flame.

INFRASONIC (elec.) in fra son' ic: Sound frequencies beyond the audio frequency range.

INGOT (metal) in' got: The first solid form which steel takes after leaving the furnace, usually large rectangular blocks.

INHIBITOR (space) in hib' i tor: A sub-stance bonded, taped or dip-dried onto a solid propellant to restrict the burn-ing surface and to give direction to the burning process.

INHIBITORS (auto.) in hib' i tors: Addi-tives to oil to retard deterioration.

INITIAL (graphics) ini' tial: A large letter used at the beginning of a text division or a paragraph.

INJECTION MOLDING in jec' tion mold' ing: A molding process used by the plastics industries, in which heat softened plastic is forced into cool mold of the desired shape.

INK (graphics) ink: A combination of pigment, varnish and driers used in printing.

INK BALLS (graphics) ink balls: A leather ball stuffed with cotton and formerly used for inking forms.

INKING IN (draft.) ink' ing in: Applying ink to a drawing.

INK KNIFE (graphics) ink knife: A thin flexible blade used for mixing inks.

INLAY (const.) in lay': The setting into a prepared recess in a base material; a piece of wood or metal for ornamental purposes.

INLET (air cond.) in' let: The suction or inlet side of a pump or compressor.

IN-LINE ENGINE (auto.) in-line en'-gine: An engine with cylinders arranged in a straight line.

INORGANIC (paint. and dec.) in-or gan' ic: Composed of matter other than vegetable or animal.

INORGANIC COLORS (paint. and dec.) in or gan' ic col' ors: Chemical colors obtained by combining two or more inorganic chemicals.

IN PHASE (elec.) in phase: Two waves of the same frequency are in phase when they pass through their maximum and minimum values at the same instant with the same polarity.

INPUT (automation) in' put: Information from any source, man, machine, process, or product fed into a machine.

INPUT (elec.) in' put: The power or signal delivered to a device or circuit.

INPUT ELEMENT (elec.) in' put el' e-ment: The section of a computer that provides the information to be processed. Information may be on punched card, tapes or typewriter, etc.

INPUT IMPEDANCE (elec.) in' put im-ped' ance: The impedance of the input terminals of a circuit or device, with the input generator disconnected.

INSCRIBE (draft.) in scribe': To draw a geometrical figure inside another figure.

INSERTED TOOTH CUTTER (metal) in-sert' ed tooth cut' ter: A milling cutter with removable teeth of high speed steel, mounted in a steel blank.

INSERTING (automation) in sert' ing: An assembly operation where a smaller part is inserted into a major part. One part acts as the carrier of the other on the assembly line.

INSERTION LOSS (elec.) in ser' tion loss: Loss in a transmission system as the result of inserting some device or apparatus. It is usually expressed in db.

INSIDE CORNER WELD (weld.) in' side cor' ner weld: Two metals fused together; one metal is held 90 deg. to the other. The fusion is performed inside the vertex of the angle.

INSPECTION (automation) in spec' tion: The examination of a piece of work for defects, errors and flaws. Its purpose is to cull out unsatisfactory pieces and prevent the production of unsatisfactory pieces.

INSTANTANEOUS VALUE (elec.) in-stan ta' ne ous val' ue: Any value between zero and maximum depending upon the instant selected.

INSTRUMENTATION (automation) in-

stru men ta' tion: The sensing and
display of pertinent information.

INSULATE (const.) in' su late: To use
necessary materials in a building structure to prevent the passage of heat,
cold and sound.

INSULATING VARNISH (paint. and dec.)
in su lat' ing var' nish: A varnish
especially designed for the electrical
insulation of wires, coils and electrical
appliances.

INSULATION (air cond.) in su la' tion:

  SOUND, The treatment of a room or
compartment to inhibit the emission or
transmission of sound.

  THERMAL ,The treatment of a room
or compartment to minimize the flow of
heat; the material used to resist the
flow of heat.

INSULATION (elec.) in su la' tion: Materials which are poor conductors of
electricity used to cover wires and
components to prevent short circuits
and accidental shock hazards.

INSULATION RESISTANCE (elec.) in-
su la' tion re sis' tance: The resistance to current leakage through and
over the surface of insulating material.

INSULATORS (e l e c .) in su la' tors:
Substances containing very few free
electrons and requiring large amounts
of energy to break electrons loose from
the influence of the nucleus.

INSULET (elec.) in' su let: A conduit
fitting for a horizontal service entrance.

INTAGLIO (crafts) in ta' glio: A design,
figure or pattern cut into the material.

INTAGLIO (graphics) in ta' glio: Any

engraved surface where the design is
cut into the metal.

INTAKE SILENCER (auto.)   in' take
si' lenc er: A drum-like container
attached to the air intake of a carburetor, containing nonflammable filter
material and frequently an oil bath.
The device cleans the air entering the
carburetor and muffles disturbing
noises.

INTAKE STROKE (auto.) in' take stroke:
The downward stroke of the piston
during which the air-fuel mixture is
drawn into the cylinder.

INTAKE VALVE (auto.) in' take valve:
Valve in the intake port of cylinder.

INTARSIA (wood.) in tar' si a: A form
of inlaying in which the design is sawed
in wood or metal and glued into a
corresponding recess cut in a solid
piece of wood.

INTEGRATOR CIRCUIT (elec.) in' te-
gra tor cir' cuit: A wave forming cir-

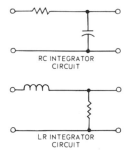

RC INTEGRATOR
CIRCUIT

LR INTEGRATOR
CIRCUIT

cuit with a long time constant, the output of which represents the average
energy content of the input signal.

INTENSE COLOR (paint. and dec.) intense' col' or: A strong vivid color

INTENSITY (H)(elec.) in ten' si ty: Th
magnetizing force per unit length o
magnetic circuit; the level of sound
the value of current.

INTERCARRIER SOUND (elec.) in ter-car'ri er sound: In a TV receiver it is a method of using the same IF amplifiers for both sound and picture information. The picture IF and associated sound IF beat together to produce the sound IF frequency.

INTERCEPTOR (plumb.) in ter-cep'tor: A type of trap designed to prevent passage of such substances as oil and grease into the sewer.

INTERCOM (elec.) in'ter com: A term used to describe an audio communication system between several locations such as between offices in a factory or business.

INTERCONTINENTAL BALLISTIC MIS-SILE (ICBM) (space) in ter con-ti nen'tal bal lis'tic mis'sile: A ballistic missile with sufficient range to strike at strategic targets from one continent to another.

INTERELECTRODE CAPACITANCE (elec.) in ter e lec'trode ca pac'i-tance: Capacitance between the metal elements in an electron tube.

INTERFERENCE (elec.) in ter-fer'ence: Any disturbance interferring with the reception of signals.

INTERFEROMETER (metal) in ter fer-om'e ter: A direct measuring instrument which measures distances in terms of wave lengths of light.

INTERGALACTIC SPACE (space) in-ter ga lac'tic space: That part of space conceived as having its lower limit at the upper limit of interstellar space and extending to the limits of space.

INTERLACE SCANNING (elec.) in ter-lace' scan'ning: The process in tele-vision of scanning all odd lines and then all even lines to reproduce picture. Used in the United States.

INTERLOCK (elec.) in ter lock': A safety switch on doors of cabinets containing high voltages. If door is opened, the high voltage circuits are disabled.

INTERMEDIATE FREQUENCY (elec.) in ter me'di ate fre'quen cy: The difference frequency obtained by beat-ing the incoming signal against the local oscillator frequency.

INTERMITTENT WELD (weld.) in ter-mit'tent weld: Joining two pieces and leaving unwelded sections in the joint.

INTERMODULATION (elec.) in ter-mod u la'tion: The modulation of one complex wave by another, producing complex waves representing the sum and difference frequencies.

INTERNAL COMBUSTION (auto.) in-ter'nal com bus'tion: An engine which develops power through the expansive force of a fuel which is fired in a closed chamber or cylinder.

INTERNAL RESISTANCE (elec.) in ter'-nal re sis'tance: Refers to the internal resistance of the source of voltage or emf. A battery or generator has internal resistance which may be represented as a resistor in series with the source.

INTERNAL THREAD (metal) in ter'nal thread: The thread on the inside of a part.

INTERNATIONAL MORSE CODE (elec.) in ter na'tion al morse code: See MORSE CODE.

INTERPLANETARY SPACE (space) in-ter plan'e ta ry space: That part of space conceived from the standpoint of the Earth, to have its lower limit at the upper limit of translunar space, and extending to beyond the limits of the solar system, some several billion miles.

INTERPOLES (elec.) in' ter poles: Auxillary poles located midway between the main poles of a generator to establish a flux for satisfactory commutation.

INTERRUPTED CONTINUOUS WAVE (ICW) (elec.) in ter rupt' ed con tin'- u ous wave: A continuous wave radiated by keying the transmitter into long and short pulses of energy (dashes and dots) conforming to a code such as the Morse Code.

INTERRUPTER (elec.) in ter rupt' er: A switching device which opens and closes a circuit many times per second.

INTERSTAGE (e l e c.) in ter' stage: Existing between stages, such as an interstage transformer between two stages of amplifiers.

INTERSTELLAR FLIGHT (space) inter stel' lar flight: Flight between stars, strictly between orbits around the stars.

INTRINSIC SEMICONDUCTOR (e l e c.) in trin' sic sem' i con duc' tor: A semiconductor with electrical characteristics similar to a pure crystal.

INVAR (elec.) in var': An alloy of steel and nickel used as resistance material.

INVAR (metal) in var': A nickel alloy which possesses a low coefficient of expansion at room temperatures.

INVERSE FEEDBACK (elec.) in verse' feed' back: S e e DEGENERATIVE FEEDBACK.

INVERSE PEAK VOLTAGE (elec.) inverse' peak volt' age: The highest

negative instantaneous peak voltage that can be applied to the plate of an electron tube without damage to the tube.

INVERSE SQUARE LAW (e l e c.) in verse' square law: The law by which a physical quantity decreases in value as the square of the distance. Ex: Illumination decreases in intensity as the square of the distance from the source.

INVERT (plumb.) in vert': The lowest part of the inside of a horizontal pipe.

INVERTED JOINT (plumb.) in vert' ed joint: A fitting installed upside down.

INVERTED SPEECH (elec.) in vert' ed speech: Scrambled speech to provide security. Speech is made unintelligible by inverting the frequencies. At the receiving end the frequencies are again inverted into intelligence.

INVERTER (elec.) in vert' er: An electromechanical system for changing direct current to alternating current.

INVISIBLE LINE (draft.) in vis' i ble line: A dotted line used to represent hidden surfaces and intersections on a drawing.

INVOLUTE (draft.) in' vo lute: A spiral curve generated by a point on a chord as it unwinds from a circle or a polygon.

IODINE NUMBER (paint. and dec.) i' o- dine num' ber: A means of identifying and specifying qualities of oils, resins and waxes, based on the fact that different qualities of these products will absorb different quantities of iodine.

ION (elec.) i' on: An atom which has lost or gained some electrons. It may be positive or negative depending on the net charge.

ION ENGINE (space) i' on en' gine: A type of engine in which the thrust to propel the missile or spacecraft is obtained from a stream of ionized atomic particles, generated by atomic fusion, fission, or solar energy.

IONIC (graphics) i on' ic: A type face.

IONIC VALENCE BOND (elec.) i on' ic va' lence bond: Atoms joined together so that electrons in the outer ring of one atom contribute their electrons to the outer ring of another atom. Example: hydrogen and oxygen combine to form water.

IONIZATION (elec.) i on i za' tion: An atom is said to be ionized when it has lost or gained one or more electrons.

IONIZATION (paint. and dec.) i on i-za' tion: Breaking up of molecules into two or more oppositely charged ions.

IONIZATION POTENTIAL (elec.) i on-i za' tion po ten' tial: The voltage applied to a gas filled tube at which ionization occurs.

IONOSPHERE (elec.) i on' o sphere: An atmospheric layer from 40 to 350 miles above the earth, containing a high number of positive and negative ions.

ION SPOT (elec.) i' on spot: A brown spot formed at the center of a picture tube as a result of ion bombardment.

ION TRAP (elec.) i' on trap: A fixed magnet placed around the neck of a picture tube to prevent ions from reaching the screen.

IR DROP (elec.): See VOLTAGE DROP.

I^2R LOSS (elec.): The loss in a line due to current and resistance. The loss is heat.

IRON BLUE (paint. and dec.) iron blue: Blue pigment which depends on iron content to provide blue color.

IRON DRIERS (paint. and dec.) iron dri' ers: Dark brown in color and have high tinting strength which limits use to colored finishes.

IRON OXIDE (paint. and dec.) iron ox'-ide: Iron oxide is available in three forms: red, brown and yellow. It is sold under a variety of names, such as Red Oxide, Jeweler's Rouge, Venetian Red, Ferric Oxide, Indian Red, Red Ochre, Mineral Rouge, Spanish Oxide, Turkey Red, etc.

IRON (Symbol Fe.) (metal) iron: The most important of all metallic elements for the industrial world. It is marketed in many forms, types and alloys. It is the basic part of steel.

IRON-CORE INDUCTOR (elec.) iron-core in duc' tor: An inductor wound on an iron core.

IRON VANE METER (elec.) iron vane me' ter: A meter based on the principle of repulsion between two concentric vanes placed inside a solenoid.

IRRADIATION (air cond.) ir ra di a'-tion: The exposure of food to radiation in order to kill certain bacteria.

IRREGULAR CURVE (draft.) ir reg' u-lar curve: A flat plastic guide for drawing irregular curves and arcs.

IRREGULAR CURVES

ISENTROPIC (air cond.) is en trop' ic: Describing a reversible adiabatic process.

I-SIGNAL (elec.) i-sig'nal: In TV. The color TV signal containing the orange or cyan picture information.

ISO (air cond.) i'so: A Greek prefix meaning the same or at a constant value; identical; equal.

ISOBARIC (air cond.) i so bar'ic: A change taking place at a constant pressure.

ISOCLINIC LINE (elec.) i so clin'ic line: An imaginary line around the earth, all points on which have the same magnetic inclination or dip.

ISOGONIC LINE (elec.) i so gon'ic line: An imaginary line around the earth all points on which have the same declination.

ISOMETRIC PAPER (draft.) i so met'ric pa'per: Specially ruled paper with isometric guide lines for isometric sketching.

ISOMETRIC PROJECTION (draft.) i so met'ric pro jec'tion: An object so drawn that its principle edges or axes make equal angles with the plane of projection and are therefore foreshortened equally.

ISO-OCTANE (auto.) i'so-oc'tane: A high anti-knock fuel used as a reference fuel in performing anti-knock tests.

ISOTHERMAL (air cond.) i so ther'mal: A change taking place at a constant temperature.

ISOTROPIC (elec.) i so trop'ic: Having the same properties in all directions.

ITALIC (graphics) i tal'ic: A sloping style of type originally designed by Aldus Manutius and named in honor of Italy.

ITALIC QUADS (graphics) i tal'ic quads: To send an apprentice for "Italic quads" is a joke.

IVORY BLACK (paint. and dec.) i'vo ry black: A high grade bone black pigment. Its name is accounted for by the fact that it was formerly made by charring or burning ivory.

IZOD (metal) i'zod: An impact testing machine, where one end of a sample is supported in a vise in a vertical position, and the opposite end is struck by a pendulum hammer.

JACK (const.) jack: A mechanical device to multiply lifting force.

JACK (elec.) jack: A plug-in device for connecting headphones, microphones, etc. Many jacks have multiple connections and contain switches which are operated when the plug is inserted.

JACK ARCH (const.) jack arch: An ordinary flat arch.

JACK PLANE (wood.) jack plane: An all purpose plane, usually about 14" long.

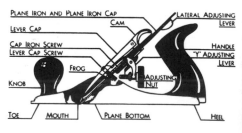

JACK RAFTER (const.) jack raft'er: A short rafter extending from the wallplate to a hip or from valley rafter to the ridge.

JACOBS CHUCK (metal) ja'cobs chuck: An automatic three jaw chuck used for holding drills and cutting tools. The chuck is tightened by using a special gear type key.

JAMB (const.) jamb: The vertical parts of a door frame.

JAMMING (elec.) jam' ming: Intentional interference with radio signals.

JAM NUT jam nut: A lock nut; a nut tightened against another nut to lock it in place.

JAN (elec.) jan: JOINT ARMY NAVY.

JAPAN (paint. and dec.) ja pan': A drying agent used in paint.

JAPAN COLOR (paint. and dec.) ja pan' col' or: Colored paste made by grinding high-quality colors in hard drying varnish.

JAPAN DRYER (paint. and dec.) ja pan' dry' er: Varnish gum with a large proportion of metallic (lead, cobalt, manganese, etc.) salts added to hasten drying.

JAPANESE LACQUER (paint. and dec.) jap a nese' lac' quer: Varnish made from sap of a tree which grows in Japan. Lacquer becomes very hard and black as it dries.

JARNO SYSTEM (metal) jar' no sys'-tem: A system of dimensioning tapers by diameters and length. The taper is .6 inch per foot in all sizes.

JERK (space) jerk: A vector denoting the time rate of change of an acceleration.

JET (auto.) jet: A hole or orifice of a specific size to limit the flow of fuel in a carburetor.

JET (graphics) jet: A small projection

on the bottom of type as it comes from the mold.

JET AIRCRAFT (space) jet air' craft: A vehicle which breathes air and is propelled by the thrust of exhaust gases.

JETAVATOR (space) jet a va' tor: A control surface that may be moved into or against a rocket's jet stream, used to change the direction of the jet flow.

JET ENGINE (space) jet en' gine: A reaction engine that takes in air from outside as an oxidizer to burn fuel and ejects a jet of hot gases backward to create thrust, the gases being generated by the combustion within the engine.

JET STEERING (space) jet steer' ing: The use of fixed or movable jets on a space vehicle to steer it along a desired trajectory.

JET STREAM (space) jet stream: The stream of gas or fluid expelled by any reaction device, especially the stream of combustion products expelled from a jet engine or rocket motor; a narrow band of high velocity wind especially near the base of the stratosphere.

JEWEL BEARING (elec.) jew' el bear' ing: Bearings used in precision instruments.

JEWELER'S SAW (crafts) jew' el er's saw: A fine hand operated saw, similar to a coping saw, but using a thin blade suitable for cutting metals.

JIB (const.) jib: The swinging boom of a crane.

JIG (metal) jig: A device that holds the work and guides the tool during cutting operations.

JIG BORER (metal) jig bor' er: A special vertical spindle milling machine for very accurate boring and drilling.

JIG GRINDER (metal) jig grind'er: Similar to a jig borer, but uses a grinding wheel as a high speed cutter.

JIG SAW (wood.) jig saw: A wood working machine for cutting intricate curves such as found in a jigsaw puzzle. Cutting is done by the up and down motion of a fine saw blade suspended between two chucks. The lower chuck is driven by cam or crank action.

JIMMY (wood.) jim'my: A short crowbar.

JOB (automation) job: A group of related operations, usually performed at one station.

JOB INK (graphics) job ink: Ink used on the job press.

JO BLOCKS (metal) jo blocks: Precisely made steel blocks used by industry as standard of measurement.

JOB PRESS (graphics) job press: Any printing press used for job printing. Now includes small cylinder presses as well as platen presses.

JOB PRINTING (graphics) job print'ing: Small scale printing operation.

JOB SHOP job shop: The shop in which short runs of products or parts are made. General purpose machines are used and precision is not as great as in the toolroom. Machines are arranged by operation, rather than any consideration of flow of production.

JOG (graphics) jog: To straighten the edges of a pile of sheets of paper.

JOINER (const.) join'er: A V-shaped

tool used to compress and finish mortar joints.

JOINERY (wood.) join'er y: The art or trade related to the joining of wood by various joints.

JOINT (const.) joint: The act of fitting materials together; the point at which parts are joined together.

JOINT (wood.) joint: Method of fastening wood parts together. See crosslap, finger, etc., for illustrations.

JOINT (weld.) joint: A connection between two pieces; the point or line between two pieces.

JOINT, UNIVERSAL joint, u ni ver'sal: A connection between two shafts which

permits movement in any direction and still conveys a positive motion.

JOINTER (wood.) joint'er: A power driven jointing plane with a rotary cutting head mounted in bearings at center of table. Work, supported by fence and table, is fed into rotary cutter. Is used for smoothing surfaces and straightening edges of boards. See illustration, page 191.

JOINTER PLANE (wood.) joint'er plane: A plane, usually 20-24 in. long, for planing very long edges of boards.

JOINTING (const.) joint'ing: The finishing of exterior mortar joints between brick or stone.

JOINT RUNNER (plumb.) joint run'ner: An incombustible type of packing which is placed around a joint to hold the molten lead in place until solidified.

JOIST HANGER (const.) joist hang' er: A metal strap or stirrup used to suspend floor joists.

JOISTS (const.) joists: Horizontal wood or metal beams used for the support of floors and ceilings.

J OPERATOR (J) (elec.) J op' er a tor: An imaginary number used to indicate the square root of a negative number. +J indicates 90° rotation of a vector in a counterclockwise direction. -J indicates 90° rotation in a clockwise direction.

JOULE (elec.) joule: Unit of energy equal to one watt-second.

JOULE, JAMES PRESCOTT (1818-1889) (elec.): This English scientist began his life's work as a brewer. His interest in electricity led to many fundamental discoveries. He is remembered by his studies determining the equivalence of heat and work.

JOURNAL (auto.) jour' nal: The part of a shaft which rotates within the bearing.

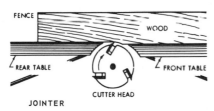

JOINTER

JOURNEYMAN jour' ney man: A tradesman who has served his apprenticeship and is qualified to perform the skills of his trade.

JOURNEYMAN PAINTER (paint. and dec.) jour' ney man paint' er: One who has had at least three years experience and schooling as an apprentice.

JUMPER (elec.) jum' per: A short wire, usually with clips on each end, for making temporary connections.

JUNCTION (elec.) junc' tion: The region in a semiconductor between a P and an N crystal; the region formed by alloying an impurity to a semiconductor crystal.

JUNCTION BOX (elec.) junc' tion box: A metal box in which connections of several wires are made; a distribution box.

JUNCTION DIODE (elec.) junc' tion di' ode: A PN junction, having unidirectional current characteristics.

JUNCTION TRANSISTOR (elec.) junc'-tion tran sis' tor: A transistor consisting of a thin layer of N or P type crystal between P or N type crystals. Designated as NPN or PNP.

JUSTIFICATION (graphics) just i fi-ca' tion: To make a line fit a given measure.

JUXTAPOSITION OF COLORS (paint. and dec.) jux ta po si' tion of col' ors: Placing colors side by side, or close together. Complementary colors such as blue and orange in juxtaposition accentuate each other.

KALSOMINE (paint. and dec.) kal' so-mine: Another name for Calcimine.

KAOLIN (crafts) ka' o lin: Clay used in making porcelain.

KAOLIN (paint. and dec.) ka' o lin: Inert pigment, which tends to impart easy brushing properties to paint products in which it is used; a fine white clay used to make porcelain.

KAOLINITE (paint. and dec.) ka' o lin-ite: Hydrous aluminum silicate.

KAPOK ka' pok: A fibre from a tropical tree used as a filler for pillows and mattresses.

KARAT (crafts.) kar' at: One twenty-fourth of a troy pound. Used as a means to express the proportion of pure gold contained in an alloy.

KAURI GUM (paint. and dec.) kau' ri gum: A fossil copal found in New Zealand.

KEEPER (elec.) keep' er: A soft iron bar placed across the poles of a permanent magnet to preserve its magnetism.

KELVIN DEGREES (elec.) kel' vin degrees': A temperature scale which starts at absolute zero (-273.16° C.).

KENNELLY-HEAVISIDE LAYER (elec.): See HEAVISIDE LAYER.

KERN (graphics) kern: The part of the face of type which projects beyond the body.

KERF (wood.) kerf: A cut made by a saw.

KEROSENE (paint. and dec.) ker' o sene: A distillate obtained in petroleum refining, which evaporates slowly.

KETTLE BODIED OIL (paint. and dec.) ket' tle bod' ied oil: Oil which has been held at an elevated temperature until the oil has thickened.

KEY (elec.) key: A manually operated switch used to interrupt the r-f radiation of a transmitter; a manually operated lever type switch used in sending code signals in telegraphy or radio communication.

KEY (metal) key: A rectangular piece of metal, used to positively fasten a pulley or gear to a shaft.

KEY CLICK FILTER (elec.) key click fil' ter: A filter in the keying circuit of a transmitter to prevent surges of current and prevent sparking at the key contacts.

KEYHOLE SAW (wood.) key' hole saw: A saw similar to a compass saw with a thinner blade. Used for small internal cut-outs.

KEYING (elec.) key' ing: The process of causing a cw transmitter to radiate an rf signal when the key contacts are closed.

KEYING, SYSTEMS OF (elec.)

CATHODE, The key is inserted in the grid and cathode circuits of the keyed stage.

GRID-BLOCK, Keying a stage by applying a high negative voltage on the grid of the tube.

PLATE, The key is inserted in the plate circuit of the stage to be keyed.

KEY PLATE (graphics) key plate: Any plate used as a guide to get other plates into register.

KEYSTONE (const.) key' stone: The stone placed in the center of an arch.

KEYSTONE DISTORTION (elec.) key'-stone dis tor' tion: In TV, a distortion which causes the picture to be trapezoidal in shape.

KEYWAY (metal) key' way: The groove in the shaft or in the hole of a gear or pulley, to fit the key.

KICK (elec.) kick: In television, it is the name of an unwanted light from some reflecting surface.

KILN (crafts.) kiln: A furnace for firing.

KILN DRY (wood.) kiln dry: A method of artificially curing lumber by saturating it uniformly in a steam chamber and then drying it by heat for a specified time.

KILN DRYING (paint. and dec.) kiln dry' ing: Drying of wood, paint, varnish or lacquer in room or compartment with heat and humidity regulated.

KILO (elec.) kil' o: Prefix meaning one thousand times. Ex: Ten kilohms means ten thousand ohms.

KILOCYCLE (elec.) kil' o cy cle: One thousand cycles.

KILOGAUSS (elec.) kil' o gauss: One thousand gausses.

KILOGRAM kil' o gram: One thousand grams; 2.204 pounds.

KILOMETER (auto.) kil' o meter: A unit in the metric system of measurement. It is equal to 5/8 of a mile.

KILOWATT (elec.) kil' o watt: One thousand watts.

KILOWATT-HOUR (kwh) (elec.) kil' o-watt-hour: Means 1000 watts per hour. Common unit of measurement of electrical energy for home and industrial use. Power is priced by the kwh.

KINESCOPE (elec.) kin' e scope: The image reproducing tube in the television receiver. Sometimes called the "picture tube."

KINESCOPE RECORDING (elec.) kin' e-scope re cord' ing: The recording of a program from a monitor kinescope on film with sound track, for playback at a later date.

KINETIC ENERGY ki net' ic en' er gy: Energy possessed by a moving body as a result of its motion.

KINGPIN (auto.) king' pin: A steel pin used to fasten and support the steering knuckle to the axle in the front end of an automobile. The pin permits free right and left movement of the front wheels.

KINGPIN INCLINATION (auto.) king' pin in cli na' tion: The tilt from vertical of the kingpins in the front wheel suspension of an automobile.

KING POST (const.) king post: A central upright support for the tie beam to which the rafters of a roof are fastened.

KINK kink: A short cut or unusual method of doing some shop work.

KIRCHHOFF'S CURRENT LAW (elec.) kich' hoff's cur' rent law: At any junction of conductors in a circuit, the algebraic sum of the currents is zero.

KIRCHHOFF'S LAW OF VOLTAGES (elec.) kirch' hoff's law of volt' ages: In a simple circuit, the algebraic sum of the voltages around a circuit is equal to zero.

KLYSTRON (elec.) klys' tron: A high frequency vacuum tube employing a cathode, control grid, single-cavity resonator with buncher grids and a repeller electrode.

KNIFE knife: A cutting tool consisting of a handle to which is attached a blade with a sharp cutting edge.

KNIFE SWITCH (elec.) knife switch: A manually operated switch in which the circuit is opened or closed by a knife-like blade contacting and sliding into a metal slot.

KNOB (elec.) knob: A porcelain insulator and support for an electrical conductor; a form of handle for a control shaft.

KNOCK (auto.) knock: Rapping or pinging noises in an engine as a result of detonation of fuels under high compression.

KNOCKED DOWN knocked down: Abbreviated KD; complete in its various parts, but unassembled.

KNOCKING (auto.) knock' ing: Sounds from an engine resulting from broken or worn parts such as pistons, wrist pins, and bearings; sounds produced by premature detonation of fuel due to incorrect timing or improper fuel.

KNOCKOUT (elec.) knock' out: A partially punched hole in a metal box or panel, which may be easily removed by striking with a hammer.

KNOT (wood.) knot: An imperfection in wood caused by a branch off-shoot when the tree is growing; a nautical mile which equals 6080.27 ft. or 1.15 statue miles.

KNOTTING (wood.) knot' ting: The covering of knots in wood with a special compound such as shellac to prevent the knot from showing through on the painted surface.

KNUCKLE JOINT (metal) knuck' le joint: A joint between two shafts in which an eye on one shaft is engaged in a fork on the other. A pin through the joint holds them together.

KNURL (metal) knurl: The process of marking the surface of work by rolling depressions in the surface.

KNURLING TOOL (metal) knurl' ing tool: A tool used in a lathe to produce a knurled surface.

KRAFT (graphics) kraft: A strong, tough, natural colored paper.

KRAFT PAPER kraft pa' per: A strong brown paper used for wrapping.

KYANIZE (const.) ky' an ize: To impregnate wood with mercuric chloride to prevent decay.

LABOR-SAVING MATERIAL (graphics) la' bor-sav' ing ma ter' i al: Material cut or cast to regular pica lengths.

LAC (paint. and dec.) lac: A natural resin secreted by certain insects which live on the sap of trees in India and other Oriental countries. Marketed in various forms: seed lac, button lac, shellac.

LACEWOOD (wood.) lace' wood: Sometimes called the silky oak. It is a native of Australia. It is a decorative wood marked by small silky spots.

LACING (metal) lac' ing: Rawhide strips used to fasten the ends of a leather belt; the metal fasteners used to join leather belts.

LACQUER (paint. and dec.) lac' quer: Finishing material that dries by the evaporation of the thinner or solvent. There are many different types of lacquers, the most important being that based on cellulose nitrate. Besides the cellulosic compound, lacquers contain resins, placticizers, solvents, and diluents.

LACQUER FILM (graphics) lac' quer film: A lacquer coat film used for making stencils for silk screen work.

LADDER (wood.) lad' der: Two parallel uprights connected by evenly spaced rungs. It is an aid to climbing.

LADDER BACK (wood.) lad' der back:

A chair having horizontal slats in its back.

LADLE (metal) la'dle: A receptacle used for transporting and pouring molten metal.

LAG (elec.) lag: The amount, expressed in degrees, that one wave is behind another.

LAGGING ANGLE (elec.) lag'ging an'gle: The angle the current lags the voltage in an inductive circuit.

LAG SCREW (const.) lag screw: A heavy wood screw with a square head.

LAKE PIGMENT (paint. and dec.) lake pig'ment: Pigment made by putting an organic dye on a base of fine particles of inert or translucent pigment.

LAMBDA (elec.) lamb'da: Greek letter λ . Symbol for wavelength.

LAMINATED CONSTRUCTION (const.) lam'i nat ed con struc'tion: Built up in layers to secure maximum strength.

LAMINATIONS (elec.) lam i na'tions: Thin sheets of steel used in cores of transformers, motors and generators.

LAMP (elec.) lamp: An artificial source of light.

ARC, A lamp produced by an arc between two carbon electrodes.

BLACK LIGHT, Lamps which emit ultraviolet light.

FLUORESCENT, A lamp, usually tubular, which produces light by the ultraviolet radiation striking a phosphor coating on inside of light.

GLOW, A lamp consisting of two electrodes in a bulb of inert gas. Used as indicator light.

INCANDESCENT, A lamp which produces light by heat. Modern lamps use a tungsten filament in an evacuated bulb or in an inert gas.

MERCURY VAPOR, A lamp which produces light as a current flows through mercury vapor.

PILOT, An indicator light.

LAMPBLACK lamp'black: Finely divided carbon derived from burning gas or oil. It is used in paint, ink and rubber.

LAMPBLACK (paint. and dec.) lamp'black: a fine black soot produced by incomplete combustion of tars and oils and other forms of carbon. It is used as a pigment in paints.

LAMPHOLDER (elec.) lamp'hold er: A socket to hold an electric light bulb. They are made in a variety of types and sizes, with or without switches.

LANCE (metal) lance: An oxygen cutting tool consisting of a length of black pipe connected to a regulated supply of oxygen.

LAND (elec.) land: The surface on a record between adjacent grooves in mechanical recording.

LANDING (const.) land'ing: A platform in a flight of stairs or at the end of a stairway.

LANDING ROCKET (space) land'ing rock'et: A manned space vehicle operated to transfer passengers and cargo from a satellite or larger orbiting spacecraft to the surface of a planet.

LAP (metal) lap: Usually a soft material such as brass or lead charged with a fine cutting abrasive.

LAPIDARY (crafts.) lap' i dar y: The craft of gem cutting.

LAP JOINT (weld.) lap joint: A joint in which the edges of the two metals to be joined overlap one another.

LAP JOINT (wood.) lap joint: A joint made by cutting away one half of each

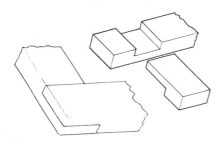

mating piece and lapping together so that surfaces are flush.

LAPPED JOINT (wallpaper) paint. and dec.) lapped joint: Joint made by trimming one selvedge and overlapping the other.

LAPPING (metal) lap' ping: The process of finishing a surface by using a lap.

LAP SIDING (const.) lap sid' ing: See BEVEL SIDING.

LARD OIL (metal) lard oil: An animal fat oil used as a cutting tool lubricant.

LARRY (metal) lar' ry: A long handled tool with a curved blade, used to mix hair into coarse plaster.

LASER (space) la' ser: Light Amplification by Stimulated Emission of Radiation. A device for producing light by emission of energy stored in a molecular or atomic system when stimulated by an input signal.

LATENT HEAT (air cond.) la' tent heat: See HEAT, LATENT.

LATERALS (const.) lat' er als: Diagonal bracing between members to increase rigidity.

LATEX (paint. and dec.) la' tex: A milky substance from some plants, usually white in color. It is a mixture of proteins, gums and carbohydrates; a milky viscous fluid extruded from rubber trees.

LATHE (metal) lathe: A machine tool which holds a piece of work between two rigid supports called centers or in a device such as a face plate or chuck. Spindle carrying work is rotated, while

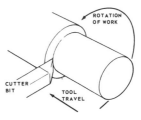

a cutting tool which is supported on a carriage which slides over the bed, is brought into contact with the work.

LATHE DOG (metal) lathe dog: A clamping device used to drive work in a lathe, by means of a faceplate. See illustration, page 197.

LATHE SHEARS (metal) lathe shears: The machine top of the lathe bed.

LATHS (const.) laths: Thin strips of wood nailed to wall studs to support plaster.

LATRINE (plumb.) la trine': A toilet consisting of a continuous trough of running water.

L – ATTENUATOR (elec.)L – at ten' u- a tor: Two gang controlled variable resistors connected one in parallel with the load and the other across the load so that the load voltage may be varied while maintaining a constant current through the source.

LATTICE (const.) lat' tice: Decorative work made by crossing thin strips of wood, laths or bars to form a network.

LAUNCH PAD (space) launch pad: A concrete or other hard surface area on which a missile launcher is positioned.

LAUNCHER (space) launch' er: A structural device designed to physically support and hold a missile in position for firing.

LAVATORY (plumb.) lav' a to ry: A sink fixture for washing hands and face.

LAWN (crafts) lawn: A fine mesh gauze used as a sieve for clay.

LAWS OF MAGNETISM (elec.) laws of mag' ne tism: Like poles repel; unlike poles attract.

LAY (draft.) lay: The predominate direction of tool marks on a surface.

LAYER (weld.) lay' er: The thickness of a weld made by a single pass of the welding torch.

LAYING OUT (draft.) lay' ing out: The process of marking out work to full size.

LAYOUT (draft.) lay' out: A working plan of a job.

LAYOUT BENCH (metal) lay' out bench: A bench with a flat level top design for layout work.

LC CIRCUIT (elec.) lc cir' cuit: A circuit containing both inductance and capacitance. Its resonant frequency is determined by the product of L and C.

L/C RATIO (elec.) L/C ra' tio: The ratio of inductance to capacitance.

LEACH leach: To separate soluble components, by using action of percolating water or other liquid; dissolving out of by action of percolating liquid.

LEAD (leed) (elec.) lead: Short connecting wire.

LEAD (graphics) lead: A strip of metal two points thick used for spacing between lines of type.

LEAD (metal) lead: The distance a screw moves axially in one revolution.

LEAD ACID CELL (elec.) lead a' cid cell: A secondary cell which uses lead peroxide and sponge lead for plates, and sulfuric acid and water for electrolyte.

LEAD BATH (metal) lead bath: A molten lead bath for heating pieces of steel within the range of 650 to 1700 degrees F.

LATHE DOG

LEAD BURNING (elec.) lead burn' ing: A process of lead fusion similar to welding used to connect terminal strips on cells in a battery.

LEAD CARBONATE, BASIC (paint. and dec.) lead car' bon ate, ba' sic: A type of white lead pigment.

LEAD DRIER (paint.) and dec.) lead dri' er: Almost water-white drier which works on body of paint film. Various combinations of lead, cobalt and other driers are used in formulating many modern finishes.

LEADED ZINC OXIDE (paint. and dec.) leaded zinc ox' ide: White pigment made by combining lead sulphate and zinc oxide.

LEADER (draft.) lead' er: A continuous line terminated by an arrowhead used as a pointer between dimensions or notes and the part to which the information applies.

LEADERS (graphics) lead' ers: Periods or dots cast in en, em, 2 em and 3 em widths. They are used in tables to lead the eye from one point to another; a dotted line.

LEAD HOLE (metal) lead hole: A guide hole drilled in metal to serve as a center for a larger hole.

LEAD-IN (elec.) lead-in: The connecting wires between the antenna and a receiver.

LEADING ANGLE (elec.) lead' ing an' gle: The angle the current leads the voltage in a capacitive circuit.

LEADING EDGE (elec.) lead' ing edge: The front or rising portion of a pulse.

LEAD JOINT (plumb.) lead joint: A joint made when connecting soil pipe. The space between the bell and spigot of the pipe is calked and then filled with molten lead which is calked again to make a tight joint.

LEAD OXIDE (paint. and dec.) lead ox' ide: Compound in several combinations of lead and oxygen, e.g., litharge and red lead.

LEAD PEROXIDE PbO_2 (elec.) lead per-

ox' ide: The lead compound used as the positive plates of a lead-acid storage battery.

LEAD SCREW (metal) lead screw: A long screw which transmits power from gear box to apron. Positive mechanical linkage to this screw is provided for thread cutting or frictional linkage for feeding during general machining.

LEAD SPONGE (elec.) lead sponge: A porous lead used as the negative plates of a lead-acid storage battery.

LEAD SULPHATE, BASIC (paint. and dec.) lead sul' phate, basic: A type of white lead.

LEAD TETRAETHYL (auto.) lead tetra eth' yl: An anti-knock compound used in gasoline.

LEAD WIRE (weld.) lead wire: Electric cables connecting the welding machine to the electrode holder or the ground clamp.

LEAD WOOL (plumb.) lead wool: Shredded lead, used for calking and packing joints.

LEAFING (paint. and dec.) leaf' ing: The overlapping arrangement of aluminum or gold bronze powders in a paint, similar to that of fallen leaves.

LEAF SPRING (auto.) leaf spring: A spring used in automobiles and wagons made up of several flat plates placed on top of each other.

LEAGUE league: 15840 ft. = 5280 yds. = 3 miles.

LEAKAGE (elec.) leak' age: Current flow over the surface or through a path of high insulation value.

LEAKAGE RESISTANCE (elec.)

leak' age re sis' tance: Opposition to a leakage current.

LEAK DETECTOR (air cond.) leak detec' tor: A device used to discover leaks in a refrigeration system.

LEAN MIXTURE (auto.) lean mix' ture: A fuel mixture which contains too much air in proportion to gasoline.

LEAN-TO (const.) lean-to: A small building or shelter whose rafters lean against another building or wall.

LEATHERCRAFT (crafts.) leath' ercraft: The craft of decorating and tooling leather.

LEATHERETTE (crafts.) leath er ette': Imitation leather.

LECHER WIRES (elec.) lech' er wires: A two wire transmission line used as a resonant line to measure wavelength.

LECLANCHE CELL (elec.) le clanche' cell: The scientific name for the common dry cell.

LEDGE (const.) ledge: A shelf projection from a wall.

LEDGERS (const.) ledg' ers: Horizontal boards fastened to scaffolding timbers during erection around a building.

LEDGER STRIP (const.) ledg' er strip: A strip of wood nailed to the side of a girder on which joists rest.

LEFT HAND RULE (elec.) left hand rule: A method, using your left hand, to determine polarity of an electromagnetic field or direction of electron flow.

LEFT HAND SCREW (metal) left hand screw: A screw which advances when

turned from right to left or counterclockwise.

LEFT HAND THREAD (metal) left hand thread: A thread so cut or machined that it is necessary to turn a mating nut in a counterclockwise direction to advance on the thread.

LEGEND (draft.) leg' end: A key to identify certain symbols and representations on a drawing or map.

LENS (weld.) lens: A specially treated glass through which a welder may look at an intense flame without being injured by the harmful rays, or glare, radiating from this flame.

LENZ'S LAW (elec.) lenz's law: The induced emf in any circuit is always in such a direction as to oppose the effect that produces it.

LEROY (draft.) le' roy: Device used by draftsmen to improve quality of lettering.

LET-IN let-in: Sinking or cutting to embed or insert one part into surface of another.

LETTER BOARD (graphics) let' ter board: A board with strips of wood around three edges. Used to store composed type.

LETTERPRESS PRINTING (graphics) let' ter press print' ing: Letters and designs to be reproduced are raised above nonprinting area of type or plate. Ink is applied to raised areas by means of inking rollers.

LETTER SIZE DRILLS (metal) let' ter size drills: Drills which are sized according to letters A to Z. Diameters are expressed in thousands of an inch and range from approximately 15/64 to 13/32 inches.

LEVEL (elec.) lev' el: A specified value of amplitude of a wave; the measured amplitude of a signal wave.

LEVEL (wood.) lev' el: A tool used to determine if a surface is horizontal or vertical; a wood or metal straight-edge containing one or more small glass

tubes partly filled with alcohol so as to leave an air bubble, which moves to the center of the tube when in an exact horizontal or vertical position.

LEVELING (paint. and dec.) lev' el ing: The formation of a smooth film on either a horizontal or vertical surface, independent of the method of application.

LEVELING ROD (const.) lev' el ing rod: A rod used by the surveyor as a target rod. They may be targets or self-reading rods.

LEVER le' ver: A rigid bar or arm turning against a fulcrum or around an axis.

LEYDEN JAR (elec.) ley' den jar: A capacitor made by covering a glass jar on the inside and outside with thin metal.

L-HEAD ENGINE (auto.) l-head en' gine: An engine with valves arranged in line in the engine block, operated from a single camshaft.

LIBRATION (space) li bra' tion: A real or apparent oscillatory motion, particularly the apparent oscillation of the moon.

LIFESPAN (space) life' span: The time duration between a satellite's achieving

an orbit and its falling back to the Earth or disintegrating.

LIFTER (metal) lift' er: A tool used by the molder in a foundry to remove small particles of sand which may have fallen into a mold cavity after pattern is removed.

LIFTING (paint. and dec.) lift' ing: Softening of undercoat by solvents used in coats which follow. Usually caused by not allowing sufficient time for the undercoat to harden before applying additional coats.

LIFTOFF (space) lift' off: The initial motion along the trajectory of a space vehicle as it rises from the launch stand under rocket propulsion; the take-off.

LIGATURE (graphics) lig'a ture: A type character on which two or more letters are cast on one body.

LIGHT (const.) A window pane; a division in a window sash for a pane of glass.

LIGHT FACE (graphics) light face: A type face with very narrow major and minor elements.

LIGHT FLARE (elec.) light flare: A white spot appearing in a televised picture due to a misplaced or mis-directed spot light.

LIGHT LEVEL (elec.) light lev'el: The general illumination intensity of a scene or object measured in foot-candles.

LIGHTNING ARRESTER (elec.) light'-ning ar res' ter: A protective device in a lead-in or transmission line which protects equipment from the effects of lightning.

LIGHTNING ROD (elec.) light' ning rod:

Pointed metal rod mounted at top of building or mast and connected by cable to moist earth. Reduces chance of damage by lightning.

LIGHT WAVE (elec.) light wave: A wave of visible light.

LIGHT YEAR (space) light year: Distance traveled in year by light which covers 186,284 miles in one second.

LIMBA (Terminalia Superba) (wood) lim' ba: Light blond wood from Congo in Africa. Often sold under name of Korina. Has open grain and about same texture and hardness as mahogany.

LIME (const.) lime: Calcium oxide obtained by heating limestone.

LIME PASTE (paint. and dec.) lime paste: Used in whitewash. Eight gallons of lime paste can be made by slaking 25 pounds of quick lime in ten gallons of water.

LIMESTONE (const.) lime' stone: A popular building stone; also used to make lime; calcium carbonate.

LIMIT (automation) lim' it: The extreme condition allowable for a system or process.

LIMITS (draft.) lim' its: The extreme acceptable dimensions of a part.

LIMITER (elec.) lim' it er: A stage or circuit that limits all signals at the same maximum amplitude.

LIMIT GAGE (metal) lim' it gage: A snap gage, preset to allow slight variations in work dimensions. GAGE has "go" and "no go" settings.

LIMONITE (metal) li' mo nite: Iron ore, similar to hematite, but containing water.

LINE (air cond.) line: Commonly refers to a pipe conveying liquid or gas.

LINE (elec.) line: A wire or cable; an electrical conductor; a trace on a television tube. In the American System there are 525 lines to each complete television picture.

BOP, a voltage surge which shows up as increased brightness on a TV screen.

CORD, a two wire conductor used to connect a piece of electric equipment to the power source.

CORD RESISTOR, a built-in resistance in a line cord to cause a voltage drop.

DROP, voltage loss due to conductor resistance.

FILTER, a special circuit to prevent electrical disturbances and noise developed in the power source from entering equipment attached to source.

LINEAD (draft.) li' ne ad: A type of T square consisting of three straight-edged blades which can be clamped at any desired angles. It is used to draw lines toward a vanishing point outside the limits of the drawing.

LINEAL FOOT (const.) lin' e al foot: A foot in distance in a straight line.

LINEAR (elec.) lin' e ar: In a straight line; a mathematical relationship in which quantities vary in direct proportion.

LINEAR ACCELERATOR (elec.) lin' - e ar ac cel' er a tor: A machine used to accelerate particles or electrons along a straight enclosed tube by means of high frequency electromagnetic waves.

LINEAR AMPLIFIER (elec.) lin' e ar am' pli fi er: An amplifier whose output is in exact proportion to its input.

LINEAR DETECTOR (elec.) lin' e ar de tec' tor: A detector using linear portions of the characteristic curve on both sides of the knee. Output is proportional to input signal.

LINEAR DEVICE (elec.) lin' e ar device': An electronic device or component whose current-voltage relation is a straight line.

LINEARITY (elec.) li ne ar' i ty: The velocity of the scanning beam. It must be uniform for good linearity.

LINEAR MEASUREMENT lin' e ar mea' sure ment: Measurement on flat surfaces.

LINE DROP (elec.) line drop: The voltage drop due to resistance in an electrical conductor; IR drop.

LINE ENGRAVING (graphics) line engrav' ing: An engraving in which the image is represented by lines.

LINE FREQUENCY (elec.) line fre' quen cy: The frequency of the source voltage; in television, it is the number of lines scanned per second.

LINE GAUGE (graphics) line gauge: The printer's measuring stick graduated in nonpareils and picas.

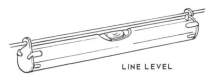

LINE LEVEL

LINE LEVEL (wood.) line lev' el: A small level with hooks on each end so that it may be supported on a line.

LINER (auto.) lin' er: A metal liner or replaceable tube put in an engine cylinder or bearing.

LINE SHAFT (metal) line shaft: Several shafts connected together in line, from which countershafts and secondary shafts receive their power.

LINES OF FORCE (elec.) lines of force: A graphic representation of electrostatic and magnetic fields showing direction and intensity.

LINES, Type of (draft.) lines, type of:

BORDER LINE, a heavy line used to frame or as a border for a drawing.

BREAK LINE, lines used to show that part of an object is removed in order to reduce its size to the limits of the drawing.

CENTER LINE, a line used to indicate the center of arcs and circles.

CROSS SECTION LINES, parallel lines used to represent cut-away portions or sections of a drawn object. Also, various methods of cross section lining indicate the type of material from which the object is made.

CUTTING PLANE LINE, a line designating the location of a plane cutting through an object.

DIMENSION LINES, lines used to indicate the size or measurements between points on a drawing.

HIDDEN LINE, a dashed line representing invisible edges of a drawn object.

PHANTOM LINE, lines used to show alternate positions of a moving part of an object or the line of motion.

VISIBLE OUTLINE, lines representing visible edges of a drawn object.

LINING PAPER (paint. and dec.) lin' ing pa' per: Wallpaper without a ground (over-all background color), used mostly for wall conditioning.

LINOLEUM AND OIL CLOTH VARNISHES (paint. and dec.) li no' le um and oil' cloth var' nish es: Special highly flexible and elastic varnishes.

LINOTYPE (graphics) lin' o type: Trade name of a machine invented by Ottmar Mergenthaler in 1886, which assembles matrices from which are cast slugs or lines of type that may be used for printing.

LINSEED OIL (paint. and dec.) lin' seed oil: Vegetable oil obtained by crushing seed of flax plant. Drying properties accentuated by heating oil to 130 to 200 degrees C. to form what is known as "boiled linseed oil." Metallic salts or driers are added to increase the rate of drying.

LINTEL (const.) lin' tel: The horizontal support over a door or window.

LIP (metal) lip: The cutting edge of a machine tool.

LIQUEFACTION (air cond.) liq ue fac' - tion: The change to the liquid state.

LIQUID AIR liq' uid air: Air changed to liquid by a series of controlled processes of compression and cooling by expansion.

LIQUID DRIERS (paint. and dec.) liq' uid dri' ers: Solution of driers in paint thinners.

LIQUID PROPELLANT (space) liq' uid pro pel' lant: Any liquid ingredient fed to the combustion chamber of a rocket engine.

LIQUID WOOD FILLER (paint. and dec.)

liq' uid wood fill' er: Varnishes of low viscosity, usually containing extending pigment, for use as a first coating on open grain woods. Its purpose is to afford a non-absorbent surface for succeeding coats of varnish. It is frequently colored so as to stain and fill in one operation.

LIQUOR (air cond.) liq' uor: A refrigerant consisting of ammonia and water.

LITER li' ter: The standard French liquid measure; equals 1.0567 liquid quart.

LITHARGE (metal) lith' arge: Lead-monoxide in a fused form.

LITHARGE (paint. and dec.) lith' arge: A yellowish-red oxide of lead; lead monoxide.

LITHOGRAPHY (graphics) li thog' raphy: A planographic method of printing from grained zinc or aluminum plates. The process is based on the repulsion between grease and water. The design is put on the surface of a greasy material and then water and ink are applied. The greasy parts of the design repel the water, but absorb the ink.

LITHOL RED (paint. and dec.) lith' ol red: Pigment which is bright red with bluish cast.

LITHOPONE (paint. and dec.) lith' o-pone: White pigment made from barium sulphide and zinc sulphate.

LITHOPRINTING (draft.) lith' o printing: A photo-offset method of producing many copies of a drawing.

LITZ WIRE (elec.) litz wire: A conductor made of a group of small wires each insulated from the other, but joined at the ends.

LIVE (elec.) live: A term used in television to designate a real show as opposed to film or video tape.

LIVE AXLE (auto.) live ax' le: The axle and wheel rotate together.

LIVE CENTER live cen' ter: The center which fits the live or moving spindle in the headstock.

LIVERING (paint. and dec.) liv' er ing: Coagulation of varnish finishing material into a viscous, rubber-like mass.

LIVER OF SULPHUR (crafts) liv' er of sul' phur: A sulphur compound used for oxidizing metal.

LIVE TESTING (space) live test' ing: The testing of a rocket engine or aerospace vehicle by actually launching it.

LOAD (air cond.) load: The required rate of heat removal for a refrigeration system.

LOAD (automation) load: To insert several smaller parts into a major part. Term used in fabrication and assembly.

LOAD (elec.) load: The resistance connected across a circuit which determines current flow and energy used.

LOAD FACTOR (air cond.) load fac' tor: The ratio between actual load and maximum production capacity.

LOAD FACTOR (elec.) load fac' tor: The average power consumed divided by the maximum power.

LOADING (metal) load' ing: The filling of pores of a grinding wheel with the material being ground.

LOADING A CIRCUIT (elec.) load' ing a cir' cuit: The effect of connecting a voltmeter across a circuit. The meter will draw current and the effective resistance of the circuit is lowered.

LOADING COIL (elec.) load' ing coil: An inductor inserted in a transmission line to change its characteristic impedance.

LOAD LINE (elec.) load line: A line drawn on the characteristic family of curves of an electron tube when used with a specified load resistor representing plate current at zero and maximum plate voltage.

LOAM (metal) loam: A mixture of sand and clay used in molding.

LOBLOLLY PINE (wood.) lob' lol ly pine: A coarse grain, soft fiber pine wood used mostly for house framing in the southern part of the United States.

LOCAL ACTION (elec.) lo' cal ac' tion: A defect in voltaic cells caused by impurities in the zinc, such as carbon, iron and lead. These impurities form many small internal cells which contribute nothing to the external circuit. The zinc is wasted away, even when cell is not in use.

LOCAL OSCILLATOR (elec.) lo' cal os cil la' tor: An oscillator in a superheterodyne receiver, the output of which is mixed with the incoming signal to produce the intermediate frequency.

LOCKER PLANT (air cond.) lock' er plant: A cold storage and refrigeration plant usually containing many small lockers for individual or family use.

LOCK-UP (graphics) lock-up: Locking up forms for press.

LOCK WASHER (metal) lock wash' er: A special washer to prevent nuts from coming loose under vibration.

LODESTONE (elec.) lode' stone: A natural magnet, so called a "leading stone" or lodestone because early navigators used it to determine directions.

LOG (elec.) log: A record kept at radio transmitters showing types of emission, power output and frequency and other information required by the FCC.

LOGARITHM log' a rithm: The exponent of the power to which the base must be raised to produce the number. The base is usually 10 or e. The whole number of the logarithm is known as the characteristic; the decimal fraction as the mantissa.

LOGARITHMIC GRAPHS (draft.) log a - rith' mic graphs: Graph paper ruled with parallel horizontal and vertical lines spaced proportional to the logarithms of numbers.

LOGARITHMIC SCALE (elec.) log a - rith' mic scale: A scale on which distances are proportional to the logarithms of the numbers with which the scale is numbered.

LOGGIA (const.) log' gia: A gallery or portico open to the air, projecting from or built into a building. Its open side is usually surrounded by a colonnade.

LOGICAL FUNCTIONS (automation) log' i cal func' tions: An expression referring to a definite state of condition.

AND FUNCTION, an output is obtained only with a combined group of input signals.

OR FUNCTION, an output is obtained with any one of a group of input signals.

NOT FUNCTION, an output is obtained only when there is no input signal.

MEMORY FUNCTION, an output is

continually obtained unless an input signal is applied.

LOGOTYPE (graphics) log' o type: See LIGATURE.

LOKTAL BASE (elec.) lok' tal base: A base for a small electron tube which locks it firmly in place by means of a metallic center post.

LONG (crafts) long: Clay which is very plastic and workable.

LONG-OIL VARNISH (paint. and dec.) long-oil var' nish: Varnish with a large percentage of oil to gum resin--usually more than 25 gallons of oil to 100 pounds of resin. Long-oil varnish is more elastic, and more durable than short-oil varnish. Spar varnish is a typical example of long-oil varnish.

LONG TON long ton: 2240 pounds.

LOOKOUT (const.) look' out: A short wooden bracket which supports the roof overhang.

LOOM (elec.) loom: Flexible nonmetallic tubing used to cover wires to provide additional insulation and protection.

LOOP (elec.) loop: A closed circuit.

LOOSE COUPLING (elec.) loose cou'-pling: Coupling less than critical coupling; very little transfer of energy.

LOOSE FIT (metal) loose fit: Class Fit 1. A large tolerance used when accuracy is not essential.

LORAN (elec.) lor' an: A direction finding system employing the principle of the difference in time required for pulsed radio signals to arrive at a point from a pair of synchronized transmitters.

LOSS (elec.) loss: Dissipation of energy without useful work.

LOSS FACTOR (elec.) loss fac' tor: The products of the dielectric constant and the power factor in a capacitor.

LOST MOTION (metal) lost mo' tion: See BACK LASH

LOUDNESS (elec.) loud' ness: A quality of sound determined by auditory sensation.

LOUDSPEAKER (elec.) loud' speak er: A device to convert electrical energy into sound energy.

DYNAMIC, a speaker consisting of a voice coil moving in a strong magnetic field.

ELECTRODYNAMIC, a speaker which uses an electromagnetic field.

PM, a speaker which uses a fixed permanent magnetic field.

ELECTROSTATIC, a speaker in which mechanical forces are produced by electrostatic fields. Sometimes called a capacitor speaker.

LOUVER (const.) lou' ver: A ventilating window, usually in the gable end of a house. It is made of inclined horizontal slats which permit air to pass with protection against weather.

LOUVRE (elec.) lou' vre: A type of grill construction placed in front of a loudspeaker. The sloping sections of the louvre hide the speaker, but permit sound to pass; a slotted opening.

LOW BRASS (metal) low brass: Yellow brass alloy with approximately 80 percent copper and 20 percent zinc. It is very ductile and easily drawn or formed into shapes.

LOW CARBON STEELS (metal) low car' bon steels: Generally those steels with a carbon content below .3 of one percent. It does not harden except by casehardening treatment.

LOWER CASE (graphics) low' er case: One of the small letters; minuscule - not capitals.

LOW GEAR (auto.) low gear: The slowest forward speed in an automobile gear chain.

LOW LEVEL MODULATION (elec.) low lev' el mod u la' tion: Modulation of a stage before the final r-f amplification stage.

LOW SIDE (air cond.) low side: The part of a refrigerator system below evaporator pressure.

LOW TENSION (elec.) low ten' sion: Low voltage.

LOW VOLTAGE WIRING (elec.) low volt' age wir' ing: A method of house wiring where low voltage relays are used for switching lighting circuits.

LOX (space) lox: Acceptable symbol for liquid oxygen.

L PAD (elec.) L pad: A combination of two variable resistors, one in series and the other across the load, which is used to vary the output of an audio system and match impedances.

LPG or LP GAS (auto.) LPG or LP gas: A mixture of petroleum compounds such as butane and propane. For storing and transporting LPG is compressed and cooled to its liquid state.

L-SECTION FILTER (elec.) L-sec' tion fil' ter: A filter consisting of a capacitor and an inductor connected in an inverted L configuration.

LUBRICATION SYSTEM (auto.) lu bri - ca' tion sys' tem: The system of pumps, reservoirs, pipes and controls to supply lubricating oils to moving parts of an engine.

LUBRICATING SYSTEM TYPES (auto.) lu bri cat' ing sys' tem types:

PRESSURE FEED, oil is forced by pump through oil channels in connecting rods and crank shaft. All moving parts are force lubricated.

SPLASH, oil is picked up by dippers and splashed as droplets and mist to upper parts of engine such as valves, piston pins, rings and cylinder walls.

SPLASH-PRESSURE, a combination of splash and pressure. Usually main bearings, camshaft bearings and valves are pressure fed. Connecting rod bearings, piston pins and cylinder walls are lubricated by dippers and splash.

LUDLOW (graphics) lud' low: A machine for casting lines of type from hand set matrices.

LUG (metal) lug: A projection from a casting of irregular shape.

LUG (auto.) lug: The bolts used to fasten the wheels on a car, called lug bolts.

LUGS (elec.) lugs: Terminals; terminals placed on the ends of a wire to facilitate rapid connection.

LUMBER (const.) lum' ber: Timber cut to size for marketing such as studs, boards, etc.

LUMBERJACK (wood.) lum' ber jack: Worker employed in logging or other operations in lumber industry.

LUMBER SCALE (const.) lum' ber scale: A specially graduated scale used by the lumberman to determine the number of board feet in a rough sawed board.

LUMEN (elec.) lu' men: A unit of measurement for the flow of light.

LUMEN BRONZE (metal) lu' men bronze: An alloy of 86 percent zinc, 10 percent copper and 4 percent aluminum. It is used for high speed bearings.

LUMINANCE (elec.) lu' mi nance: The photometric quantity of light radiation, a term referring to brightness in TV.

LUMINANCE CHANNEL (elec.) lu' mi nance chan' nel: Circuits in a color TV designed to pass only the luminance or monochrome signal.

LUMINANCE SIGNAL (elec.) lu' mi - nance sig' nal: In color TV. Contains brightness and detail information.

LUMINESCENCE (elec.) lu mi nes' - cence: The property of a phosphor to radiate light when bombarded by electrons.

LUMINOSITY (elec.) lu' mi nos i ty: The quality of emitting or giving out light.

LUMP LIME (const.) lump lime: Lime made from limestone burned in a kiln.

LUNAR BASE (space) lu' nar base: A projected installation on the surface of the Moon for use as a base in scientific or military operations.

LUNAR GRAVITY (space) lu' nar grav'- i ty: The attraction of particles and masses toward the gravitational center of the Moon.

LUNAR PROBE (space) lu' nar probe: A probe for exploring and reporting on conditions on or about the Moon.

LUNAR SPACE (space) lu' nar space: Space near the Moon.

LUSTER lus' ter: The reflection of light from a smooth surface.

LUTE (const.) lute: To make a joint airtight by sealing with clay; a straightedge for leveling off clay in a brick mold by removing the excess.

LYE (const.) lye: A powder or solution derived from a substance containing an alkali; sodium or potassium hydroxide.

LYOPHILIZATION (air cond.) ly oph i-li za' tion: The dehydration of a frozen substance under conditions of sublimation.

MACHINABILITY (metal) ma chin' a - bil ity: The characteristics of a material to be machined.

MACHINE (metal) ma chine': A device for transforming or transferring energy.

MACHINE COMPOSITION (graphics) ma chine' com po si' tion: Composing by using type setting machines.

MACHINE DISPERSION (automation) ma chine' dis per' sion: The index of dispersion is the range or standard deviation of a sample of measurements. It indicates the capabilities of the machine.

MACHINE DRAWING (draft.) ma chine' draw' ing: A drawing or the art of drawing machines and machine parts with necessary specifications, dimensions and information for manufacturing.

MACHINE LANGUAGE (automation) machine' lan' guage: Coded signals which direct the operation of a machine.

MACHINE RATING (elec.) ma chine' rat' ing: The load which can be normal-ly applied to a machine for continuous operation without overheating.

MACHINE SCREWS ma chine' screws: A common variety of screw fastener used for general assembly of machine work. They are made in coarse and

ROUND HEAD   FILLISTER   FLAT HEAD
           HEAD

fine threads and with a variety of heads. Machine screws vary in diameter from $^{\#}0$ (.060) to 1/2 (.50) inches and in lengths from 1/8 to 3 inches.

MACHINE TOOL (metal) ma chine' tool: Name given to a power driven machine used to shape solid work by removing metal, or by deformation of the metal.

MACHINIST (metal) ma chin' ist: A person trained to operate machine tools, including the making and fitting of machine parts.

MACH NUMBER (elec.) mach num' ber: The ratio of flight speed to the speed of sound.

MADDER (paint. and dec.) mad' der: Coloring matter originally derived from the pulverized root of a plant cultivated in Europe and Asia Minor. Now largely made synthetically; synthetic coal-tar dye; bright red, crimson.

MADDER LAKE (paint. and dec.) mad' der lake: Transparent red pigment made by precipitating extract from madder root upon metallic salt base.

MAGIC EYE (elec.) mag' ic eye: See ELECTRON-RAY TUBE.

MAGNALIUM (metal) mag na' li um: An

alloy of aluminum and magnesium (2–10%). It can be easily forged and machined and is very strong.

MAGNESIA (metal) mag ne' si a: Commercial basic magnesium carbonate; a light white powder derived from calcining magnesium carbonate; it is used as medicine for symptoms of stomach acidity and constipation.

MAGNESIUM SILICATE (paint. and dec.) mag ne' si um sll' I cate: White extender pigment which adds "fluffiness" to products in which it is used.

MAGNESYN (elec.) mag' ne syn: A type of remote indicating device composed of a stator wound on a toroidal form and a rotor consisting of a strong cylindrical permanent magnet.

MAGNET (elec.) mag' net: A substance that has the property of magnetism.

MAGNET CORE (elec.) mag' net core: A soft iron core of an electromagnet.

MAGNETIC AMPLIFIER (elec.) mag - net' ic am' pli fi er: A transformer type device employing a d-c control winding. The control current produces more or less magnetic core saturation, thus varying the output voltage of the amplifier.

MAGNETIC BRAKE (elec.) mag net' ic brake: A friction type mechanical brake operated by magnetic forces.

MAGNETIC CHUCK (metal) mag net' ic chuck: A strong magnet used to hold iron or steel in position for machine work.

MAGNETIC CIRCUIT (elec.) mag net' ic cir' cuit: The complete path through which magnetic lines of force may be established under the influence of a magnetizing force.

MAGNETIC CIRCUIT BREAKER (elec.) mag net' ic cir' cuit break' er: An overload protection device for an electrical circuit which opens the circuit by a magnetic switch if overloaded.

MAGNETIC COIL (elec.) mag net' ic coil: The windings of an electromagnet.

MAGNETIC DEFLECTION (elec.) magnet' ic de flec' tion: The movement of the electron beam in a cathode-ray tube by means of magnetic fields. This type of deflection is widely used in television receivers.

MAGNETIC DENSITY (elec.) mag net' ic den' si ty: The number of lines of magnetic force per unit area of field.

MAGNETIC FIELD (elec.) mag net' ic field: Imaginary lines along which a magnetic force acts. These lines emanate from the N pole and enter the S pole, forming closed loops.

MAGNETIC FLUX (symbol Φ phi) (elec.) mag net' ic flux: The entire quantity of magnetic lines surrounding a magnet.

MAGNETIC INDUCTION (elec.) mag - net' ic in duc' tion: See MAGNETIC DENSITY.

MAGNETIC LINE OF FORCE (elec.) mag' net' ic line of force: The magnetic line along which a compass needle aligns itself.

MAGNETIC MATERIALS (elec.) magnet' ic ma te' ri als: Materials such as iron, steel, nickel and cobalt which are attracted to a magnet.

MAGNETIC PERMEABILITY (elec.) mag net' ic per me a bil' i ty: The property of a material in respect to the ease with which magnetism passes through it; the ratio B/H where B equals the flux density and H equals the magnetizing force dependent upon the ampere-turns per unit length of a coil; a number symbolized by mu (u) representing the ratio of flux density produced in a substance to that which would be produced in a vacuum by the same magnetizing force.

MAGNETIC PICKUP (elec.) mag net' ic pick' up: A phono cartridge which produces an electrical output from an armature in a magnetic field. The armature is mechanically connected to the reproducing stylus.

MAGNETIC SATURATION (elec.) magnet' ic sat u ra' tion: This condition exists in a magnetic material when a further increase in magnetizing force produces very little increase in flux density. A saturation point has been reached.

MAGNETIC SCREEN (elec.) mag net' ic screen: See SHIELD.

MAGNETIC STORM (space) mag net' ic storm: A worldwide disturbance of the Earth's magnetic field.

MAGNETIC SWITCH (elec.) mag net' ic switch: A switch activated by an electromagnet.

MAGNETIC WHIRL (elec.) mag net' ic whirl: The circular magnetic fields built up around a current carrying conductor.

MAGNETISM (elec.) mag' ne tism: The invisible force of a magnet which causes it to attract steel.

MAGNETITE (metal) mag' ne tite: A heavy black iron ore, possessing magnetic properties.

MAGNETIZATION CURVE (elec.) magnet i za' tion curve: A graph produced by plotting the intensity of magnetizing

force on the X axis and the relative magnetism on the Y axis.

MAGNETIZING CURRENT (elec.) mag'-ne tiz ing cur' rent: The current used in a transformer to produce the transformer core flux.

MAGNETO (auto.) mag ne' to: A self contained generator, transformer, breaker points and distributor ignition system.

MAGNETO-HYDRODYNAMICS (space) mag ne' to-hy dro dy nam' ics: New sciences dealing with ultra-high altitude, high speed flight; examines whether an electrically charged wing or aerodynamic body passing through a sea of ions can attract these charged particles on the one side and repel them on the other side to produce lift.

MAGNETOMETER (elec.) mag ne tom'-e ter: An instrument used to measure the direction and force of a magnetic field.

MAGNETOMETER (space) mag ne -tom' e ter: An instrument used in the study of geomagnetism for measuring magnetic elements.

MAGNETOMOTIVE FORCE (F) (mmf) (elec.) mag ne to mo' tive force: The force that produces the flux in a magnetic circuit.

MAGNETOSTRICTION (elec.) mag ne-to stric' tion: The effect of a change in dimension of certain elements when placed in a magnetic field.

MAGNETOSTRICTIVE TRANSDUCER (elec.) mag ne to stric' tive trans duc'-er: A transducer which operates on the principle of magnetostriction.

MAGNET POLES (elec.) mag' net poles: Points of maximum attraction on a magnet. They are designated as North and South poles.

MAGNET WIRE (elec.) mag' net wire: Wire used for coils in relays, small transformers and meters. Wire is usually insulated with enamel coating.

MAGNITUDE (elec.) mag' ni tude: Size, greatness, extent of.

MAGNITUDE (space) mag' ni tude: Brightness of a star, first magnitude is the brightness of a candle flame at a distance of 1300 feet.

MAHLSTICK (const.) mahl' stick: A stick used to steady the hand of a painter. The stick usually has a rubber ball on one end, which rests against the surface as the painter uses the stick for support.

MAHOGANY (wood.) ma hog' a ny: The ideal cabinet wood, used by the early craftsmen of the 18th century to present designers of fine furniture. It is tough, strong but easy to work. It is deep reddish-brown in color and has a beautifully figured grain.

MAHOGANY, Philippine (wood.) ma-hog' a ny: A wood which grows in the Philippine Islands and is similar to genuine mahogany but coarser in texture.

MAIN (air cond.) main: A large pipe or duct used to distribute or collect from several branch pipes or lines.

MAIN (elec.) main: The main circuit which supplies all others.

MAIN LINE (metal) main line: The principal driving shaft for a train of pulleys.

MAIN STAGE (space) main stage: In a single stage rocket vehicle powered by one or more engines, the period when full thrust is attained.

MAIN VENT (plumb.) main vent: The vent in a building to which branch and fixture vents are connected.

MAJOR AXIS (draft.) ma' jor ax' is: The long diameter of an ellipse.

MAJOR CARRIER (elec.) ma' jor car'-ri er: Conduction through a semiconductor as a result of a majority of electrons or holes.

MAJOR DIAMETER (metal) ma' jor di-am' e ter: The largest diameter of a screw thread.

MAJUSCULE (graphics) ma jus' cule: A capital letter.

MAKE AND BREAK (elec.) make and break: A term referring to a mechanical or magnetic switch for opening and closing a circuit.

MAKE-UP (graphics) make-up: The assembly and spacing out of jobs or pages on a galley.

MAKE-UP RULE (graphics) make-up rule: A rule used by newspaper men in making up pages. Sometimes called a "hump back rule" because of its shape.

MAKEUP WATER (air cond.) make' up wa' ter: Water supplied to replace water lost by evaporation.

MALACHITE (metal) mal' a chite: Copper ore; a green basic cupric carbonate used for ornamentation and mosaics, paint pigment called "mountain green."

MALAX (crafts) ma' lax: To soften a finish material by stirring, rubbing and mixing with a thinner substance.

MALEIC RESINS (paint. and dec.) male'-ic res'ins: Resins based on reaction between maleic anhydride or maleic acid with glycerine and rosins.

MALE THREAD (plumb.) male thread: An external thread.

MALLEABILIZATION (metal) mal'le-a bil i za tion: A heat treating process to make iron more ductile and less brittle with an increase in strength.

MALLEABLE IRON (metal) mal'le a-ble iron: Specially heat treated cast iron to make it less brittle.

MALLET (wood.) mal'let: A wooden hammer.

MANDREL (metal) man'drel: Lathe accessory. Steel shaft machined to slight taper, onto which work with hole in center is pressed. Mandrel with work attached is fitted into metal lathe between centers for machining.

MANDREL (crafts) man'drel: A tapered piece of steel used as an anvil to form rings and curves.

MANDREL (metal) man'drel: A rounded stake used for forming sheet metal.

MANGANESE DIOXIDE (metal) man'-ga nese di ox'ide: A depolarizer for primary cells.

MANGANESE DRIER (paint. and dec.) man'ga nese dri'er: Compound of manganese. Classified as "through" drier as it acts on both top and body of film.

MANGANIN (elec.) man'ga nin: An al-loy of ferromanganese, copper and nickel. It is used for resistance work.

MANHOLE (plub.) man'hole: An opening to permit workmen to enter an enclosed space.

MANIFOLD (auto.) man'i fold: A system of tubes or pipes.

EXHAUST, pipes connected to the engine block at exhaust ports to carry burned gases away.

INTAKE, pipes connected to the engine block to bring air-fuel mixture from carburetor to cylinder intake port.

MANIFOLD (metal) man'i fold: A pipe with multiple outlets for connecting a group of tanks together.

MANIFOLD (plumb.) man'i fold: A pipe with a series of parallel outlets at right angles to its center line.

MANIFOLD HEAT CONTROL (auto.) man'i fold heat con trol': A thermostatically controlled butterfly valve in the exhaust manifold used to direct heat to the intake manifold during warm-up.

MANIFOLD VACUUM (auto.) man'i fold vac'u um: The state of the atmosphere within the manifolds of an operating engine.

MANILA RESINS (paint. and dec.) ma-nil'a res'ins: Natural resin, obtained by tapping agathis alba trees. Alcohol soluble.

MANOMETER (air cond.) ma nom'e-ter: A U-shaped tube used for measuring pressure differentials.

MANSARD ROOF (const.) man'sard roof: A roof with two slopes on each of four sides, the lower slope having a steeper inclination; a curb roof.

MANTEL (const.) man'tel: The ornamental shelf and other work over the fireplace in front of the chimney.

MANTISSA   man tis' sa: The decimal part of a logarithm.

MANUAL   man' u al: Done by hand; a book of instructions.

MANUAL ARTS   man' u al arts: A large group of skills performed by hand.

MANUFACTURING (automation) man u-fac' tur ing: The making of material goods for human needs and desires.

MAPLE (Acer Saccharum) (wood.) ma'-ple: A hard, heavy stiff wood which has exceptional strength. It is used extensively in home finish and furniture making.

MAPP (weld.) mapp: A stabilized methyl acetylene–propadiene fuel gas. It is a Dow Chemical Co. product.

MAR (wood.) mar: To deface; scar; scratch.

MARBLE (const.) mar' ble: A valuable and beautiful limestone with colors varying from whites, grays to browns, used for exterior and interior finish of buildings.

MARBLEIZING (paint. and dec.) mar'-ble iz ing: Finishing process used to make surface being treated look like marble.

MARCONI ANTENNA (elec.) mar co' ni an ten' na: An antenna which depends upon ground for its operation.

MARCONI, GUGLIEMO (1874–1937) (elec): The Italian inventor of the wireless. In 1901 he succeeded in transmitting wireless messages across the Atlantic. He shared the Nobel Prize with C. F. Braun in 1909.

MARINE VARNISHES (paint. and dec.) ma rine' var' nishes: Varnishes es-

pecially designed to resist long immersion in salt or fresh water and exposure to marine atmosphere.

MARKING GAUGE (wood.) mark' ing gauge: A tool used for making lines at

a uniform distance from the edge of a board.

MARKER GENERATOR (elec.) mark' er gen' er a tor: An accurate rf oscillator used as a test instrument for radio and TV alignment. Marked frequencies appear as a "pip" on the response pattern, observed on an oscilloscope.

MARQUETRY (wood.) mar' que try: Pieces of different colored woods or veneers inlaid in a piece of wood or veneer of the same thickness.

MARTENSITE (metal) mar' ten site: Principal structure element of very hard steel.

MASER (space) ma' ser: Microwave Amplification of Stimulated Emission of Radiation; the emission of stored energy in a molecular or atomic system by a microwave power supply when stimulated by an input signal.

MASKING (elec.) mask' ing: Raising the threshold of audibility of a sound by the presence of another sound called the masking sound.

MASKING TAPE (paint. and dec.) mask'-ing tape: Adhesive coated paper tape used to mask or protect parts of surface not to be finished.

MASONITE (const.) ma' son ite: The trade name for a wood fibre board used for interior wall panels.

MASONRY (const.) ma' son ry: Brick, stone, tile laid in mortar or concrete.

MASS (air cond.) mass: A quantity of matter forming a body of indefinite shape.

MASS PRODUCTION (automation) mass pro duc' tion: The manufacturing of many articles of like quality and kind by special tools and machines.

MASTER mas' ter: A tradesman possessing the qualifications of a journeyman and also the knowledge of the physical laws affecting his work and installations, laws and ordinances affecting his work, and usually business methods and procedures.

MASTER CYLINDER (auto.) mas' ter cyl' in der: The fluid reservoir and activating cylinder and piston for the hydraulic brake system of an automobile.

MASTER FOLLOWER (automation) mas' ter fol' low er: Information furnished to a machine in the form of a master workpiece or template.

MASTER GAUGE (metal) mas' ter gauge: A very accurate gauge kept in reserve for checking the accuracy of other gauges.

MASTER-KEYED mas' ter-keyed: A group of locks which may be opened by a single special key.

MASTER SWITCH (elec.) mas' ter switch: A switch which controls the operation of several other switches.

MASTIC (const.) mas' tic: Pasty material used as cement, protective coating.

MATCHED BOARDS (const.) matched boards: Boards cut with tongue and groove.

MATCHING (elec.) match' ing: See IMPEDANCE MATCHING.

MATERIALS HANDLING (automation) ma te' ri als hand' ling: The movement of materials within a manufacturing plant.

MAT FINISH (crafts) mat fin' ish: Dull finish.

MATRIX (elec.) ma' trix: A circuit which performs a color coordinate transformation by electrical means in color TV.

MATRIX (graphics) ma' trix: A brass mold used in casting letters in a type setting machine.

MATT (crafts) matt: A glazed finish without gloss.

MATTE (metal) matte: Crude copper; a mixture of copper and other metals.

MATTER (elec.) mat' ter: Physical substance of common experience. Everything about us is made up of matter.

MAUL (const.) maul: Large heavy mallet.

MAUVE (crafts) mauve: A delicate purple color.

MAXIMUM max' i mum: The greatest quantity, amount or degree; the highest possible value.

MAXIMUM POWER TRANSFER (elec.) max' i mum pow' er trans' fer: This condition exists when the resistance of the load equals the internal resistance of the source.

MAXIMUM VALUE (elec.) max' i mum

val' ue: Peak value of a sine wave either in a positive or negative direction.

MAXWELL (elec.) max' well: One single line of magnetic flux.

MAXWELL, JAMES CLERK (1831-1879) (elec.): The famous Scottish scientist who gave definite meaning to the expermintal studies in electromagnetism made by Farady. He was the author of "Treatise on Electricity and Magnetism" in 1873. He supervised the construction of the Cavendish Laboratory while a professor at Cambridge University.

MEAN mean: An average value.

MEAN EFFECTIVE PRESSURE (auto.) mean ef fec' tive pres' sure: The average pressure developed in a cylinder of an engine during combustion.

MEASURE (graphics) meas' ure: The length to which a stick is set.

MECHANIC (auto.) me chan' ic: A skilled workman who repairs and assembles machinery.

MECHANICAL AXIS (elec.) me chan'- i cal ax' is: See Y AXIS.

MECHANICAL BRAKES (auto.) me- chan' i cal brakes: A system of brakes in which pressure is applied to the braking shoes through mechanical linkage of rods, cams and levers.

MECHANICAL DRAWING (draft.) me- chan' i cal draw' ing: Drawing by means of instruments such as triangles and T square. The term of mechanical drawing is used to describe all types of engineering and architectural drafting including projections and perspective drawings.

MECHANICAL EFFICIENCY (auto.) me-

chan' i cal ef fi' cien cy: In an automotive engine, it is equal to the brake horsepower divided by the indicated horsepower.

MECHANICAL ENGINEER (metal) me- chan' i cal en gi neer' : One who has been trained and is expert in the design, construction and operation of mechanical devices.

MECHANIZATION (automation) mech- a ni za' tion: Refers to machines in the first and second order of automaticity including semi-automatic machines.

MEDIAN me' di an: The average; middle.

MEDIUM FIT (metal) me' di um fit: Class 3 Fit; used for sliding and running fits which require greater accuracy than a "free fit."

MEDIUM VALUE (color) (paint. and dec.) me' di um val' ue: Color midway between a dark color and a light color.

MEDULLARY RAY (wood.) med' ul lary ray: Lines of dense cells radiating in star fish fashion from the center of a tree to the cambrium layer.

MEETING RAIL (wood.) meet' ing rail: The horizontal wood or metal bar dividing the upper and lower sash of a window.

MEGA (elec.) meg' a: Prefix meaning one million times.

MEGACYCLE (elec.) meg' a cy cle: One million cycles. Megahertz.

MEGAVOLT (elec.) meg' a volt: One million volts.

MEGGER (elec.) meg' ger: A meter for measuring resistance in high ranges up to 1,000 megohms.

MEGOHM (elec.) meg' ohm: One million ohms.

MEGOHMMETER (elec.) meg ohm' meter: See MEGGER.

MELT (air cond.) melt: Change of state from solid to liquid by addition of heat.

MELTING POINT (air cond.) melt' ing point: The melting temperature at a given pressure.

MELTING POINT (paint, and dec.) melt' ing point: Temperature at which a specific solid changes to a liquid.

MEMORY (automation) mem' o ry: The part of a control system in which data is stored for future use. Also termed STORAGE AND MEMORY STORAGE.

MEMORY CIRCUIT (elec.) mem' o ry cir' cuit: A circuit by which information can be stored. The circuit may exist in either ON or OFF position.

MEMORY SECTION (elec.) mem' or y sec' tion: See STORAGE.

MENTOR (automation) men' tor: A limited purpose computer used for control and instrumentation.

MERCURY mer' cu ry: A silver colored liquid metal with a specific gravity of 13.6. It is obtained from cinabar or mercuric sulphide ores.

MERCURY CELL (elec.) mer' cu ry cell: A type of dry primary cell which produces a steady high current by the chemical action between mercuric oxide and zinc.

MERCURY VAPOR LAMP (elec.) mer'-cu ry va' por lamp: The Cooper Hewitt lamp, which produces light by passing an electric current through mercury vapor.

MERCURY VAPOR RECTIFIER (elec.) mer' cu ry va' por rec' ti fi er: A hot cathode diode tube which uses mercury vapor instead of a high vacuum.

MESH (metal) mesh: A net-like structure; the openings formed by a series of crossed wires or strings.

METABOLISM me tab' o lism: Chemical and physical changes constantly occurring in living organisms with associated release of energy for all vital processes.

METAL (metal) met' al: Element characterized by such properties as ductility, malleability, fusibility, elements of high thermal and electrical conductivity; elements which readily form positive ions; an inclusive term meaning all metallic substances and their alloys.

METALENE NAILS (crafts) met' al lene nails: Furniture upholstery nails with large round or flat heads.

METAL FINISHING (metal) met' al fin' - ish ing: The final finishing of a metal object, by polishing or buffing or coating to produce a desired appearance.

METAL GATHERING (automation) met' al gath' er ing: A process in which a section of a tube or rod is gathered into a heavy mass at either or both ends or in the middle.

METALIZE (metal) met' al ize: To treat, cover or impregnate with a metal or metallic compound.

METAL LATH (const.) met' al lath: A fabricated metal material used as a backing and support for plaster.

METALLIC RECTIFIER (elec.) metal' lic rec' ti fi er: A rectifier made of copper oxide, based on the principle that electrons flow from copper to copper oxide but not from copper oxide to copper. It is a unidirectional conductor.

METALLIC SOAP (paint. and dec.) metal' lic soap: A compound of metal and organic acid. Metallic soaps are used as driers, fungicides, suspending agents, flatting agents.

METALLOGRAPHY (metal) met' al logra phy: The study of the microscopic structure of metals.

METALLURGY (metal) met' al lur gy: The study of the properties of metals; the science of smelting and refining metallic ores.

METAL PRIMER (paint. and dec.) met'- al prim' er: First coating applied in finishing metal.

METAL SPINNING (crafts) met' al spin'- ning: The art of producing circular and hollow shapes from malleable metals, by shaping the metal over a preformed mold with special tools as the work turns at high speeds in a lathe.

METAL SPRAYING (metal) met' al spray' ing: Adding a protective metal coating to an object by spraying an atomized metal on it. The spray metal is atomized by feeding a wire through a hydrogen-oxygen flame.

METEOR BUMPER (space) me' te or bump' er: Thin shield, comparable in thickness with the diameter of the meteor to be intercepted, around a space vehicle and designed to thermally dissipate the energy of the meteoritic particles.

METER me' ter: Unit of length = 39.37 inches. An instrument for measuring specified units and rates. Ex: Flowmeter, kilowatt-hour meter.

METER (elec.) me' ter: An instrument used to measure electrical quantities; a unit of length in the metric system. One meter = 39.37 inches.

METERING ORIFICE (auto.) me' ter ing or' i fice: A small hole which limits the flow of gasoline to the venturi of a carburetor. The size of the orifice may be controlled by a tapered pin in its center.

METERING PIN (auto.) me' ter ing pin: A pin used in a metering orifice to regulate the flow of liquid.

METERING ROD (auto.) me' ter ing rod: A tapered pin, used to control the flow through a jet. As the pin is inserted further into the jet the effective flow area is decreased.

METHANE meth' ane: Marsh gas; an odorless gas formed by the decomposition of vegetable matter.

METHODS STUDY (automation) meth'- ods stud' y: The restudy of a product for possible simplification and reduction of cost, and re-evaluation of methods of production.

METHYL ACETATE (paint. and dec.) meth' yl ac' e tate: A colorless, volatile, inflammable liquid with a distinct odor of apples. It is used as a solvent for lacquers.

METRIC met' ric: A system of measurement using the meter (39.37 inches) as the standard.

METRIC SCREW THREAD (metal) met'- ric screw thread: The system of designating screw thread measurements based on the metric system.

MEZZANINE (const.) mez' za nine: A gallery; a secondary floor between the main floor and the first floor of a building.

MHO (elec.) mho: Unit of measurement of conductance.

MICA (elec.) mi' ca: A semi transparent mineral used for insulation and as a dielectric in capacitors.

MICA CAPACITOR (elec.) mi' ca capac' i tor: A capacitor made of metal foil plates separated by sheets of mica.

MICA PIGMENT (paint. and dec.) mi' ca pig' ment: Extender pigment made from silicates of aluminum and potassium which are split into verv thin plates or sheets.

MICARTA (elec.) mi car' ta: An insulating material similar to Bakelite.

MICA UNDERCUTTER (elec.) mi' ca un der cut' ter: A tool used to cut the mica below the segments of a commutator.

MICRO mi' cro: Prefix meaning one millionth of.

MICROAMPERE (elec.) mi' cro am' - pere: One millionth of an ampere; 1×10^{-6} ampere; .000001 amperes.

MICROFARAD (uf) (elec.) mi cro far' - ad: One millionth of a farad.

MICROHENRY (uh) (elec.) mi' cro henry: One millionth of a henry.

MICROINCH mi' cro inch: One millionth of an inch.

MICROMETER (metal) mi crom' e ter: A direct reading caliper for measuring dimensions, which employs an accurate screw which may be revolved in a fixed nut to vary the opening between the measuring faces.

MICROMETER COLLARS (metal) microm' e ter col' lars: Graduated collars on control wheels of machines, usually marked in thousandths of an inch.

MICROMETER, INSIDE (metal) microm' e ter, in side' : A micrometer for inside measurements. It is equipped with a variety of rods. The rod may be extended by rotating the micrometer thimble. It is read directly in thousandths of an inch.

MICROMETER, SCREW THREAD (metal) mi crom' e ter, screw thread: See SCREW THREAD MICROMETER.

MICROMHO (elec.) mi' cro mho: One millionth of a mho.

MICROMICRO (elec.) mi' cro mi cro: Prefix meaning one millionth of one millionth of.

MICROMICROFARAD (uuf) (elec.) micro mi cro far' ad: One millionth of one millionth of a farad. Picofarad.

MICROMINIATURIZATION (elec.) micro min i a tur i za' tion: The techniques of circuitry where several components such as resistors and transistors are etched or deposited on a tiny section of semiconductor material.

MICRON (air cond.) mi' cron: Unit of

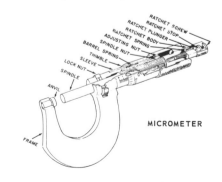

MICROMETER

measurement = one meter x 10^{-6} ; one millionth of a meter.

MICROPHONE (elec.) mi' cro phone: An energy converter that changes sound energy into corresponding electrical energy.

MICROPHONES, TYPE OF (elec.) mi' - cro phones, types of:

CAPACITOR, output is produced by a variation in capacitance between a sound diaphragm and a back plate.

CARBON, output is obtained by the variation of the resistance of carbon granules. Carbon is compressed by linkage to a sound diaphragm.

CRYSTAL, sound impinged upon diaphragm distorts crystal which produces signal output due to piezoelectric effect.

DYNAMIC, employs a moving coil in a magnetic field. Action is the reverse of the dynamic speaker.

RIBBON, signal is produced by sound acting on metallic ribbon suspended in magnetic field.

VELOCITY, a microphone which responds to the instantaneous velocity of sound wave.

MICROPHONICS (elec.) mi' cro phonics: Distortion as a result of slight vibrations of tube elements.

MICROPHOTOGRAPH (graphics) micro pho' to graph: A photograph at a reduction; a small photograph of a large object.

MICROSECOND (elec.) mi cro' sec ond: One millionth of a second.

MICROSWITCH (elec.) mi' cro switch: A trade name for a very sensitive switch.

MICROVOLT (elec.) mi' cro volt: One millionth of a volt; 1×10^{-6} volts or .000001 volts.

MICROWAVE (elec.) mi' cro wave. Electromagnetic waves with a wave length of less than one meter.

MICROWAVE REFLECTOR (elec.) mi' - cro wave re flec' tor: A disk or parabolic shaped reflector to guide microwave beams.

MIG (welding) mig: Abbreviation for Metal Inert Gas Welding. Type of welding in which arc is surrounded by gas which keeps atmosphere away, and does not react with electrode or base metal.

MIKE (elec.) mike: An abbreviated term for microphone.

MIL mil: Unit of thickness, 1/1000 in. (.001 in.).

MILDEW (const.) mil' dew: Mold which forms on objects exposed to moisture.

MILDEW (paint. and dec.) mil' dew: Whitish or spotted discoloration caused by parasitic fungi.

MILD STEEL (metal) mild steel: Low carbon steel; steel which does not harden but can be casehardened.

MIL-FOOT (elec.) mil-foot: A wire which is one mil in diameter and one foot long.

MILITARY AUTOMATION (automation) mil' i tar y au to ma' tion: Automation of energy and information to deliver an offensive projectile to the enemy and also detect and intercept enemy offensive action.

MILL FILE (metal) mill file: A common single cut flat file, ten or twelve inches in length.

MILLI mil' li: Prefix meaning one thousandth of.

MILLIAMMETER (elec.) mil li am'me ter: A meter which measures in the milliammeter range of currents.

MILLIAMPERE (elec.) mil' li am' pere: One thousandth of an ampere; 1×10^{-3} amperes or .001 amperes.

MILLIHENRY (mh) (elec.) mil' li henry: One thousandth of a henry.

MILLIMETER mil li me' ter: One thousandth of a meter; .03937 inches.

MILLING (metal) mill' ing: The process of cutting metals with multiple tooth rotary cutters.

MILLING CUTTERS, Types of (metal) mill' ing cut' ters, types of:

ANGULAR CUTTERS, mills which have teeth at some oblique angle to the axis of the cutter.

CONCAVE CUTTERS, a formed milling cutter with half circle concave teeth.

CONVEX CUTTERS, a formed milling cutter with half circle convex teeth.

DOUBLE ANGLE CUTTERS, cutters with double oblique angles to the axis of the cutter.

END MILL, a chuck held miller with teeth on its periphery and end.

FLY CUTTER, a small square cutter mounted in an arbor.

PLAIN, straight or spiral teeth on the periphery only, for cutting flat surfaces.

SHELL END MILL, end mills over two inches in diameter which are detachable from shank.

SIDE MILLING, a plain milling cutter with teeth also on the sides.

SLITTING SAW, a thin plain milling cutter.

MILLING MACHINE (metal) mill' ing ma chine' : A machine which uses a rotary cutter to remove material from the work. The cutter may be mounted

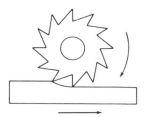

on either a horizontal or vertical spindle depending upon the type of machine. The work is fastened to a table which is mechanically fed into contact with the cutter.

MILLING OPERATIONS (metal) mill' ing op er a' tions:

ANGULAR, cutting flat surface at an angle to axis of cutter.

FACE, cutting at right angles to axis of cutter.

FLUTE, cutting spiral flutes or grooves on drills.

FORM, cutting an irregular surface with form cutter.

GANG, using two or more cutters on one arbor.

PLAIN, production of flat surfaces.

SLAB, same as plain milling.

STRADDLE, using two cutters which straddle the work and cut both sides at once.

MILLWORK (wood.) mill' work: Finish woodwork, machined and may be partially assembled at the mill.

MILLIVOLT (elec.) mil' li volt: One thousandth of a volt; 1×10^{-3} volts or .001 volts.

MILL WHITE (paint. and dec.) mill white: White paint used to augment illumination on interior wall surface of industrial plants, office and school buildings.

MILLWRIGHT mill' wright: A skilled mechanic who specializes in the installation of machinery in a mill.

MILORI BLUE (paint. and dec.) milor' i blue: An iron blue pigment.

MINARET (const.) min' a ret: A slender tower-like structure.

MINERAL BLACK (paint. and dec.) min' er al black: A natural black pigment based on graphite.

MINERALOGY (metal) min' er al o gy: The science of minerals including identification and classification.

MINERAL OIL (paint. and dec.) min' er al oil: Oil obtained from petroleum by distillation or other processes.

MINERAL SPIRITS (paint. and dec.) min' er al spir' its: Petroleum product which has about the same evaporation rate as gum turpentine.

MINIMUM min' i mum: The least quantity or amount; the lowest value or point.

MINING (metal) min' ing: Extracting minerals from the earth.

MINION (graphics) min' ion: The name of a type size.

MINOR AXIS (draft.) mi' nor ax' is: The shorter diameter of an ellipse.

MINOR CARRIER (elec.) mi' nor car' ri er: Conduction through a semiconductor opposite to major carrier. Ex: If electrons are the major carrier, then holes are the minor carrier.

MINOR DIAMETER (metal) mi' nor diam' e ter: The smallest diameter of a screw thread.

MINUS (symbol -) (elec.) mi' nus: Negative terminal or junction of a circuit.

MINUSCULE (graphics) mi nus' cule: A lower case letter.

MINUTEMAN (space) min' ute man: An Air Force intercontinental ballistic missile whose designed range is 5,500 nautical miles. Powered by three stage solid propellant rocket engines.

MISALIGNMENT (auto.) mis a lign'ment: In automotive mechanics this term refers to the out of adjustment condition of the front end of a car and steering mechanism such as toe-in, camber and caster. Poor alignment causes hard steering and excessive tire wear.

MISCIBLE (paint. and dec.) mis' ci ble: Capable of being mixed. Examples: lacquer thinner is miscible with lacquer, water and alcohol are miscible.

MISMATCH (elec.) mis match' : Incorrect matching of a load to a source.

MISSILERY (space) mis' sile ry: The art of science of designing, developing, building, launching, directing and sometimes guiding a missile.

MISSING (auto.) mis' sing: A term used

to describe rough engine operation due to failure of one or more cylinders to fire.

MISSION TYPE (wood.) mis' sion type: A particular furniture design identified by massive structure and straight lines. It is usually dark in color and made of oak.

MITER (const.) mi' ter: The cutting of moldings or trim at a 45° angle and joined so that they form a right angle.

MITER BOX (wood.) mi' ter box: A box-like device with fixed or adjustable guides to hold miter saw so that desired angles may be cut accurately.

MITER GEAR (metal) mi' ter gear: A bevel gear with a pitch cone at an angle of 45 degrees with its axis. Two mating bevel gears transmit power at a right angle.

MITER JOINT (const.) mi' ter joint: A joint made when two pieces are cut at

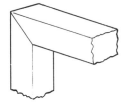

a 45° angle and jointed so that they form a right angle.

MITER SAW (wood.) mi' ter saw: A long backsaw used with a miter box for cutting various angles.

MITER SQUARE (wood.) mi' ter square: A try square with provisions on the head for laying out 45 degree miters.

MITER VISE (wood.) mi' ter vise: A clamping device to hold mitered parts together during fitting, gluing and nailing.

MITOGRAPHY (graphics) mi to' graphy: The art of silk screen process printing.

MIXER (elec.) mix' er: A multigrid tube used to combine several input signals.

MIXER (audio) (elec.) mix' er: A system of variable risistors or pads used to mix signals from various program sources.

MIXING CHAMBER (weld.) mix' ing cham' ber: That part of the welding torch where the welding gases are intimately mixed prior to combustion.

MKS (elec.) Meter-kilogram-second unit.

MMF (elec.) Abbreviation for magneto-motive force.

MOBILITY (elec.) mo bil' i ty: The velocity of current carriers in a semiconductor. The ratio of the velocity of the carrier to the applied electric field, expressed as cm^2 /volt, sec.

MOBILITY (paint. and dec.) mo bil' i-ty: The degree to which a material flows.

MOCK-UP (metal) mock-up: A mechanical device, simulating an actual machine or part, used as a training device.

MODELING (crafts) mod' el ing: Shaping by smoothing and pressure such as modeling clay.

MODERN (graphics) mod' ern: A type face design characterized by straight serifs and thin hair lines.

MODULAR CONSTRUCTION (const.) mod' u lar con struc' tion: The use of standard units of size in manufacture and construction.

MODULAR UNITS (automation) mod' -

u lar u' nits: Semi-products designed for flexible arrangements to suit requirements.

MODULATED CONTINUOUS WAVE (mcw) (elec.) mod u lat' ed con tin' u ous wave: A carrier wave amplitude modulated by a tone signal of constant frequency.

MODULATION (elec.) mod u la' tion: The process by which the amplitude or frequency of a sine-wave voltage is made to vary according to variations of another voltage or current called the modulation signal.

MODULATION INDEX (elec.) mod u- la' tion in' dex: The ratio between the amount of frequency deviation in FM to the frequency of the modulating signal.

MODULATION PERCENT (elec.) mod- u la' tion per cent' : In FM radio; a frequency swing of ±75 kc. In TV, a frequency swing of ±25 kc. for 100% modulation.

MODULATION PRODUCT (elec.) mod- u la' tion prod' uct: Sideband frequencies resulting from modulation of a radio wave.

MODULE (metal) mod' ule: (English measurement) The reciprocal of the diametral pitch on a gear.

MODULUS mod' u lus: A number, co-efficient or quantity which measures a force, function or effect.

MODULUS OF ELASTICITY (metal) mod' u lus of e las tic' i ty: The ratio of the stress in pounds per square inch applied to a metal specimen to the elongation in fractions of an inch for each inch of the original specimen length.

MOGUL (elec.) mo gul': A large socket or receptacle used with lights of over 300 watts.

MOHAIR (crafts) mo' hair: A fabric made of Angora goat hair.

MOH'S SCALE (metal) moh's scale: A hardness scale in which numbers 1-10 have been assigned to specific substances. An unknown substance is compared to a standard substance.

MOISTURE (paint. and dec.) mois' ture: Finely divided particles of water; water causing slight wetness or dampness.

MOISTURE CONTENT OF WOOD (paint. and dec.) mois' ture con' tent of wood: The amount of water contained in wood, usually expressed as a percentage of the weight of oven-dry wood.

MOLD (metal) mold: The pattern or hollow form in which molten metal is poured to make a desired shape. In foundry, the pattern is packed in sand, then the pattern removed and the metal poured in through an opening called a sprue.

MOLDING (const.) mold' ing: Any pieces of wood cut and milled to a special shape or pattern.

MOLDING CUTTERS (wood.) mold' ing cut' ters: Cutters used on a spindle

shaper. They are manufactured in a variety of accepted shapes and contours.

MOLDING SAND (metal) mold' ing sand: Special sands used for molding in a foundry.

MOLECULAR THEORY (elec.) molec' u lar the' o ry: The theory that all matter is made up of minute particles called "molecules" each having the same properties as the whole part of a particular substance.

MOLECULE (elec.) mol' e cule: The smallest division of matter. If further subdivision is made, the matter will lose its identity.

MOLYBDENITE (metal) mo lyb' denite: The most common of ores of molybdenum. It is a greasy graphite-like ore and is found in small quantities in granite, gneiss and limestone.

MOLYBDENUM (metal) mo lyb' denum: A metallic element used chiefly as an alloy for steels and cast iron. It produces a very hard steel which is used for machine cutting tools.

MOMENT mo' ment: The product of a specified force, mass or volume and its perpendicular distance from its axis or fulcrum.

MOMENTUM mo men' tum: The product of mass and velocity; the impetus of a moving object.

MONEL METAL (metal) mo nel' met' - al: An alloy of 60% nickel, 38% copper and a small amount of aluminum.

MONITOR (elec.) mon' i tor: To listen or to view a radio or TV broadcast for purposes of checking.

MONO-BLOCK (auto.) mon' o-block: A type of engine block construction when all cylinders are contained in one casting.

MONOCHROMATIC HARMONY (paint. and dec.) mon o chro mat' ic har' - mo ny: Color harmony formed by using shades and tints of a single color.

MONOCHROME TELEVISION (elec.) mon' o chrome tel' e vi sion: Black and white pictures.

MONOPROPELLANT (space) mon o-pro pel' lant: A rocket propellant in which the fuel and oxidizer are pre-mixed, ready for immediate use.

MONOSCOPE (elec.) mon' o scope: A TV test camera with a fixed image called a test pattern.

MONOTONE (graphics) mon' o tone: All one color; a type face in which various elements are all equal in width.

MORDANT (crafts) mor' dant: A corrosive preparation used in etching of metals.

MORPHY (metal) mor' phy: A common name for the hermaphrodite caliper.

MORSE CODE (elec.) An international system where letters, numbers and symbols are represented by dashes and dots, or dahs and dits. It is used in radio communications. The emission of the transmitting station is keyed to conform to coded characters which contain the message information. Also called the International Morse Code.

MORSE TAPER (metal) Morse ta' per: A system of standard dimensions for tapers.

MORTAR (const.) mor' tar: A mixture of sand and cement used in masonry.

MORTAR BOARD (const.) mor' tar board: A hawk; a square board with a handle underneath on which a mason holds mortar.

MORTAR BOX (const.) mor' tar box: A large box or container used for mixing mortar, plaster and concrete.

MORTAR JOINT (const.) mor' tar joint: The seam filled with mortar joining bricks or blocks.

MORTISE (const.) mor' tise: A hole or recess in a piece of wood to receive a tenon.

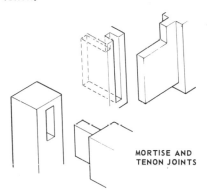

MORTISE AND TENON JOINTS

MORTISE CHISEL (wood.) mor' tise chis' el: A heavy bodied wood chisel for cutting mortises.

MORTISE GAUGE (wood.) mor' tise gauge: A combination marking gauge used for laying-out the size and depth of a mortise.

MORTISE LOCK (wood.) mor' tise lock: A lock, such as on a door, which is fitted into a mortise.

MOSAIC (elec.) mo sa' ic: The photo sensitive surface used in an Iconoscope TV camera tube.

MOTHER (elec.) moth' er: In disk recording, it is a mold obtained by electroforming from the original master.

MOTIF (crafts) mo tif' : The predominate decorative scheme, design or ornamentation.

MOTOMETER (auto.) mo tom' e ter: A speedometer; a speed counter.

MOTOR (elec.) mo' tor: A device which converts electrical energy into mechanical energy.

MOTOR (elec.) mo' tor:

INDUCTION, a common type of a-c motor in which power is delivered to the stator windings. A current is induced in the rotor which consists of closed loops mounted in the rotating core. The interaction between fields produces rotation.

REPULSION INDUCTION, an a-c motor which operates as a repulsion motor during starting and as an induction motor while running.

SHADED POLE, an induction motor with a short circuited auxilliary winding on each pole face. The interaction of fields produces a partial rotation required for starting.

SPLIT PHASE, an induction motor which will start on single phase current, due to displacement in phase created by unequal reactances of the starting and running windings.

SYNCHRONOUS, a motor whose speed is dependent upon the frequency of the applied voltage and the number of field poles.

MOTOR, AIR (air cond.) mo' tor, air: An air pressure activated device generally used to open and close valves.

MOTOR ANALYZER (auto.) mo' tor an-a lyz' er: A combination of meters and instruments used in tune-up and trouble shooting an automotive engine.

MOTORBOATING (elec.) mo' tor boating: Low frequency oscillation of an audio amplifier due to excessive re-generation.

MOTOR GENERATOR (elec.) mo' tor gen' er a tor: An electric motor driv-ing a generator used to convert a–c to d–c or d–c to a–c.

MOTOR REACTION (elec.) mo' tor re-ac' tion: The opposing force to rotation developed in a generator, created by the load current.

MOTOR STARTER (elec.) mo' tor start' er: A hand or automatic variable resistance box used to limit the current to a motor during the time it is in-creasing to rated speed. As speed in-creases, the resistance is decreased.

MOTORS, Types of d–c (elec.) mo' tors, types of d–c:

COMPOUND, uses both series and parallel field coils.

SERIES, field coils are connected in series with armature circuit.

SHUNT, field coils are connected in parallel with armature circuit.

MOTTLED (crafts) mot' tled: Spotted; a variety of colors and shades, varie-gated finish.

MOVIEOLA (elec.) mov' ie o la: A de-vice to edit motion picture film.

MU (elec.) mu: Greek letter (u) used to represent the amplification factor of a vacuum tube; magnetic permeability; the prefix meaning one millionth of.

MUCILAGE (crafts) mu' ci lage: Glue; an adhesive made of vegetable gums from certain plants.

MUCK BAR (metal) muck bar: A bar of wrought iron after it has passed through

the muck rolls. A shape of wrought iron during manufacturing when a bloom is reduced by mucking rolls.

MUD SILL (const.) mud sill: A founda-tion timber placed directly on the ground.

MUFACTOR (elec.) mu fac' tor: In vacuum tubes, it is equal to the change in plate voltage to a change in grid voltage while holding the plate current at a constant value.

MUFFLE (crafts – auto.) muf'fle: A chamber in a ceramic kiln used for fir-ing clay; to reduce noise by passing the exhaust of an engine through a muffler.

MUFFLE FURNACE (crafts) muf' fle fur' nace: A small high temperature furnace used for annealing and enam-eling metals.

MUFFLER (auto.) muf' fler: A tank con-taining a series of holes and baffle plates connected between the exhaust manifold and the tailpipe. Its purpose is to absorb and muffle the noise of the engine exhaust.

MULLION (const.) mul' lion: A slender vertical dividing bar between lights of a window or screen.

MULTI-COLOR SPRAYING (paint. and dec.) mul' ti-col' or spray' ing: Spray-ing a surface with two or more differ-ent colors at one time from one gun. The multiple colors exist separately within the material and when sprayed create an interlacing color network with each color retaining its individuality.

MULTIELEMENT TUBE (elec.) mul' -ti el e ment tube: Electron tube with more elements than a cathode, plate and grid.

MULTIGRID TUBE (elec.) mul' ti grid

tube: A special tube with 4, 5 or 6 grids.

MULTIMETER (elec.) mul' ti me ter: A combination volt, ampere and ohm meter.

MULTIPLANER PROJECTION (draft.) mul' ti plan er pro jec' tion: See MULTIVIEW PROJECTION.

MULTIPLE DISK CLUTCH (auto.) mul' - ti ple disk clutch: A mechanical clutch system using a number of disks, part of which are driving and the others driven. They are held in contact by compression springs. Operation of the foot pedal releases the spring pressure and disengages the clutch.

MULTIPLE POINT CUTTING TOOLS (metal) mul' ti ple point cut' ting tools: Cutting tools such as drills, reamers, routers, milling cutters and tools used for hobbing, tapping, sawing and broaching.

MULTIPLE REVOLUTION (draft.) mul' ti ple rev o lu' tion: See SUCCESSIVE REVOLUTION.

MULTIPLEX (elec.) mul' ti plex: A method employed in radio and telephone communications where several messages are transmitted in one or both directions over a single transmission path.

MULTIPLEXER (elec.) mul' ti plex er: A mechanical or electrical device for sharing a circuit by two or more coincident signals.

MULTIPLIER (elec.) mul' ti pli er: A precision resistor connected in series with a voltmeter to increase its range.

MULTIPOLAR (elec.) mul' ti po lar: Having two or more poles or field coils.

MULTIUNIT TUBES (elec.) mul' ti u nit tubes:

HEXODE, six elements with four grids.

HEPTODE, seven elements with five grids.

OCTODE, eight elements with six grids.

TWIN DIODE, two diodes in one envelope.

TWIN DIODE-TRIODE, a diode and triode in one envelope.

TWIN DIODE-TETRODE, a diode and tetrode in one envelope.

TWIN PENTODE, two pentodes in one envelope.

MULTIVIBRATOR (elec.) mul' ti vi bra tor: An oscillator employing two tubes or transistors in such a way that the output of one is coupled to the input of the other (and vice versa) by means of a resistance capacitance coupling network.

MULTIVIBRATORS, Type of (elec.) mul' ti vi bra tors, Types of:

ASTABLE, a free-running multivibrator.

BISTABLE, a single-trigger pulse switches conduction from one tube to the other. See FLIP-FLOP and ECCLES-JORDAN.

CATHODE COUPLED, both tubes have a common cathode resistor.

FREE-RUNNING, frequency of oscillation depending upon value of circuit components. Continuous oscillation.

MONOSTABLE, one trigger pulse is required to complete one cycle of operation.

ONE SHOT, Same as MONOSTABLE.

PLATE COUPLED, the plates of the tubes and grids are connected by RC networks.

MULTIVIEW PROJECTION (draft.) mul' ti view pro jec' tion: Views of an object as projected upon two or more picture planes in orthographic projection.

MUNTIN (const.) mun' tin: The small dividers between window panes.

MUNTZ METAL (metal) muntz met' al: An alloy of copper (60%) and zinc (40%). Used in ship building.

MURIATIC ACID, mu' ri at' ic ac' id: A dilute form of hydrochloric acid.

MUSH COIL (elec.) mush coil: A coil not wound in regular layers, sometimes called scramble wound.

MUSIC WIRE (metal) mu' sic wire: A high quality steel wire with great tensile strength and resilience without hardness.

MUTTON QUAD (graphics) mut' ton quad: An EM.

MUTUAL CONDUCTANCE (elec.) mu' - tu al con duc' tance: See TRANSCONDUCTANCE.

MUTUAL INDUCTANCE (M) (elec.) mu' tu al in duc' tance: When two coils are so located that the magnetic flux of one coil can link with the turns of the other coil so that a change in flux of one coil will cause an emf in the other, there is mutual inductance.

MYLAR (elec.) my' lar: A DuPont trade name for polyester film used in the manufacture of high quality recording tapes.

MYRTLE (wood.) myr' tle: California laurel; a strong hard greenish yellow wood which is attractive for veneers.

NAIL (wood.) nail: A device for fastening wood together, a wire, headed on one end and pointed on the other. Used as a wood fastener. Nails are sized by the term "penney" which is the number of pounds per 1000 nails. They are manufactured in a large variety of wire sizes, lengths and heads and for special purposes.

NAILSET (wood.) nail' set: A punch type tool used to set the head of a nail below the surface of the wood.

NAILSET

NAPHTHA naph' tha: A cleaning solvent; a distillate of petroleum between gasoline and benzine.

NAPHTHA (paint. and dec.) naph' tha: An inflammable, volatile oily liquid produced by the fractional distillation of petroleum. It is between gasoline and benzine. Used as a solvent and as fuel.

NASA (space) nasa: National Aeronautics and Space Agency.

NATIONAL COARSE (NC) (metal) na' - tion al coarse: See THREADS.

NATIONAL ELECTRIC CODE (elec.) A set of rules and regulations to be used by the electrician when installing electric wiring, appliances and machinery.

NATIONAL FINE (NF) (metal) na' tional fine: Series of screw threads,
characterized by 60 deg. angle formed
by sides of thread and small flat at
thread crest and root. NF series has

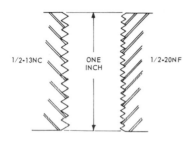

1/2-13NC   ONE INCH   1/2-20NF

more threads per inch than NC (National Coarse) series. See drawing for
comparison of NC and NF threads.
Both have same geometric shape.

NATIONAL PLUMBING CODE (plumb.)
na' tion al   plumb' ing   code: The
recommendations and requirements for
plumbing published jointly by the
American Society of Mechanical Engineers and the American Public Health
Association.

NATURAL GAS nat' u ral gas: Gas
formed in the earth, particularly in
oil regions. It is an excellent fuel and
is widely used in both home and industry.

NATURAL MAGNET (elec.) nat' u ral
mag' net: Magnets found in natural state
in the form of a mineral called Magnetite.

NATURAL RESINS (paint. and dec.) nat'-
u ral res' ins: Essentially the result
of exudation of trees. Divided into two
large classes, dammars and copals.
Resins are usually named after the
locality in which they are found or the
port of shipment.

NAVAL STORES (paint. and dec.) na' val
stores: A group of products derived
from the pine tree such as turpentine,
rosin and pine oil.

NEAT CEMENT (const.) neat ce ment'
A pure cement mixture, with no sand.

NEAT'S FOOT OIL (crafts) Neat's foot
oil: An oil used as a preservative and
softener of leather.

NEBULAE (space) neb' u lae: Galactic
nebulae are clouds of interstellar matter whose presence is revealed either
because they are illuminated by a
bright star or because they noticeably
weaken the light from stars in a particular region of the sky; unborn stars.

NEC (elec.)   NATIONAL   ELECTRIC
CODE.

NECKING (metal) neck' ing: Cutting a
narrow groove in the work by turning
on lathe.

NEEDLE (elec.) nee' dle: The pointer
on a compass; the indicating pointer
on a meter; a part of a phonograph
pickup which rides in the grooves of
a record.

NEEDLE BEARING   (auto.)   nee' dle
bear' ing: An antifriction bearing using
a large number of needlelike rollers.

NEEDLE CASE (metal) nee' dle case:
See STAKE.

NEEDLE-HANDLE FILES (metal) nee' _
dle-han' dle files: A group of very fine
files for delicate work. They are made
in a variety of shapes and sizes.

NEEDLE VALVE (plumb.) nee' dle valve:
A valve which controls flow through a
jet by the insertion or withdrawal of a
needlelike pin in the jet.

NEGATIVE (graphics) neg' a tive: A
photographic image with lights and
shades in reverse to those of the
original image.

NEGATIVE G (space) neg' a tive g: The opposite of "positive g." In a gravitational field or during an acceleration the human body is so positioned that the force of inertia acts on it in a foot-to-head direction.

NEGATIVE, symbol (-) (elec.) neg' a-tive, symbol (-): The point in a circuit with the greatest electron concentration.

BIAS, the voltage applied to the control grid of an electron tube. It is usually negative.

CHARGE, having an excess of electrons.

NEGATIVE FEEDBACK (elec.) neg' a-tive feed' back: See DEGENERATIVE FEEDBACK.

NEGATIVE GHOSTS (elec.) neg' a tive ghosts: A ghost picture in television when the black and white areas are reversed.

NEGATIVE ION (elec.) neg' a tive i' on: An atom which has gained electrons and is negatively charged.

NEGATIVE RESISTANCE (elec.) neg' a-tive re sis' tance: A condition in a circuit where an increase in voltage produces a decrease in current.

NEGATIVE TEMPERATURE COEFFI-CIENT (elec.) neg' a tive tem' per a-ture co ef fi' cient: A negative change in characteristics such as frequency or resistance, as a result of a positive change in temperature.

NEON (elec.) ne' on: A rare gas. It has low resistance and good electrical conductivity.

NEON GLOW LAMP (elec.) ne' on glow lamp: A cold cathode, gas filled diode.

NETWORK (elec.) net' work: Two or more components connected in either series or parallel.

NEUTRAL (elec.) neu' tral: Neither positive or negative.

NEUTRAL CONDUCTOR (elec.) neu' tral con duc' tor: The grounded wire in a two wire system; the grounded third wire in a three wire system.

NEUTRALIZATION (elec.) neu tral i-za' tion: The process of feeding back a voltage from the plate of an amplifier to the grid, 180° out of phase, to prevent self-oscillation.

NEUTRAL FLAME (weld.) neu' tral flame: Flame which results from combustion of perfect proportions of oxygen and the welding gas.

NEUTRAL POSITION (elec.) neu' tral po si' tion: In a generator, it is the point at which the armature conductors are not cutting across the magnetic field and do not produce a voltage.

NEUTRAL WIRE (elec.) neu' tral wire: The balance wire in a three wire electrical distribution system.

NEUTRINO (elec.) neu tri' no: An uncharged particle resulting from the breakdown or decay of a neutron into a proton, an electron and a neutrino.

NEUTRODYNE (elec.) neu' tro dyne: The control of feedback in a radio circuit by neutralizing capacitors.

NEUTRON (elec.) neu' tron: A particle which is electrically neutral.

NEWEL POST (const.) new' el post: A post usually ornamented, placed at the foot of a staircase which acts as the starting support for a handrail.

NEWS INK (graphics) news ink: Ink used on absorbent paper.

NEWTON (elec.) new' ton: A unit of force which will give a one kilogram mass an acceleration of one meter per second ^{2}

NEWTON, ISAAC (1642–1727) (elec.) The famous English scientist and mathematician. He is known as the inventor of calculus and formulated the theory of gravitation.

NEWTON'S LAWS OF MOTION

1. Every body continues in a state of rest or in uniform motion in a straight line, unless acted upon by a force to change its state of rest or motion.

2. If a body is acted upon by several forces, it is acted upon by each of these forces as if the others did not exist.

3. To every action there is always an equal reaction.

NIBBLER (metal) nib' bler: A shear type metal cutting tool used for cutting irregular shapes in sheet metal. It cuts in little bits or nibbles.

NICHE (const.) niche: A recess in a wall.

NICHROME (elec.) ni' chrome: A high resistance wire made of an alloy of nickel and chromium. It is used for heating elements.

NICK (graphics) nick: A groove in the shank of a type character to enable the compositor to distinguish between different fonts of type when distributing, and to indicate, both by sight and touch, which is the bottom of a letter.

NICKEL (metal) nick' el: (Ni); a metallic element. It is a hard white metal with a specific gravity of 8.63. It is used as an alloy in steel and for plating.

NICKEL CADMIUM CELL (elec.) nick' - el cad' mi um cell: An alkaline cell with a paste electrolyte hermetically sealed. Used in aircraft.

NICKEL SILVER (elec.) nick' el sil' ver: Called German silver; an alloy of zinc, copper and nickel.

NIGGLING (crafts) nig' gling: To be too fussy; too elaborate in detail; putter around.

NIPPERS (wood.) nip' pers: A pincer tool with sharp jaws for cutting.

NIPPLE (plumb.) nip' ple: A short piece of pipe, threaded on each end. They are

made in all sizes and are classified as close, short and long nipples.

NITRIDING (metal) ni' trid ing: Producing a hard surface on low carbon steel by heating in an atmosphere of ammonia gas.

NITROCELLULOSE (paint. and dec.) nitro cel' lu lose: A substance used in lacquers made from cellulose treated with nitric acid; also used in explosives and photographic films; cellulose nitrate.

NODE (elec.) node: The point at which the amplitude in a stationary-wave system is zero.

NOGGING (const.) nog' ging: Brick used to fill spaces between studs and timbers.

NOISE (elec.) noise: Any undesired interference to a signal.

NOISE FIGURE (elec.) noise fig' ure: In transistors, the ratio of the actual noise power to the theoretical noise power, expressed in decibels.

NOISE LIMITER (elec.) noise lim' i ter: A special circuit which blocks sudden bursts of noise through the receiver.

NO LOAD VOLTAGE (elec.) no load volt' age: The terminal voltage of a battery or supply when no current is flowing in external circuit.

NOMINAL SIZE (draft.) nom' i nal size: The designating size without specifying any limits; the conventional size.

NOMOGRAPH (draft.) nom' o graph: A diagram by which equations may be solved by placing a straightedge between known values and reading the unknown where the straightedge intersects its scale.

NONCONDUCTOR (elec.) non con duc' - tor: An insulator; material which does not conduct electricity.

NON-DRYING OILS (paint. and dec.) non-dry' ing oils: Oils which are unable to take up oxygen from the air and change from a liquid to a solid state. Mineral oils are non-drying oils.

NONFERROUS (metal) non fer' rous: Metals that contain little or no iron.

NON-GRAIN-RAISING STAIN (NGR Stain) (paint. and dec.) non-grain-rais' ing stain: Wood stain which does not raise the grain of the wood.

NONINDUCTIVE (elec.) non in duc' - tive: A component or circuit which has a minimum of inductance.

LOAD, a load which has very little self-inductance. Current and voltage will be in phase.

RESISTOR, a wire wound resistance which has a minimum inductance at high frequencies.

WINDING, a type of winding in which magnetic fields cancel each other and provide a noninductive resistance.

NONISOMETRIC LINES (draft.) non iso-met' ric lines: Lines in pictorial draw-

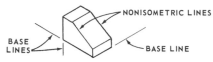

ing which are not parallel to one of three base lines as used in isometric drawings.

NONLINEAR DEVICE (elec.) non lin' - e ar de vice' : An electronic device or component whose current-voltage relation is not a straight line.

NONMAGNETIC (elec.) non mag net' ic: Materials which are not attracted by a magnet.

NON-METALLIC SHEATHING (elec.) non-me tal' lic sheath' ing: See LOOM.

NONPAREIL (graphics) non par eil' : 6 point type; a unit of measure equal to one-half pica or about one-tenth of an inch.

NONRESONANT LINE (elec.) non res' - o nant line: A line which has no standing waves. It is either infinitely long or terminated by its characteristic impedance.

NON-VOLATILE (paint. and dec.) non-vol' a tile: Portion of a product which does not evaporate at ordinary temperature.

NORMAL (elec.) nor' mal: The usua position or state of a device or circuit.

NORMALIZE (metal) nor' mal ize: A

heat treatment to eliminate internal stresses and obtain uniform grain structure in metals.

NORMALLY CLOSED (NC) (elec.) nor'-mal ly closed (nc): Refers to a switch or relay in its nonactivated state.

NORMALLY OPEN (NO) (elec.) nor'-mal ly o' pen (no): Refers to a switch or relay in its nonactivated state.

NORTH POLE (elec.) north pole: The concentration of magnetic lines of force at one end of a magnet. Magnetic lines are considered as leaving the North Pole; the direction toward which a compass points.

NOSE CONE (space) nose cone: The shield that fits over, or is, the nose of an aerospace vehicle built to withstand high temperatures generated by friction with air particles.

NOSE RADIUS (metal) nose ra' di us: The radius of the round between the side and end cutting edge angles.

NOSINGS (const.) nos' ings: The rounded and projected edges of stair treads.

NOTCHING MACHINE (metal) notch' ing ma chine': A sheet metal cutting machine employing dies to cut out rectangular and square corners. It is used extensively in box and chassis construction.

NOT CIRCUIT (elec.) not cir' cuit: A circuit that produces no output, if input signal is present.

NOVA (space) no' va: Star which undergoes a sudden and enormous increase in brightness.

NOVELTY SIDING (const.) nov' el ty sid' ing: Wood siding milled to a special design.

NOZZLE (plumb.) noz' zle: Outlet from the end of a pipe, a hose or a faucet. A nozzle usually reduces the size of the water stream or changes its shape.

NOZZLE (weld.) noz' zle: See TIP.

NOZZLE BLOCK (space) noz' zle block: The "throat" of a wind tunnel which regulates the air flow and velocity.

NUCLEAR FUEL (space) nu' cle ar fuel: A fuel that consists of a nuclear reactor controlled so as to produce a form of energy than can be used in an engine or motor.

NUCLEAR PROPULSION (space) nu'-cle ar pro pul' sion: Propulsion by means of atomic energy.

NUCLEONICS (elec.) nu cle on' ics: The branch of physics dealing with the science of small particles and the release of energy from the atom.

NUCLEUS (elec.) nu' cle us: The core of the atom.

NULL (elec.) null: The zero point.

NULL INDICATOR (elec.) null in' di-ca tor: A meter designed to indicate the balance of a circuit; indicator for no current or no voltage in a circuit.

NUMBER DRILLS (metal) num' ber drills: Small twist drills numbered from 1 to 80 and sized in thousandths of an inch. No. 1 is .228 inches in diameter and No. 80 is .0135 inches in diameter.

NUMERALS (graphics) nu' mer als: Numbers; the arabic numerals are 1, 2, 3, etc., the roman numerals are I, II, III, IV, V, etc.

NUMERICAL CONTROL (automation) nu mer' i cal con trol': Information furnished to a machine in which the data concerning the workpiece is arranged in numerical form and translated into punched tape or card codes.

NUMERICAL POSITIONING CONTROL
(automation) nu mer' i cal po si' tioning con trol': A system of machine and tool control used in automation.

NUT (metal) nut: A small metal block made in a variety of shapes such as

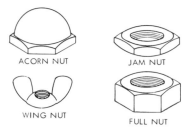

ACORN NUT   JAM NUT

WING NUT   FULL NUT

square and hexagonal which is drilled and internally threaded to match a bolt.

NUTDRIVER (elec.) nut' driv er: A small socket wrench mounted on a screwdriver type handle.

NUT QUAD (graphics) nut quad: An EN; one half an EM.

OATMEAL PAPER (paint. and dec.) oat' meal pa' per: Wallpaper made by sprinkling sawdust over an adhesive surface.

OAK, RED (wood.) oak, red: A coarse textured, hard and durable wood, reddish brown in color with a very attractive grain. It is hard to work.

OAKUM (plumb.) oa' kum: Old hemp rope soaked in oil to make it waterproof and resistant to rot.

OAK, WHITE (wood.) oak, white: A valuable timber tree in the United States. The wood is light brown in color and close grained.

OBEY (automation) o bey': The ability of a machine to follow orders.

OBLIQUE PROJECTION (draft.) oblique' pro jec' tion: An object so drawn that one of its principal faces is parallel to the plane of projection, and is projected in true size and shape. The third set of edges is oblique to the plane of projection at some convenient angle.

OBTUSE ANGLE (draft.) ob tuse' an'_gle: An angle greater than 90 degrees.

OCCULATION (space) oc cul ta' tion: The disappearance of a body behind another body of larger apparent size.

OCHRE (paint. and dec.) o' chre: Earth pigment, which is yellow in color.

OCTAGON (draft.) oc' ta gon: An eight sided plane geometric figure.

OCTAGON SCALE (wood.) oc' ta gon scale: A scale usually found on the

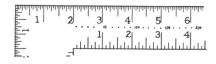

tongue of the carpenter's square which is used to lay out a figure with eight equal sides.

OCTAL BASE (elec.) oc' tal base: A tube base with eight pins and a keyed center post for correct placement.

OCTAL SOCKET (elec.) oc' tal sock' et. A socket for an octal base tube.

OCTAVE (elec.) oc' tave: The interval between frequencies which have a 2 to 1 ratio.

OCTAVE (space) oc' tave: The relationship between two frequencies having the ratio of 1 to 2.

OCTODE (elec.) oc' tode: An electron tube with eight elements or electrodes.

OCULOGYRAL ILLUSION (space) oc-u lo gy' ral il lus' ion: The apparent movement of an object in the same direction as that in which one seems to be turning due to stimulation of the semicircular canals of the inner ear.

ODOMETER (auto.) o dom' e ter: A device which registers the distance travelled in miles.

OERSTED (elec.) oer' sted: Unit of magnetic intensity equal to one gilbert per centimeter.

OERSTED, HANS CHRISTIAN (1777-1851) (elec.) The Danish scientist who studied and lectured at the University of Copenhagen. He discovered the relationship between electricity and magnetism when laboratory experiments demonstrated that a magnetic field appeared around a current carrying conductor.

OFFCUT (graphics) off' cut: Small sections of paper stock left over after cutting original stock to required size.

OFFICE AUTOMATION (automation) of' fice au to ma' tion: The automation of machines to provide service, such as information handling, accounting, billing, inventory, etc. Automatic data processing for routine paper work.

OFF ITS FEET (graphics) off its feet: Type leaning to one side or other resulting in inperfect print.

OFF-PEAK SYSTEM (air cond.) off-peak sys' tem: A system which is so controlled that it will not operate and use power during peak periods.

OFFSET (graphics) off' set: An ink smudge resulting from carrying so much ink on a sheet that some of it sticks to the bottom of the sheet above it.

OFFSET CUTTING PLANE (draft.) off' - set cut' ting plane: Two or more parallel cutting planes offset, to show interior of object in greater detail without invisible lines.

OFFSET PRINTING (graphics) off' set print' ing: A planographic process,

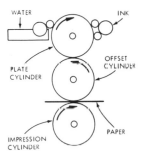

wherein the ink from the form is first offset on a rubber blanket instead of being transferred directly to the sheet.

OGEE CURVE (draft.) o gee' curve: An S shaped curve.

OHM (symbol Ω) (elec.) ohm: The unit of measurement of resistance.

OHM, GEORGE SIMON (1787-1854) (elec.) The German scientist who discovered the relationship between voltage, amperage and resistance now called Ohm's Law. He taught at the University of Munich.

OHMIC HEATING (metal) ohm' ic heat'-ing: Heating metal by a current through the metal overcoming the resistance of the metal; resistance heating.

OHMIC RESISTANCE (elec.) ohm' ic re-sis' tance: The resistance of a con-ductor due to its size, length and material.

OHMMETER (elec.) ohm' me ter: A meter used to measure resistance in ohms.

OHM'S LAW (elec.) Ohm's law: The mathematical relationship between cur-rent, voltage and resistance discovered by George Simon Ohm.

$$I = \frac{E}{R} \quad E = IR \quad R = \frac{E}{I}$$

OHMS-PER-VOLT (elec.) ohms-per-volt: Unit of measurement of sensitivity of a meter.

OIL BATH (metal) oil bath: A bath of hot oil for tempering steel up to tem-peratures of 500 deg. F.

OIL CAPACITOR (elec.) oil ca pac' i-tor: A capacitor using oil impregnated paper as a dielectric.

OIL COLORS (paint. and dec.) oil col' -ors: Colors ground to form of paste, in linseed oil.

OIL CONTROL RING (auto.) oil con-trol' ring: Special piston rings de-signed to compensate for irregularities in cylinder bore and assure a good seal.

OIL COOLER (auto.) oil cool' er: A radiator type device with cooling fins. Heat is absorbed by surrounding air as the oil passes through the cooler.

OIL FILTER (auto.) oil fil' ter: A filter in the oil system which removes dirt, carbon and dust from lubricating oils during engine operation.

OIL LENGTH (paint. and dec.) oil

length: Oil length in varnish is mea-sured by the oil in gallons per hundred pounds of resin. A long oil varnish is tougher than a short oil varnish. Rub-bing varnish is a typical short oil varnish and spar varnish is a typical long oil varnish.

OIL PAN (auto.) oil pan: A metal pan fastened to the bottom of the engine block, which seals and protects the crank shaft and bearings. It also serves as an oil reservoir and cooler.

OIL PUMP (auto.) oil pump: A gear type pump used to circulate the lubrication oil to moving parts and bearings in an engine.

OIL SEPARATOR (air cond.) oil sep' -a ra tor: A device used to separate oil from refrigerant.

OIL SOLUBLE (paint. and dec.) oil sol' u ble: Capable of being dissolved in oil.

OIL SPIT (auto.) oil spit: A hole drilled in a bearing which permits a spit or stream of oil when the hole is indexed with the oil-passage hole in the con-necting rod. It is used to lubricate the inside surfaces of a cylinder.

OIL STAIN (Penetrating) (paint. and dec.) oil stain: Wood stain consisting of oil-soluble dies and solvents such as turpentine, naptha, benzol, etc. Pen-etrates into pores of wood.

OIL STILL (air cond.) oil still: An oil separator device employing distillation for separation.

OMNIDIRECTIONAL (elec.) om ni di-rec' tion al: Response is independent of direction; all directions.

ONE AND ONE HALF STAGE (space) one and one half stage: A rocket wherein all rocket motors utilize a single propellant source. When the first desired velocity is attained, only rocket motors are jettisoned. When final desired velocity is attained, the propellant tanks and remaining motors are jettisoned.

ONE POINT PERSPECTIVE (draft.) one point per spec' tive: A drawing of an object so that two sets of its principal edges are parallel to the picture plane and the third set of edges is perpendicular to the picture plane. This third set of lines will converge toward a single vanishing point in perspective.

ONE SHOT OSCILLATOR (elec.) one shot os' cil la tor: See MULTIVIBRATOR.

OPAQUE (graphics) o paque' : A term used in lithography to describe a water-soluble solution used to cover holes or block out undesirable portions of a negative.

OPAQUE (paint. and dec.) o paque' : Impervious to light; not transparent.

OPEN CIRCUIT (elec.) o pen cir' cuit: Circuit broken or load removed. Load resistance equals infinity.

OPEN-GRAIN WOODS (paint. and dec.) open-grain woods: Woods of loose, open formation with minute openings between the fibers, such as oak and walnut.

OPEN-HEARTH (metal) o' pen-hearth: A steel making furnace, so called because hearth or floor of the furnace is exposed to the flames which melt the steel.

OPEN PIT (metal) o' pen pit: A method of mining, when ores are near to the surface of the earth.

OPEN PLUMBING (plumb.) o' pen plumbing: Installation of plumbing so that drain pipes and traps are exposed and open to inspection.

OPEN WIRING (elec.) o' pen wir' ing: Electric wiring fastened to surfaces with porcelain knobs; knob and tube wiring.

OPERATIONAL VIEWPOINT (automation) op er a' tion al view' point: The manner or method by which a desired operation can be performed.

OPERATION NUMBER (automation) op er a' tion num' ber: A number indicating the position of an operation in a sequence.

ORANGE MINERAL (paint. and dec.) or' ange min' er al: Red lead prepared by roasting basic carbonate white lead.

ORANGE PEEL (paint. and dec.) or' ange peel: Spray painting defect, in which the lacquer coat does not level down to a smooth surface but remains rough, like the peeling of an orange.

ORBIT (space) or' bit: The path described by a celestial body in its revolutions around another body.

OR CIRCUIT (elec.) or cir' cuit: A circuit with two or more inputs and one input signal must be present to produce an output signal.

ORDER OF AUTOMATICITY (automation) or' der of au to ma tic' i ty: A classification of tools and machines by their adaption to automatic control.

ORGANIC (paint. and dec.) or gan' ic: Compounds produced by plants and animals.

ORGANIC COMPOUND (air cond.) or gan' ic com' pound: Chemical compounds produced by the life process. Compounds containing carbon.

ORIFICE (weld.) or' i fice: Opening through which gases flow. It is usually the final opening or any opening controlled by a valve.

ORTHICON (elec.) or' thi con: See IMAGE ORTHICON.

ORTHOGRAPHIC PROJECTION (draft.) or tho graph' ic pro jec' tion: A projection on a picture plane formed by perpendicular projectors from the object to the plane.

OSCAR (space) oscar: Letters symbolic of Orbiting Satellite Carrying Amatuer Radio; a sub-satellite designed and built by Amateur Radio Operators, "Hams."

OSCILLATOR (elec.) os' cil la tor: An electron tube generator of alternating current voltages.

OSCILLATORS, Types of (elec.) os'-cil la tors, Types of:

ARMSTRONG, an oscillator using a tickler coil for feedback.

COLPITTS, an oscillator using a split tank capacitor as a feedback circuit.

CRYSTAL-CONTROLLED, an oscillator controlled by the piezoelectric effect.

ELECTRON COUPLED OSCILLATOR (ECO), a combination oscillator and power amplifier utilizing the electron stream as a coupling medium between the grid and plate tank circuits.

HARTLEY, an oscillator using inductive coupling of a tapped tank coil for feedback.

PUSH-PULL, a push-pull circuit utilizing interelectrode capacitance of each tube to feed back energy to grid circuit to sustain oscillation.

RC OSCILLATORS, oscillators depending upon the charge and discharge of a capacitor in series with a resistance.

TRANSITRON, an oscillator utilizing negative transconductance.

TUNED PLATE TUNED GRID, an oscillator utilizing tuned circuits in both grid and plate circuits.

ULTRAUDION, an oscillator, similar to a Colpitts, but employing the grid-to-cathode and plate-to-cathode interelectrode capacitances for feedback.

OSCILLOGRAPH (elec.) os cil' lograph: An instrument which provides a permanent visual trace of a waveform or shape.

OSCILLOSCOPE (elec.) os cil' loscope: A test instrument, using a cathode-ray tube, permitting observation of a signal.

OSOPHONE (elec.) os' o phone: A telephone receiver designed for a partially deaf person. In this device, sound vibrations are applied directly to the bones in the head

OTTO CYCLE (auto.) ot' to cy' cle: Same as FOUR CYCLE.

OUTER SPACE (space) out' er space: See AEROSPACE.

OUTLET BOX (elec.) out' let box: A metal box, equipped with clamps, used to terminate a cable or conduit. Connections are made in the box. A variety of covers and plates are available to close the box.

OUTLINE SECTIONING (draft.) out' line sec' tion ing: Used on large section-lined surfaces. Only the outline is emphasized by section lines; center portions are left blank.

OUT OF PHASE (elec.) out of phase: A term used to describe alternating current or voltage waveforms which do not pass through their maximum and minimum values simultaneously.

OUT OF PLUMB (const.) out of plumb: Not vertical.

OUTPUT (air cond.) out' put: Capacity; work done; net work produced by a system.

OUTPUT (automation) out' put: The effect of useful work.

OUTPUT (elec.) out' put: The energy from a circuit or device.

OUTPUT DEVICE (automation) out' put de vice': The final section of a computer which handles and records the solutions to problems. It may consist of high speed readout devices such as a card punching unit, a typewriter, or tape recorder.

OUTPUT METER (elec.) out' put me' - ter: A meter connected in the output of a circuit. It may read in watts, db's, voltage or current.

OUTPUT STAGE (elec.) out' put stage: The final stage in an electronic circuit. It is usually a power amplifier which drives the output device. Example: final amplifier stage in an audio system which drives the speaker.

OUTPUT TRANSFORMER (elec.) out' - put trans form' er: An impedance matching transformer which matches the output impedance of the final stage to the impedance of the transducer such as a speaker.

OUTRIGGER (const.) out' rig ger: A rafter extension to provide shape and nailing grounds for a boxed overhang on a building.

OUTSIDE CORNER WELD (weld.) out' - side cor' ner weld: Welding pieces together positioned at an angle to each other. The weld and fusion is made on the outside corner of the joint.

OVER-COMPOUNDING (elec.) o' ver-com pound' ing: See GENERATORS; a generator is over-compounded when the voltage increases with an increase in load.

OVERDAMPING (elec.) o' ver damping: More than the required damping to prevent oscillation.

OVERDRIVE (auto.) o' ver drive: A special gear ratio, permitting lower engine speeds at high car speeds, for more economical operation and less engine wear.

OVERHANG (graphics) o' ver hang: Anything which sticks out beyond the main body of the type or slug.

OVERHEAD POSITION (weld.) o' ver-head po si' tion: A weld made on the underside of the joint with the face of the weld in a horizontal plane.

OVERLAP (weld.) o ver lap': Extending the welding metal beyond the toe of the weld.

OVERLAY (graphics) o' ver lay: When preparing a form of type or plates for printing, it is necessary to put more impression on some parts than on others. A proof is pulled and the sheet spotted up. If this sheet is put on the tympan or cylinder, it is called an overlay; if it is put under or back of the form, it is called an underlay.

OVERLOAD (elec.) o' ver load: A greater load applied to a circuit or device than the circuit was designed to carry.

OVERLOAD CAPACITY (elec.) o' ver-load ca pac' i ty: The capacity of a machine, device or circuit to perform beyond its rated capacity for a short interval of time.

OVERMODULATION (elec.) o ver mod-u la' tion: A condition when the modulating wave exceeds the amplitude of the continuous carrier wave, thereby reducing the carrier wave power to zero.

OVERRUNNING CLUTCH (auto.) o' ver-run ning clutch: A device consisting of a shaft and a housing linked together by hardened rollers operating in tapered slots. As the shaft starts to rotate, the rollers move into the smaller ends of the tapered slots and lock the shaft and housing together. If the housing should be driven at a greater speed the rollers retract and disconnect the shaft.

OXALIC ACID (paint. and dec.) ox al' - ic ac' id: A colorless, poisonous crystalline acid derived from the oxalis plants or prepared synthetically. It is used in dyeing and bleaching.

OXIDANT (space) ox' i dant: An oxidizer. In a rocket propellant a substance such as liquid oxygen, nitric acid, or the like that yields oxygen for burning the fuel.

OXIDE (metal) ox' ide: A compound consisting of oxygen and one or more other elements.

OXIDIZE (metal) ox'i dize: To combine

oxygen with one or more other elements. Metal is oxidized when combined with oxygen and burned with cutting torch; soldering flux dissolves oxides that form due to air contacting metal surface.

OXIDIZING FLAME (weld.) ox' i diz ing flame: Flame produced by an excess of oxygen in the torch mixture, leaving some free oxygen which tends to burn the molten metal.

OXYACETYLENE WELDING (weld.) ox-y a cet' y lene weld' ing: See OXYGEN-ACETYLENE WELDING.

OXYGEN (weld.) ox' y gen: A gas formed of the element oxygen. When it very actively supports combusion, it is called burning; when it slowly combines with a substance, it is called oxidation.

OXYGEN-ACETYLENE CUTTING (weld.) ox' y gen a cet' y lene cut'-ting: Cutting metal using the oxygen jet which is incorporated with an oxygen-acetylene, preheating flame or flames.

OXYGEN-ACETYLENE WELDING (weld.) ox' y gen-a cet' y lene weld' - ing: A method of welding, using as a fuel a combination of the two gases - oxygen and acetylene.

OXYGEN CYLINDER (weld.) ox' y gen cyl' in der: A specially built container manufactured according to I.C.C. standards and used to store and ship certain quantities of oxygen.

OXYGEN-HYDROGEN FLAME (weld. ox' y gen-hy' dro gen flame: The chemical combining of oxygen with the fuel gas hydrogen.

OXYGEN-LP GAS FLAME (weld.) ox' - y gen-LP gas flame: Chemical combining of oxygen with the fuel gas LP (liquefied petroleum).

OXYGEN REGULATOR (weld.) ox' y gen reg' u la tor: An automatic valve used to reduce cylinder pressures to torch pressures and to keep the pressures constant.

OZALID PRINTS (draft.) oz' a lid prints: A printing process which produces black, blue or maroon lines on a white background.

OZALID PRINT (graphics)   oz' a lid print: A print made on ozalid paper which prints by contact without reversing the image.

OZONE (air cond.) o' zone: Triatomic oxygen, O_3, used as an air purifier and for the elimination of odors; a bluish gas with a penetrating odor.

OZONE (elec.) o' zone: Oxygen produced by an electrical discharge.

OZONE LAYER (space) o' zone lay' er: Layer in the atmosphere about 20 miles above sea level which strongly absorbs solar ultraviolet radiation.

OZONOSPHERE (space)   o zon' o-sphere: A stratum in the upper atmosphere at an altitude of approximately 40 miles having a relatively high concentration of ozone.

PACKAGING (automation) pack' ag ing: Preparing a product for delivery to the consumer.

PACK HARDEN (metal) pack hard' en: A process in which mild steel parts are given a hard outer surface by being buried in a container of carbonaceous material and heated in a furnace.

PACKING (air cond.) pack' ing: The stuffing around a valve or shaft to prevent fluid leakage.

PACKING (plumb.) pack' ing: Soft rope

like material used to seal joints. The packing is compressed in the joint.

PAD (elec.) pad: A resistance network for reducing signal strength without introducing an impedance mismatch.

PAD (space) pad: A permanent or semi-permanent load-bearing surface constructed or designed as a base upon which a launcher can be placed. Short for launch pad.

PADDER (elec.) pad' der: A small variable capacitor usually connected in series with a larger capacitor.

PAINT (paint. and dec.) paint: An adhesive coating which is applied as a thin film to various surfaces for decoration, protection, aid to morale, safety, sanitation, illumination, fire-retarding and other purposes.

PAINT BASE (wood.) paint base: .The composition of paint such as lead or zinc.

PAINT COATING (paint. and dec.) paint coat' ing: Paint in position on a surface.

PAINT DRIER (paint. and dec.) paint dri' er: Special compositions added to paint to improve its drying qualities.

PAINT GAUGE (paint. and dec.) paint gauge: An instrument used to measure the thickness of paint coatings.

PAINT REMOVER (paint. and dec.) paint re mov' er: A mixture of active solvents used to remove paint and varnish coatings.

PAINT THINNER (wood.) paint thin' ner: Turpentine and petroleum spirits added to heavy bodied paint to improve its application and coverage.

PALE (const.) pale: A sharpened fence picket.

PALETTE KNIFE (crafts) pal' ette knife: A thin flexible blade knife used for mixing color pigments and inks.

PALETTE KNIFE (graphics) pal' ette knife: See INK KNIFE.

PALM FIBER (crafts) palm fi' ber: An upholstery material secured from the outer husks of coconuts.

PALNUT (metal) pal' nut: A single thread lock nut.

PAN (elec.) pan: The rotation of a TV camera to follow the action in the televised scene.

PANCHROMATIC (graphics) pan chromat' ic: Sensitive to all colors.

PANE (const.) pane: A term used to describe each piece of glass in a window; light.

PANEL (const.) pan' el: A piece of wood, framed on four sides by molding, used to fill an opening, such as a door panel.

PANEL (graphics) pan' el: A section of a type composition separated from the main body by a border enclosure.

PANEL BOARD (elec.) pan' el board: A control board containing switches, fuses or breakers and usually meters for operating and monitoring an electrical machine or system.

PANEL BOX (elec.) pan' el box: A fuse or switch box used in electrical wiring, from which branch currents are distributed.

PANEL SAW (wood.) pan' el saw: A handsaw with very fine teeth, used for finish cutting thin woods and panels.

PANTOGRAPH (draft.) pan' to graph: A device used in drafting for enlarging or reducing the scale of a drawing while copying.

PANTRY (const.) pan' try: A small room adjoining the kitchen used for food storage.

PAPER CAPACITOR (elec.) pa' per capac' i tor: A capacitor with metal foil plates separated by waxed paper.

PAPER DRILL (graphics) pa' per drill: A special drill for drilling holes in stacks of paper.

PAPIER MACHE (const.) pa' pier mache' : A substance made of ground paper and glue. When molded into shapes it is widely used for ornamentation.

PARABOLA (draft.) pa rab' o la: A curve generated by a point moving so that its locus in any position is equidistant from a fixed point (focus) and a fixed line (directrix).

PARABOLIC (draft.) par a bol' ic: Shaped like a parabola.

PARABOLIC REFLECTOR (elec.) par a bol' ic re flec' tor: A light or sound reflector used to direct energy into a narrow beam. Reflecting surface conforms to a parabolic curve.

PARAFFIN OIL (paint. and dec.) par' af fin oil: Light gravity mineral oil used as a lubricant in wood finishing.

PARAGLIDER (space) par a glid' er: A flexible-winged kite-like vehicle designed as a reentry vehicle or to aid in the recovery of launched vehicles.

PARALLAX (elec.) par' al lax: The error introduced in meter reading as the result of not viewing the meter from directly in front.

PARALLAX (space) par' al lax: The apparent displacement of an object, or the apparent difference in its direction of motion, if viewed from two different points.

PARALLEL CELLS (elec.) par' al lel cells: A method of connecting cells so that all positive terminals are interconnected and all negative terminals are interconnected.

PARALLEL CIRCUIT (elec.) par' al lel cir' cuit: A circuit which contains two or more paths for electrons supplied by a common voltage source.

PARALLEL FEED (elec.) par' al lel feed: Also called SHUNT FEED. A circuit arrangement whereby the dc and ac components of a signal flow in different paths.

PARALLELOGRAM (draft) par al lel' o gram: A four sided geometric figure with opposite sides parallel to each other.

PARALLEL RESONANCE (elec.) par' - al lel res' o nance: A parallel circuit of an inductor and a capacitor at a frequency when the inductive and capacitive reactances are equal. The current in the capacitive branch is 180° out of phase with the inductive current and their vector sum is zero.

PARALLEL RULE (draft.) par' al lel rule: A movable straightedge used in drafting, which maintains its horizontal position at all times by means of a pulley and cord attachment at each end.

PARALLEL PROJECTION (draft.) par' - al lel pro jec' tion: See ORTHO-GRAPHIC PROJECTION.

PARALLELS (metal) par' al lels: Long rectangular blocks of accurately machined and finished steel, used to rest or support work.

PARAMAGNETIC (elec.) par a magnet' ic: Materials which have a permeability greater than one. Materials which are attracted by a magnet.

PARAMETER (elec.) pa ram' e ter: A constant whose value varies depending upon application.

PARAPET (const.) par' a pet: A low wall around the edge of a roof or along a bridge to prevent people from falling.

PARAPHASE AMPLIFIER (elec.) par' - a phase am' pli fi er: See PHASE SPLITTER.

PARA RED (paint. and dec.) par' a red: Pigment which is a coal tar product. Brilliant, opaque, non-fading, but has tendency to bleed.

PARASITIC ARRAY (elec.) par a sit' ic ar ray' : A dipole antenna with one or more director and reflector elements.

PARASITIC OSCILLATION (elec.) par-a sit' ic os cil la' tion: Oscillations in a circuit resulting from circuit components or conditions, occuring at frequencies other than that desired.

PARASITIC SUPPRESSOR (elec.) par-a sit' ic sup pres' sor: A component, such as a resistor, placed in a circuit to prevent parasitic oscillations.

PARCHMENT (graphics) parch' ment: Dried animal skin; vegetable parchment is made by treating paper in a bath of heated sulfuric acid.

PARGETING (const.) par' get ing: A thin coat of plaster on a stone or brick wall.

PARING (wood.) par' ing: To cut off in thin strips or layers; a method of wood turning in which the tool is made to cut the wood as opposed to scraping.

PARKER-KALON (metal) park' er-ka' -lon: A self tapping screw fastener.

PARMELEE WRENCH (plumb.) par' -mel ee wrench: A special wrench which wraps around a pipe and holds it by friction and clamping action. It leaves no mark on the pipe, so is used extensively with finished or plated pipes.

PARQUETRY (wood.) par' quet ry: Mosaic wood floors; floors finished with parquet blocks.

PARSEC (space) par' sec: A unit of measure for instellar space equal to 3.26 light years.

PARTED PATTERN (metal) part' ed pat' tern: A pattern, used in foundry work, which is divided into two parts to facilitate the removal of pattern from the sand mold.

PARTIAL AUXILIARY (draft.) par' tial aux il' ia ry: An auxiliary view of an inclined part of an object, excluding the remainder of the object which would be distorted.

PARTIAL SECTION (draft.) par' tial sec' tion: See BROKEN SECTION.

PARTING (metal) part' ing: The separating joint between two sections of a mold.

PARTING SAND (metal) part' ing sand: A fine composition dusted over the drag of a mold to prevent the cope from sticking to it.

PARTING STRIP (const.) part' ing strip: A thin strip of wood forming the center of a channel in which the upper and lower sash of a double hung window slide.

PARTING TOOL (metal) part' ing tool: A relatively thin offset-cutting tool used for cutting material at specified length in the lathe.

PARTITION (const.) par ti' tion: A wall which subdivides an area.

PARTS FORMER (metal) parts form'-er: An automatic multiple die machine.

PARVENU (draft.) par' ve nu: In extremely bad taste; sometimes referred to Victorian Gothic architecture.

PASCAL'S LAW pas' cal's law: Pressure applied to a given area of a fluid enclosed in a vessel is transmitted with undiminished force in every direction. This pressure acts at right angles to every portion of the surface of the container with equal force on equal areas.

PASS (weld.) pass: Weld metal created by one progression along the weld.

PASSIVE (space) pas' sive: Reflecting a signal without transmission.

PASTED PLATES (elec.) past' ed plates: Plates for lead acid cells formed by a lead oxide paste in a grid of lead antimony alloy.

PASTEL (crafts) pas' tel: Ground coloring pigments mixed with gum and formed into a crayon; term used to describe soft and pale colors; a picture drawn with pastel crayons.

PASTEURIZATION (air cond.) pas teur-i za' tion: A heat treating process for raw milk to destroy bacteria without changing the chemical composition of the milk.

PASTE WOOD FILLER (paint. and dec.) paste wood fill' er: A compound supplied in the form of a stiff paste for filling the open grain of hardwoods, such as oak, walnut and mahogony.

PA SYSTEM (elec.) PA sys' tem: Public Address System; an audio amplifier system of sufficient power to amplify voice and sound to large groups of people.

PATCH BOARD (elec.) patch board: A panel with numerous jacks, used to interconnect a number of circuits.

PATENT BASE (graphics) pat' ent base: Metal bases for printing plates.

PATINA (crafts) pat' i na: The film on metal formed by age and exposure.

PATTERN (metal) pat' tern: The exact replica of a finished casting except that it is slightly larger to provide for shrinkage. Patterns usually are made of wood.

PATTERN MAKER'S SAW (wood.) pat' tern mak' er's saw: A special type of backsaw with very fine teeth used in pattern making and cabinet making.

PATTERN MAKING (metal) pat' tern mak' ing: The trade or art of making wooden patterns to be used in sand casting.

PAWL (auto.) pawl: A device consisting of a hinged tongue engaging a gear. It is used to limit or lock the motion of a gear; used to produce cogwheel effect.

PAYLOAD (space) pay' load: The load carried by an aircraft, spaceship or rocket over and above that necessary for the operation of the vehicle.

PEAK (elec.) peak: The maximum value of a sine wave; the highest voltage, current or power reached during a particular cycle or operating time.

PEAKER (elec.) peak' er: See PEAKING OSCILLATOR.

PEAKING COIL (elec.) peak' ing coil: A small inductor in a high frequency circuit to reduce the distributed capacitance effect.

PEAKING OSCILLATOR (elec.) peak' ing os cil la' tor: A shock-excited oscillator utilizing a parallel-resonant low Q circuit in its plate circuit.

PEAK INVERSE VOLTAGE (elec.) peak in' verse volt' age: The value of voltage applied in a reverse direction across a diode.

PEAK INVERSE VOLTAGE RATING (elec.) peak in' verse volt' age rat' ing: The inverse voltage a diode will withstand without arcback.

PEAK LOAD (elec.) peak load: The maximum load applied to a generator or system at some interval of time.

PEAK TO PEAK (elec.) peak to peak: The measured value of a sine wave from peak in a positive direction to peak in a negative direction.

PEAK VALUE (elec.) peak val' ue: The maximum value of an alternating current or voltage.

PEARL (graphics) pearl: A five point type size.

PEARLING (wood.) pearl' ing: Carving of small circles and curves to decorate a surface.

PEARL LACQUER (paint. and dec.) pearl lac' quer: Lacquer into which has been suspended guanine crystals.

PEARLLITE (metal) pearl' lite: A saturated mixture of cementite and ferrite.

PEBBLE DASH (const.) peb' ble dash: To finish a plaster or cement wall by dashing pebbles against the surface.

PECK (wood.) peck: A term used to describe channels and pitted areas of decay in wood. Found in cedar and cypress.

PEDESTAL (elec.) ped' es tal: The value of the video signal representing black value of picture. Blanking pulse.

PEDESTAL HEIGHT (elec.) ped' es tal height: The difference between the black level of a composite video signal and its average value, representing the overall brightness of the picture.

PEELING (paint. and dec.) peel' ing: Detachment of a paint film in relatively large pieces. Paint applied to a damp or greasy surface usually "peels." Sometimes it is due to moisture back of the painted surface.

PEEN (metal) peen: The smaller end of a hammer head opposite the hammering head. Ex: Ball peen hammer.

PEG (wood.) peg: A wood pin, for fastening wooden parts together.

PELLUCID (paint. and dec.) pel lu' cid: Transparent; clear.

PELTIER EFFECT (elec.) pel' tier effect': The action of an electric current flowing through a junction of two dissimilar substances to remove heat from the space around the junction.

PENDANT (crafts) pen' dant: A hanging ornamentation.

PENDANT SWITCH (elec.) pen' dant switch: A push button switch hanging from a ceiling fixture.

PENETRATING STAIN (paint. and dec.) pen' e trat ing stain: Wood stain which penetrates below surface, into fibres of wood, made by dissolving oil-soluble dyes in alcohol or oil.

PENETRATION (weld.) pen e tra' tion: Extent the fusion goes into the base metal as measured from the surface of the base metal.

PENNY (const.) pen' ny: Term used to indicate nail length, abbreviated by letter d. Starts with 2d nail which is 1 in. long; increases 1/4 in. for each penny. Applies to common, box, casing, finishing nails. Small nails are identified by actual length and gauge.

PENTAGON (draft.) pen' ta gon: A five sided plane geometric figure.

PENTAGRID CONVERTER (elec.) pen' ta grid con vert' er: A tube with five grids.

PENTAGRID MIXER (elec.) pen' ta grid mix' er: See PENTAGRID CONVERTER.

PENTAVALENT (elec.) pen ta va' lent: A semiconductor impurity having five valence electrons. Donor impurities.

PENTODE (elec.) pen' tode: An electron tube with five elements including cathode, plate, control grid, screen grid and suppressor grid.

PENT ROOF (const.) pent roof: A roof which slopes in one direction only.

PERCENTAGE OF MODULATION (elec. per cent' age of mod u la' tion: The maximum deviation from the normal carrier value as a result of modulation expressed as a percentage.

PERCENTAGE OF RIPPLE (elec.) per_cent' age of rip' ple: The ratio of the rms value of the ripple voltage to the average value of output voltage expressed as a percentage.

PERCH (const.) perch: A unit of measurement for stone.

PERFORATION (graphics) per fo ra'_tion: The punching of a line of holes in paper to permit easy tearing.

PERFORATING RULE (graphics) per_fo rat' ing rule: A piece of metal placed in the type form so that a job can be printed and perforated in one operation.

PERI (space) per' i: Prefix meaning "perigee."

PERIGEE (space) per' i gee: The orbital point nearest the earth when the earth is the center of attraction.

PERIHELION (space) per i hel' i on: That point on an elliptical orbit around the Sun which is nearest to the Sun. (The Earth's perihelion is about 91,500,000 miles from the Sun.)

PERILLA OIL (paint. and dec.) per il' la oil: Drying oil obtained from seed of a bush called Perilla Ocymoide, grown largely in China and Japan.

PERIMETER (draft.) pe rim' e ter: The outer boundary of a figure.

PERIOD (elec.) pe' ri od: The time for one complete cycle.

PERIPHERAL SPEED (metal) pe riph' _er al speed: The speed of a wheel shaft or gear at its circumference usually measured in feet per minute.

PERIPHERY (auto.) pe riph' er y: A boundary line; perimeter; the outside edge; the circumference of a circle.

PERMALLOY (elec.) perm al' loy: A high permeability alloy containing iron, nickel, cobalt, chromium, vanadium and molybdenum.

PERMANENT MAGNET (elec.) per' ma_nent mag' net: Bars of steel and other substances which have been permanent_ly magnetized.

PERMANENT SET (const.) per' ma nent set: Deformation of a steel beam or structure caused by a stress from which the beam will not return to its original shape when the stress is removed.

PERMEABILITY (symbol u) (elec.) per_me a bil' i ty: The relative ability of a substance to conduct magnetic lines of force as compared with air.

PERMEABILITY CURVE (elec.) per_me a bil' i ty curve: A curve on a graph representing the density or num_ber of lines of magnetic force produced through a material as the magnetizing force is varied.

PERMEAMETER (elec.) per me am' _e ter: An instrument used to measure the number of lines of magnetic force through a material and the magnetizing force.

PERMEANCE (P) (elec.) per' me ance: The ability of a material to carry magnetic lines of force. It is the reciprocal of reluctance. $P = \frac{1}{R}$

PERMIT (const.) per' mit: License granted by one in authority.

PERMITTIVITY (elec.) per mit tiv' i_ty: The ratio of the electric displace_ment of a medium to the electric force producing it.

PEROXIDE OF LEAD (elec.) per ox' ide of lead: A lead compound used in the plates of a storage battery.

PERPENDICULAR (draft.) per pen-
dic' u lar: Lines or planes at a right
angle to a given line or plane.

PERSISTENCE (elec.) per sis' tence: A
term used to describe the time a CRT
screen glows or fluoresces at the point
where the electron beam strikes.

PERSPECTIVE PROJECTION (draft.)
per spec' tive pro jec' tion: A drawing
in which the projecting lines converge
to a point. The view of an object as
seen by the eye at a fixed location.

PETCOCK (auto.) pet' cock: A small
valve used for draining a liquid system.

PETROL (auto.) pet' rol: British name
for gasoline.

PEWTER (crafts) pew' ter: An alloy of
tin (92%), antimony (6%) and copper
(2%).

pH: Measurement of intensity of alkalinity or acidity of a solution. On scale
with values 0 to 14, 7 represents
neutrality, less than 7 acidity, greater
than 7 increasing alkalinity.

PHANTOM SECTION (draft.) phan' -
tom sec' tion: A sectional view drawn
on a regular exterior view. The interior details are emphasized by
crosshatching the imaginary cut
surface.

PHASE (elec.) phase: The relationship
between two vectors in respect to
angular displacement.

PHASE ANGLE (elec.) phase an' gle:
The angular difference between two
sine wave vectors. This angle has been
assigned the symbol of theta (θ).

PHASE INVERTER (elec.) phase in-

vert' er: A device or circuit that
changes the phase of a signal 180°.

PHASE MODULATION (elec.) phase
mod u la' tion: A process of changing
the instantaneous frequency of r-f energy already generated at a constant
frequency.

PHASE SPLITTER (elec.) phase split' -
ter: An amplifier which produces two
waves that have exactly opposite po-
larities from a single input wave form.

PHENOL-ALDEHYDE RESINS (paint.
and dec.) phe' nol-al' de hyde res' ins:
Resins produced from phenols and formaldehyde.

PHENOLIC RESIN (paint. and dec.) phenol' ic res' in: Resin based essentially on reaction between phenol and
formaldehyde.

PHENOLIC-RESIN PRIMER-SEALER
(paint. and dec.) phe nol' ic-res' in
prim' er-seal' er: Finish well suited
for fir and other softwoods, which pen-
etrates into pores of wood, dries and
equalizes density of hard and soft
grains.

PHILLIPS SCREWDRIVER (metal) phil'-
lips screw' dri ver: A screwdriver

with a special cross point to fit the
Phillips screw head.

PHON (elec.) phon: A unit of measure
ment of loudness.

PHONE (elec.) phone: A headset;
telephone handset.

PHONETIC ALPHABET (elec.) pho
net' ic al' pha bet: A list of words i

which the first letter of each word is a letter of the alphabet. Used in radio and telephone communication to distinguish between letters having the same sound.

PHONO-CARTRIDGE (elec.) pho' no-car' tridge: A device on the end of the tone arm of a phonograph which holds the needle or stylus and contains one of the various transducers used to convert mechanical movement into electric signals.

PHONOGRAPH (elec.) pho' no graph: A machine which converts mechanical vibrations, produced from a needle running in a record, into electrical signals. These signals are amplified and the sound reproduced from a speaker.

PHOSPHOR BRONZE (metal) phos' phor bronze: An alloy of bronze and a phosphor to increase its strength.

PHOSPHORESCENCE (elec.) phos phores' cence: Continued emission of light from a phosphor after electron bombardment ceases.

PHOSPHORESCENT PAINT (paint. and dec.) phos pho res' cent paint: luminous paint which emits light after the white light has been turned off. No phosphorus is used.

PHOSPHORS (elec.) phos' phors: The chemical coating on the inside of the face of a picture tube, which has luminescent properties when bombarded with electrons.

PHOTOCATHODE (elec.) pho to cath' - ode: A cathode element which emits electrons when irradiated.

PHOTOCONDUCTIVE (elec.) pho to-con duc' tive: The property of certain

materials to increase in conductivity when exposed to light.

PHOTODIODE (elec.) pho' to di ode: A PN junction diode which conducts upon exposure to light energy.

PHOTOELECTRIC CELL (elec.) pho to-e lec' tric cell: A cell which produces an electric potential when exposed to light.

PHOTOELECTRIC EFFECT (elec.) pho-to e lec' tric ef fect' : The property of certain substances to emit electrons when subjected to light.

PHOTOELECTRONS (elec.) pho to e-lec' trons: Electrons emitted as a result of light.

PHOTOENGRAVING (graphics) pho to-en grav' ing: A process in which photographs are produced on printing plates.

PHOTOGRAVURE (graphics) pho to-gra vure' : An intaglio printing process; by the aid of photography, holes of different sizes and depths are etched in the outside surface of a copper cylinder. To break up the photographic image so that it will produce holes, it is necessary either to make the negative through a screen or lay a grain on the cylinder that will resist the action of the etching-fluid. This keeps the surface of the cylinder level. The cylinder rotates in a fountain of ink, the surplus being scraped from the surface by a "doctor," leaving the ink only in the holes. The shadows of the pictures have deep holes which give up a lot of ink, while the highlights have shallow holes and give but very little ink.

PHOTOMETER (elec.) pho tom' e ter: An instrument used to measure light intensity.

PHOTOMETRIC UNITS (elec.) pho to-met' ric u' nits: Units of measurement of illumination. Ex: footcandle.

PHOTOMICROGRAPH (graphics) pho-to mi' cro graph: An enlarged photograph of a microscopically small object.

PHOTOMICROGRAPH (metal) pho to-mi' cro graph: A photograph of a microscopic slide or object.

PHOTOMULTIPLIER (elec.) pho' to-mul' ti pli er: Phototube and amplifier. Electrons are emitted when light strikes its cathode. These electrons are directed to strike a series of secondary plates before reaching the collector plate, resulting in amplification by secondary emission.

PHOTON (elec.) pho' ton: A discrete quantity of electromagnetic energy; a quantum.

PHOTOSENSITIVE (elec.) pho to sen'-si tive: A characteristic of a material which emits electrons from its surface when energized by light.

PHOTOSPHERE (space) pho' to sphere: The outermost luminous layer of the Sun's gaseous body.

PHOTOTUBE (elec.) pho' to tube: A vacuum tube, employing a photo sensitive material as its emitter or cathode.

PHOTOVARISTOR (elec.) pho to var'-is tor: A varistor which changes resistance by illumination.

PHOTOVOLTAIC (elec.) pho to vol-ta' ic: The generation of a voltage at the junction of two materials when exposed to light.

PHTHALIC ANHYDRIDE (paint. and dec.) phthal' ic an' hy dride: A white crystalline material used in making synthetic resins.

PHYSICAL METALLURGY (metal) phys' i cal met' al lur gy: The study of the physical behavior of metals during machining, shaping and treating operations.

PHYSICAL VIEWPOINT (automation) phys' i cal view' point: To consider the manufacturing requirements to make a product in terms of tools and machines.

PI (graphics) Type fallen apart and mixed up.

PIANO WIRE (metal) pi an' o wire: See Music Wire.

PICA (graphics) pi' ca: A type size; 12 point type; a unit of length for leads, slugs, rules and furniture.

PICKET (const.) pick' et: A narrow board, often pointed at one end, used for fence making.

PICKET SHIP (space) pick' et ship: One of the ocean-going ships used on a missile range to provide added instrumentation for tracking or recovering the missiles.

PICKING "SORTS" (graphics) pick' ing "sorts:" When the type setter finds certain letters missing in his case, he goes around the shop picking "sorts" from other jobs in order to complete his own.

PICKLING (crafts) pick' ling: The plunging or suspension of an object in an acid solution to remove oxides and scale.

PICKUP (elec.) pick' up: A device which converts sound, light or movement into corresponding signals.

"PICK UP SAGS" (paint. and dec.) "pick up sags": When a too-heavy coating of paint has been applied and starts to sag, or run down the surface, the painter brushes up through the sagging paint to level it off.

PICKUP, TYPE OF (elec.) pick' up, types of:

CAPACITOR, electrical signal is produced by variation of capacitance of pickup.

CERAMIC, electric signal produced by mechanical pressure on certain manufactured ceramic materials. See PIEZOELECTRIC EFFECT.

CRYSTAL, similar to ceramic, but using rochelle salts or natural crystals to produce piezoelectric effect.

MAGNETIC, the conversion to an electric signal by movement of a conductor in a magnetic field.

PHONOGRAPH, any mechanoelectrical device which produces an electric signal output, such as a needle or stylus follows the grooves in a record.

VARIABLE RELUCTANCE, the electric signal is produced by mechanical variation of the reluctance of a magnetic circuit.

PIECE FRACTIONS (graphics) piece frac' tions: Fractions made up of more than one piece of type such as 49/100.

PICOFARAD (pf) (elec.) pi co far' ad: Same as micromicrofarad.

PICTORIAL PROJECTION (draft.) picto' ri al pro jec' tion: The class of perspective methods which present a view which resembles the likeness of the object as viewed by the eye.

PICTURE ELEMENT (elec.) pic' ture el' e ment: Small areas or dots of varying intensity from black to white which contain the visual information of a scene.

PICTURE FREQUENCY (elec.) pic' ture fre' quen cy: The number of complete pictures scanned per second in television.

PICTURE INFORMATION (elec.) pic' - ture in for ma' tion: The picture intelligence picked up by the television camera and used to modulate the television transmitter; the modulated signal between blanking pulses in the composite video signal.

PICTURE MOLD (const.) pic' ture mold: A molding installed around a room from which pictures may be hung.

PICTURE PLANE (draft.) pic' ture plane: An imaginary plane between the object and the observer.

PIE CHART (draft.) pie chart: A chart in circular form representing 100%. Statistical information is represented by pie sections of circle of a size to correspond to a percentage value.

PIER (const.) pier: The part of a wall between windows or openings; a heavy column used to support weight; heavy structures used to support the span of a bridge.

PIERCE OSCILLATOR (elec.) pierce os' cil la tor: A crystal oscillator circuit in which the crystal is placed between the plate and grid circuit of tube.

PIERCING POINT (draft.) pierc' ing point: The point at which a line or projecting element pierces a projection plane.

PIER GLASS (const.) pier glass: A large high mirror.

PIEZOELECTRIC EFFECT (elec.) pi-e zo e lec' tric ef' fect: The property of certain crystalline substances of changing their shape when an emf is impressed upon the crystal. This action is also reversible.

PIG IRON (metal) pig iron: Small solidified blocks of iron (50-100 lbs.) poured from the blast furnace.

PIGMENT OIL STAIN (Wiping stain) (paint. and Dec.) pig' ment oil stain: Wood stain consisting of finely ground, insoluble color pigments as used in paints, in solution with varnish, turpentine, mineral spirits, oil, etc. Depth of color is controlled by amount of stain wiped off.

PIGMENTS (paint. and dec.) pig' ment: Fine solid particles in paint, which are insoluble in liquid portion. May be white or colored, opaque or translucent.

PIGTAIL (elec.) pig' tail: A flexible wire extending from a component for ease of connection.

PIGTAIL SPLICE (elec.) pig' tail splice: Connecting two wires by tightly twisting together their bare ends.

PIKE POLE (elec.) pike pole: A sharply pointed pole, used by lineman to raise a telephone pole.

PILE (const.) pile: A large timber driven into the ground to support a building; timbers driven into a river bottom to support retaining walls and wharfs.

PILE (elec.) pile: An arrangement for controlling nuclear reaction in atomic energy production; a nuclear reactor.

PILLAR (const.) pil' lar: Round and decorative columns used to support the main arches of a building.

PILOT HOLE (metal) pi' lot hole: A small hole used to guide a drill for a larger hole.

PILOTLESS AIRCRAFT (space) pi' lot-less air' craft: An aircraft, unattended by a human pilot within it, but kept on course by a preset or selfreacting device or by radio command.

PILOT LIGHT (elec.) pi' lot light: A small indicating light.

PILOT LIGHT (plumb.) pi' lot light: A small flame used in gas appliances for igniting the main gas supply when it is turned on.

PINCH BAR (wood.) pinch bar: See RIPPING BAR.

PINCUSHION (elec.) pin' cush ion: A type of distortion occuring in television, when the raster appears in the shape of a pincushion with concave sides.

PINE, NORWAY (wood.) pine, Nor' way: A pale reddish wood, nonporous, straight grained and very resinous.

PINE, SUGAR (wood.) pine, sug' ar: A pinkish brown to cream colored wood, straight grained with numerous and large resin ducts. It is used for interior house finish, shingles, etc.

PINE, WHITE (wood.) pine, white: A light brown soft wood, straight grained and nonporous. Widely used for doors, window frames and other carpentry work.

PINION (auto.) pin' ion: A small gear.

PINION GEAR (metal) pin' ion gear: The smaller of a pair of gears.

PIN STRIPES (paint. and dec.) pin stripes: Fine stripes.

PIN VISE (metal) pin vise: A small handle with provision in one or both ends to hold small wires, files, taps or drills, by means of a collet or chuck.

PIPE FITTINGS (plumb.) pipe fit' tings: Various types of fittings used to join pipes together such as elbows, tees and couplings.

90 DEG. STREET ELBOW   CLOSE RETURN BEND   OPEN RETURN BEND

45 DEG. ELBOW   90 DEG. REDUCING ELBOW   SIDE OUTLET ELBOW

CROSS   Y BRANCH   CAP

STRAIGHT TEE   COUPLING   REDUCING COUPLING

PIPE pipe: A tube or hollow body used to conduct or provide a passage for a liquid, gas or finely divided solid. Pipe is made of various metals, plastic, concrete, clay, etc.

PIPE WRENCH (plumb.) pipe wrench: An adjustable wrench, with serrated jaws, which will grip a pipe so that it can be turned.

PI-SECTION FILTER (elec.) pi-sec'-tion fil' ter: A filter consisting of two capacitors and an inductor connected in a π configuration.

PISTON (auto.) pis' ton: A movable plug which fits snugly into the cylinder of an engine.

PIN VISE

PISTON DISPLACEMENT (auto.) pis' ton dis place' ment: The cubical content of the cylindrical space created as the piston moves from the top dead center to bottom dead center of its stroke. It is equal to $\frac{D^2}{4}$ x S, where D = diameter of piston and S = length of stroke.

PISTON PIN (auto.) pis' ton pin: The pin which connects the connecting rod to the piston.

PISTON RING (auto.) pis' ton ring: Rings fitted into grooves of a piston to assure a good seal between the piston and the cylinder wall.

PISTON ROD (auto.) pis' ton rod: The arm between the piston and the crankshaft.

PISTON SKIRT (auto.) pis' ton skirt: The section of a piston below the head and piston pin.

PISTON SLAP (auto.) pis' ton slap: The sudden tilting or rocking of a piston as it starts down on its power stroke.

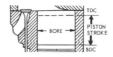

TDC
BORE
PISTON STROKE
BDC

PISTON STROKE (auto.) pis' ton stroke: Length of piston travel in cylinder.

PITCH (const.) pitch: The slope of a surface or roof.

PITCH (elec.) pitch: The property of a musical tone determined by its frequency.

PITCH (metal) pitch: The distance from

a point on one screw thread to a point on an adjacent thread taken along a straight line parallel to the axis of the thread.

PITCH (paint. and dec.) pitch: A black or dark viscous substance obtained as a residue in distilling tar. It also occurs in natural form, as asphalt.

PITCH BOARD (const.) pitch board: See BEVEL BOARD.

PITCH CIRCLE (metal) pitch cir' cle: See PITCH DIAMETER.

PITCH DIAMETER (metal) pitch di- am' e ter: Diameter of an imaginary circle that would pass through screw threads at such points as to make width of thread and width of space equal at point where they are cut by circle. Equal to major diameter of thread minus depth of thread. For gears - an imaginary circle located about mid- point on the teeth, where teeth of both gears make contact.

PITCHOVER (space) pitch' o ver: The programmed turn from the vertical that a rocket takes as it describes an arc and points in a direction other than upward.

PITH (wood.) pith: The soft spongy center of a tree.

PITH BALL (elec.) pith ball: Small balls made of the core of certain kinds of wood and plants, used in demon- strations of static electricity.

PITMAN ARM (auto.) pit' man arm: An arm used to transmit motion; a connecting rod.

PLAGES (space) pla' gas: Clouds of calcium or hydrogen vapor that show up as bright patches on the visible surface of the Sun.

PLAIN SAWING (wood.) plain saw' ing: To saw a log into boards from end to end along the length of the log.

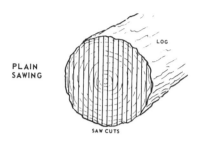

PLAIN SAWING   LOG   SAW CUTS

PLAIN TURNING (metal) plain turn' - ing: Turning straight cylindrical forms in a lathe.

PLAN (draft.) plan: A diagram; a drawing showing the shape and dimen- sions of an object or the method of assembly; a horizontal plane view of a building showing space allocations, dimensions, sizes of openings and spe- cial features.

PLANCIER (const.) plan' cier: The un- derside of a cornice to which the soffit boards are fastened.

PLANE (const.) plane: A flat surface.

PLANE (wood.) plane: A woodworking tool used to smooth the surfaces of a board or square and joint the edges of a board.

PLANER (graphics) plan' er: A block of hard wood, level and smooth on one side, used to push down the face of type to make the form plane and level.

PLANER (metal) plan' er: A machine tool for machining large flat surfaces. The work is fastened to a table and the table is reciprocated past one or more cutting tools. See illustration, page 255.

PLANER (wood.) plan' er: A machine to surface lumber. It will have controls for thickness, depth of cut and power feed.

PLANETARY ELECTRONS (elec.) plan' e tar y e lec' trons: Electrons considered in orbit around the nucleus of an atom.

PLANETARY GEARS (auto.) plan' e-tar y gears: A system of gears made up of a sun gear, planet pinions and an internal gear. So called, since the gears in place resemble our solar system.

PLANETOID (space) plan' e toid: A starlike body, one of the numerous small planets nearly all of whose orbits lie between Mars and Jupiter. Also called asteroid and minor planet.

PLANISH (crafts) plan' ish: The process of making a smooth surface by hammering lightly with highly polished hammer.

PLANK (const.) plank: A heavy board.

PLANOGRAPHIC (graphics) plan o-graph' ic: Any printing process where the ink is taken from a plane surface. See LITHOGRAPHY.

PLASMA (weld.) plas' ma: A temporary physical condition of gas after it has been exposed to and reacted to an electric arc; the region in a gaseous discharge where the positive and negative ions are in balance with no resultant charge.

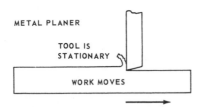

METAL PLANER

TOOL IS
STATIONARY

WORK MOVES

PLASMA JET (space) plas' ma jet: High temperature jet of electrons and positive ions that has been heated and ionized by the magnetohydrodynamic effect of a strong electrical discharge.

PLASMA JET EROSION (metal) plas'-ma jet e ro' sion: Removing large amounts of metal by impinging ionic plasma jets.

PLASTER (const.) plas' ter: A mixture of sand, water and lime with a fibrous material added for strength.

PLASTER GROUNDS (const.) plas' ter grounds: See GROUNDS.

PLASTERING (const.) plas' ter ing: The application of plaster to walls and ceiling.

PLASTER OF PARIS (crafts) plas' ter of par' is: Calcined gypsum in the form of a white powder. When mixed with water, it will set quickly. Used for casting and models.

PLASTER OF PARIS (paint. and dec.) plas' ter of par' is: A white powdery substance formed by calcining gypsum. When mixed with water it forms a paste which soon sets. Originally brought from a suburb of Paris.

PLASTICITY (metal) plas tic' i ty: The ability of a material to take deformation without fracturing.

PLASTICIZE (crafts) plas' ti cize: To make a material plastic and easy to mold.

PLASTICIZER (paint. and dec.) plas' ti-ciz er: An agent added to certain plastics and protective coatings to impart flexibility, softness, or otherwise modify the properties.

PLASTICS (crafts) plas' tics: Any of the nonmetallic compounds synthetically produced, which can be molded and shaped into a desired form.

PLAT (draft.) plat: A partial map of a city showing some specific area such as a subdivision.

PLATE (const.) plate: A timber, usually 2 x 4, running horizontally on top of wall studs. The top plate would act as a support for the roof rafters.

PLATE (draft.) plate: A name used in the drafting room for a drawing.

PLATE (elec.) plate: The anode of a vacuum tube. The element in a tube which attracts the electrons.

PLATE (graphics) plate: A metal plate so prepared that it will print an impression, when inked.

PLATE CIRCUIT (elec.) plate cir' cuit: The circuit in which plate energy of a vacuum tube is dissipated. It can include cathode, plate, loads, power source and associated components.

PLATE CLUTCH (auto.) plate clutch: A clutch in which power is transmitted from driving plate to driven plate by friction between the plates as they are held together by compression springs. A foot pedal disengages the clutch by removing the spring pressure.

PLATE CURRENT (elec.) plate cur' rent: The current which flows in the plate or anode circuit of an electron tube.

PLATE DETECTOR (elec.) plate detec' tor: The r-f signal is amplified and detected in the plate circuit. Tube is biased to approximately cutoff by cathode resistor.

PLATE EFFICIENCY (elec.) plate ef-fi' cien cy: The ratio between the useful output power to the dc input power to the plate of an electron tube.

PLATE GLASS (const.) plate glass: Flat, polished glass of high quality.

PLATE IMPEDANCE (elec.) plate imped' ance: See AC PLATE RESISTANCE.

PLATE MODULATION (elec.) plate mod-u la' tion: A modulation circuit where the modulating signal is fed to the plate circuit of the modulated stage.

PLATEN (graphics) pla' ten: That part of a printing press on which the make-ready, tympan, and guides are placed, and on which the sheet takes the impression from the type.

PLATEN PRESS (graphics) pla' ten press: A printing press in which the impression is made when a flat surface called the platen pushes the paper against the type.

PLATE RAIL (wood.) plate rail: A shelf-like molding around the interior of a room to support dishes and other decorations.

PLATERESQUE (draft.) plat er esque': A Spanish version of Renaissance architecture using ornamentation copied from designs of famous silversmiths. Platero is silversmith in Spanish.

PLATE VOLTAGE (elec.) plate volt' age: The voltage at the plate or anode of an electron tube, usually measured between plate and ground or B minus.

PLATFORM FRAMING (const.) plat' - form fram' ing: A system of framing a house, where the floor joist of each story rests on the top plates of the story below. Bearing partitions and walls rest on subfloors of each story.

PLATING (metal) plat'ing: To deposit a metal on another material by electrolysis or dipping. It is used as protection and also as decoration.

PLAY (metal) play: The motion between poorly fitted or worn parts.

PLAYBACK (elec.) play'back: To play a recording.

PLENUM (air cond.) ple'num: A chamber which receives air under pressure before distribution to various rooms.

PLIERS (metal) pli'ers: A pincerlike tool for holding small objects. They are

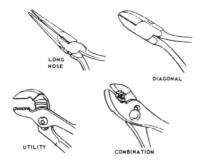

manufactured in a large variety of shapes, types and sizes for special purposes. Some have cutting edges.

PLINTH (const.) plinth: A square block base of a column or pedestal.

PLOT PLAN (draft.) plot plan: A plan showing the position of a proposed structure on the lot.

PLOW (wood.) plow: To cut a groove in wood.

PLUG (elec.) plug:

PHONO, a special audio plug used extensively in high fidelity sound systems to interconnect units.

The male terminal of a connector such as would be plugged into a socket or jack.

PLUG (plumb.) plug: An externally threaded fitting, usually with a square

head, used to close and seal the end of another fitting.

PLUG COCK (plumb.) plug cock: See GROUND KEY VALVE.

PLUG GAUGE (metal) plug gauge: A very accurate gauge for testing the internal diameters of holes in machine work.

PLUG TAP (metal) plug tap: See TAPS; an intermediate internal threading tool. Taps are used in this order: starting tap, plug tap and bottoming tap.

PLUG WELD (weld.) plug weld: Weld, which holds two pieces of metal together, made in a hole in one piece of metal which is lapped over the other piece.

PLUMB (const.) plumb: Standing vertical; perpendicular to the horizontal; parallel to a plumb line.

PLUMBAGO   plum ba'go: Another name for graphite used in making pencil leads, crucibles; as lubricant.

PLUMB BOB (const.) plumb bob: A pointed conical shaped weight to hang on a line; the weight causes the line to hang in an exact vertical position and the bob locates the point directly beneath the above position from which the line is suspended.

PLUMB CUT (const.) plumb cut: The top cut on a rafter where it joins the ridge board.

PLUMBER (plumb.) plumb'er: A person engaged in the plumbing trade.

PLUMBING (plumb.) plumb'ing: Pipes, fixtures and other apparatus concerned with introduction, distribution and disposal of water and sewage in a building.

PLUMBING CODES (plumb.) plumb'ing codes: Municipal ordinances regulating plumbing.

PLUMBER'S FRIEND (plumb.) plumb'er's friend: A cup shaped rubber device with a wooden handle. It is used to remove stoppages in waste drains by siphonage and compression.

PLUMBER'S FURNACE (plumb.) plumb'er's fur'nace: A gasoline fired pot for melting lead and heating soldering irons.

PLUMBER'S SOIL (plumb.) plumb'er's soil: A mixture of glue and lampblack used in leadwork.

PLUMB LINE (const.) plumb line: A line, weighted on one end, used to establish verticality.

PLUS (symbol +) (elec.) plus: Positive terminal or junction of a circuit.

PLY (const.) ply: A term used to describe the thickness of roofing paper.

PLYWOOD (wood.) ply'wood: Laminated sheets of wood made by glueing thin layers together.

PM SPEAKER (elec.) pm speak'er: A loudspeaker employing a permanent magnet as its field.

PN JUNCTION (elec.) pn junc'tion: A piece of N type and a piece of P type semiconductor material joined together.

POCHE (draft.) poch e': The art of outlining large letters and filling the centers with a ruling pen.

POINT (graphics) point: A unit of measurement; one-twelfth of the American pica and is .01384 inches thick. Type size is based on this unit.

POINT CONTACT (in a semiconductor) (elec.) point con'tact: A pressure contact between a semiconductor body and a metallic point.

POINT CONTACT DIODE (elec.) point con'tact di'ode: A diode consisting of a point and a semiconductor crystal.

POINTING (const.) point'ing: The filling and finishing of mortar joints.

POINTING TROWEL (const.) point'ing trow'el: A small mason's trowel used for finish work, striking joints and removal of mortar from the face of the bricks.

POINTS (graphics) points: The punctuation marks in a font of type.

POINT-SET (graphics) point-set: So called when a font of type has body widths based on a multiple of the point system.

POINT SYSTEM (graphics) point sys'tem: The casting of type bodies in widths which are multiples of the point.

POLAR COORDINATES (elec.) po'lar co o 'di nates: A vector described by its magnitude and the angle it makes with the reference line.

POLAR GRAPH (draft.) po'lar graph: A graph made with a series of equal spaced concentric circles and radial lines at equal intervals of degrees.

POLARITY (elec.) po lar'i ty: The property of a device or circuit to have poles such as North and South or positive and negative.

POLARIZATION (elec.) po lar i za'tion: Producing magnetic poles or polarity; the direction of the electric field from a radiating antenna and it is determined by the physical position of antenna; a defect in a cell caused by hydrogen bubbles surrounding the positive electrode and effectively insulating it from the chemical reaction.

POLARIZE (elec.) po' lar ize: To produce or acquire polarization.

POLAR RELAY (elec.) po' lar re' lay: A relay activated by a change in current direction.

POLAR VECTORS (elec.) po' lar vec'tors: Vectors extending from a common center or pole.

POLE (elec.) pole: One of two terminals of electric cell, battery or dynamo. Area of magnetized body at which magnetic flux density is concentrated. One end of a magnet.

POLE PIECE (elec.) pole piece: The iron laminated core around which are placed the field windings in a generator or motor.

POLE PITCH (elec.) pole pitch: The peripheral distance between the centers of two adjacent poles in a generator field.

POLE SHOE (auto.) pole shoe: The magnetic poles or cores of generator field windings.

POLISH (metal) pol' ish: To make bright and smooth by friction.

"POLISHING" (paint. and dec.) "pol' ishing" Said of wall paints where shiny spots or surfaces have resulted from washing or wiping.

POLYAMIDE (paint. and dec.) pol y-am' ide: Product used in making dripless paint.

POLYCHROME FINISH (paint. and dec.) po' ly chrome fin' ish: Finish obtained by blending together a number of colors.

POLYGON (draft.) pol' y gon: A plane geometric figure with several sides.

POLYMERIC (paint. and dec.) pol y-mer' ic: Composed of repeating chemical units. All plastics and polymers are polymeric.

POLYMERIZATION pol y mer i-za' tion: The process of joining two or more like molecules to form a new and more complex molecule whose physical properties are different.

POLYMERS pol' y mers: The products of polymerization.

POLYPHASE (elec.) pol' y phase: Consisting of currents having two or more phases.

POLYSTYRENE (elec.) pol y sty' rene: Thermoplastic material used extensively in making molded products.

POPLAR (Liriodendron Tulipifera) (wood) pop' lar: A widely used hardwood. It is soft, light and uniform in texture and density. This wood, when stained, is an excellent imitation of walnut and mahogany.

POPPET (metal) pop' pet: A type of holddown for machine work on the work table, provided with adjustable screws set at a 10° angle which give a downward thrust on the work when in use.

POPPET VALVE (auto.) pop' pet valve: A mushroom shaped valve, which is opened by a mechanism pushing against the stem.

POP VALVE (plumb.) pop valve: A safety valve which remains closed by spring pressure. Excessive pressure from within the system overcomes the spring pressure of the valve and allows it to open.

PORCH (const.) porch: A floor area extended beyond the exterior walls of a building. It is usually roofed over and may be open or enclosed.

POROSITY po ros' i ty: The property of a compound or substance to permit air, gas or fluid under pressure to pass through it.

POROSITY (weld.) po ros' i ty: Presence of gas pockets or voids in the metal.

PORT (auto.) port: Opening in a cylinder for intake and exhaust.

PORTAL (const.) por' tal: An entranceway; a door or gateway.

PORTICO (const.) port' i co: A roofed structure supported by columns, before the entrance to a building.

PORTING (auto.) port' ing: Enlarging, smoothing and streamlining the inside of the manifolds of an engine to reduce friction to the flow of gases.

PORTLAND CEMENT (const.) port' land ce ment': A hydraulic cement made by burning and grinding a mixture of clay and limestone.

POSIGRADE ROCKET (space) pos' i-grade rock' et: An auxilliary rocket which fires in the direction the rocket is pointed. It is used to separate stages of a vehicle.

POSITIVE (graphics) pos' i tive: A photographic image of an object which shows lights and shades the same as the original.

POSITIVE FEEDBACK (elec.) pos' i tive feed' back: See REGENERATIVE FEEDBACK.

POSITIVE G (space) pos' i tive g: In a gravitational field or during an acceleration, the human body is normally so positioned that the force of inertia acts on it in a head-to-foot direction.

POSITIVE ION (elec.) pos' i tive i' on: An atom which has lost electrons and is positively charged.

POSITIVE TEMPERATURE COEFFICIENT (elec.) pos' i tive tem' per a-ture co ef fi' cient: A positive change in the characteristics, such as frequency or resistance, as a result of a positive change in temperature.

POSITRON (elec.) pos' i tron: A positively charged beta particle emitted from an excited nucleus. A positive electron.

POST (const.) post: A timber fixed in an upright position and used for a support.

POST DRILL (const.) post drill: A drilling machine attached to a column, such as a round steel post.

POSTHEATING (weld.) post' heat ing: Temperature to which a metal is heated after an operation has been performed on the metal.

POST OFFICE BRIDGE (elec.) post of'-fice bridge: A type of Wheatstone Bridge in which resistances and meter are enclosed in a box. The bridge is balanced by removing brass connecting plugs which insert known resistance values into the circuit.

POT (elec.) pot: Abbreviation for potentiometer.

POTABLE WATER (plumb.) po' ta ble wa' ter: Water suitable for human consumption.

POTENTIAL DIFFERENCE (elec.) poten' tial dif' fer ence: See ELECTROMOTIVE FORCE.

POTENTIAL GRADIENT (elec.) po ten'tial gra' di ent: The difference in potential value per unit of length.

POTENTIAL HILL (elec.) po ten' tial hill: See BARRIER REGION.

POTENTIAL REGULATOR (elec.) poten' tial reg' u la tor: A device for controlling the voltage output of a generator or a circuit.

POTENTIOMETER (elec.) po ten ti om'e ter: A variable resistor, used as a voltage divider; a device used to develop electrical output signals proportional to mechanical movement.

POTHOOK (plumb.) pot' hook: A hook used to lift a pot of molten lead from a furnace.

POTTED CIRCUIT (elec.) pot' ted cir'cuit: A circuit sealed in insulating material for protection against humidity and temperature.

POTTER'S WHEEL (crafts) pot' ter's wheel: A wheel on which clay is shaped. A mass of soft clay placed on the horizontal wheel may be hand shaped as the wheel revolves.

POTTERY (crafts) pot' ter y: Fired clay products; earthenware; porcelain.

POUNCE (draft.) pounce: A commercial compound used for cleaning tracing paper before inking.

POUNDAL poun' dal: A unit of measurement in the foot-pound-second system. The force required to give a one pound mass an acceleration of one foot per second^2.

POUND-FOOT pound-foot: The unit of measurement of torque.

POUR POINT DEPRESSANT (auto.) pour point de pres' sant: An additive to oil to cause oil to flow freely at low temperatures.

POWDER METALLURGY (metal) pow'der met' al lur gy: A process by which metals are united by pressure without heat. A blend of metallic powders is fed into a precision die with a cavity that is the shape and several times deeper than the thickness of the desired piece and is compressed into a rather brittle and fragile briquet. The briquet is sintered in a furnace to produce a strong and useful object.

POWDER STAINS (paint. and dec.) pow'der stains: Stains in form of powder which are mixed with solvents to produce wood stains.

POWER (elec.) pow' er: The rate of doing work. In dc circuits $P = I \times E$.

POWER AMPLIFICATION (elec.) pow' er am pli fi ca' tion: The ratio of the output power to the input grid driving power.

POWER BRAKES (auto.) pow' er brakes: Automotive brakes operated by a hydraulic booster system. Very little pedal pressure is required when the engine is running and the booster is operating.

POWER DETECTOR (elec.) pow' er detec' tor: A detector designed to handle signal voltages having amplitudes greater than one volt.

POWER FACTOR (elec.) pow'er fac'tor: The relationship between the true power and the apparent power of a circuit.

POWER FACTOR METER (elec.) pow'-er fac'tor me'ter: A combined ammeter, voltmeter and wattmeter which indicates the value of the power factor.

POWER FEED (metal) pow'er feed: An automatic power driven feed for machine tools such as lathes, drill presses, mills, etc.

POWER JET (auto.) pow'er jet: See ECONOMIZER VALVE.

POWER LOSS (elec.) pow'er loss: Loss in a circuit due to resistance of conductors; sometimes called I^2R loss.

POWER PACK (elec.) pow'er pack: A power supply, usually a group of batteries, used to power an electronic circuit.

POWER SENSITIVITY (elec.) pow'er sen si tiv'i ty: The ratio of power output in watts to the square of the effective value of grid signal voltage. It is measured in mhos.

POWER STAT (elec.) pow'er stat: A trade name for a variable output transformer.

POWER STEERING (auto.) pow'er steer'ing: A hydraulic booster system attached to the steering mechanism of a car. When the engine is running, very little effort is required to steer the car.

POWER STROKE (auto.) pow'er stroke: The downward stroke of the piston driven by the expanding gases created by combustion.

POWER SUPPLY (elec.) pow'er sup'ply: An electronic circuit designed to provide various a-c and d-c voltages for equipment operation. Circuit may include transformers, rectifiers, filters and regulators.

POWER TRAIN (auto.) pow'er train: A mechanism that transmits power from engine or motor to the final driven unit.

POWER TRANSFORMER (elec.) pow'er trans form'er: A transformer used to convert a high voltage-low current source to a low voltage-high current source or vice versa. The power between primary and secondary remains constant.

POWER TRANSISTOR (elec.) pow'er tran sis'tor: Transistors designed to deliver a specified output power level.

POWER TUBE (elec.) pow'er tube: A vacuum tube used as a current amplifier; the tube in the final stage in an audio amplifier or a radio transmitter.

P-PLANE (draft.) p-plane: The profile plane in orthographic projection which shows the side view.

PREAMPLIFIER (elec.) pre am'pli fi er: A sensitive low level amplifier with sufficient output to drive a standard amplifier.

PRECIPITATE (paint. and dec.) pre-cip'i tate: A substance separated from a solution in concrete state by chemical action or by application of heat or cold.

PRECIPITATOR (air cond.) pre cip'i ta tor: A device to remove dust and smoke particles from the air by means of electric charges induced in the particles.

PRECIPITRON (elec.) pre cip'i tron: An electrostatic device, developed by

Westinghouse, used to remove dust, smoke and other impurities from air.

PRECISION BLOCKS (metal) pre ci' sion blocks: Precision made steel blocks used by industry as standard of measurement. Available in range of sizes with dimensional accuracy of two millionths inch. Also called Jo Blocks.

PRECISION LATHE (metal) pre ci' sion lathe: A small bench lathe for very accurate machine work.

PRECOOLER (air cond.) pre' cool er: A cooling device to remove the sensible heat from fruits and vegetables before shipment.

PREEMPHASIS (elec.) pre em' pha sis: The process of increasing the strength of signals of higher frequencies in FM at the transmitter to produce a greater frequency swing.

PREFABRICATION (const.) pre fab' rica tion: Type of construction designed to require minimum amount of assembly at the site. Prefabrication usually comprises large units manufactured or assembled at a plant.

PREHEAT (air cond.) pre' heat: To heat air, liquid or metal in advance in preparation for other processes.

PREHEATING (weld.) pre heat' ing: A welding practice to minimize conduction of heat into cold sections of metal, thus requiring greater heats at area to be welded.

PREHEATING (metal) pre' heat ing: Temperature to which a metal is heated before an operation is performed on the metal.

PREIGNITION (auto.) pre ig ni' tion: Detonation in an automotive engine due to ignition of air-fuel mixture pre-

maturely by carbon deposits or incorrect ignition timing.

PRESENTATION DRAWING (draft.) presen ta' tion draw' ing: A drawing, usually perspective, of a proposed structure to give the owner a realistic picture of the finished structure. Presentation drawings are sometimes rendered in color, and include shrubs, trees, walks and detail landscaping.

PRESSED BRICK (const.) pressed brick: Bricks subjected to pressure to eliminate imperfections of shape and texture before burning.

PRESS FIT (metal) press fit: Fitting parts together by pressure; slightly tighter than a sliding fit.

PRESSING (elec.) press' ing: A manufacturing process used to make phonograph records by press molding from a master record.

PRESSMAN (graphics) press' man: Employee who prepares forms for printing. He makes ready form and handles necessary press adjustments.

PRESSURE (air cond.) pres' sure: The force exerted by a liquid or gas, per unit of area, on a surface or wall of a container.

PRESSURE, ABSOLUTE (air cond.) pres' sure, ab' so lute: Pressure in reference to a perfect vacuum.

PRESSURE, ATMOSPHERIC (air cond.) pres' sure, at mos pher' ic: The pressure on the Earth's surface due to its atmosphere. It is equivalent to 14.696 lbs. psi or 29.921 inches of mercury at 32° F.

PRESSURE CAP (auto.) pres' sure cap: A pressure sealed cap on a radiator. The increased pressure created by heat in the cooling system increases the boiling temperature of the coolant.

PRESSURE, CRITICAL (air cond.) pres'-sure, crit' i cal: The vapor pressure corresponding to the critical temperature.

PRESSURE, DROP (air cond.) pres'-sure, drop: The loss of pressure from one end of a pipe or system to the other end, due to friction.

PRESSURE, DYNAMIC (air cond.) pres'-sure, dy nam' ic: The sum of the static pressure and velocity pressure at the point of measurement in a fluid system.

PRESSURE, GAUGE (air cond.) pres'-sure, gauge: Above atmospheric pressure.

PRESSURIZED CAPSULE (space) pres'-sur ized cap' sule: A capsule that has within it a gaseous pressure greater than the ambient pressure.

PRESSURIZED SUIT (space) pres' sur-ized suit: A garment designed to provide pressure upon the body so that respiratory and circulatory functions may continue normally.

PREVENTIVE LEADS (elec.) pre ven'-tive leads: Resistive leads used in a series a-c motor to reduce commutator sparking.

PRICK PUNCH (metal) prick punch: Similar to a center punch, except the point is sharper. Used for layout work.

PRICK PUNCH

PRIMARY (elec.) pri' ma ry: The input windings of a transformer; (auto) the

low voltage (6 or 12 volts) circuit of an automotive electrical engine.

PRIMARY CELL (elec.) pri' ma ry cell: A voltaic cell which can not be recharged; a device for transforming chemical energy into electrical energy.

PRIMARY COLOR (paint. and dec.) pri'-ma ry col' or: A color which cannot be obtained by mixing other colors.

PRIMARY COLORS (crafts) pri' ma ry col' ors: The fundamental colors (red, yellow, and blue) from which all other colors are made.

PRIMARY COLORS (elec.) pri' mar y col' ors: In color TV, the primary colors are red, blue and green. These colors are used to produce other colors of any hue.

PRIMARY FLUID (air cond.) pri' ma ry flu' id: The refrigerant in a cooling system.

PRIMARY FREQUENCY STANDARD (elec.) pri' ma ry fre' quen cy stand'-ard: The primary reference standard for verification of frequency transmitted by WWV operated by National Bureau of Standards.

PRIMARY WINDING (elec.) pri' ma ry wind' ing: The coil of a transformer which receives the energy from the a-c source.

"PRIME IN THE SPOTS" (paint. and dec.) "prime in the spots": Apply a priming coat to those spots that have been scraped, wire brushed, shellacked, have had the old paint burned off or consist of newly patched plaster.

PRIMER (paint. and dec.) prim' er: Paint applied next to surface of material being painted. First coat in painting operation.

PRIMING (const.) prim' ing: The first coat of paint on wood, used as a preservative, a filler and as a base for other coats of paint.

PRINCIPAL VIEW (draft.) prin' ci pal view: The view of an object which shows the most detail and contour of the object. Front view.

PRINTED CIRCUIT (elec.) print' ed cir'- cuit: A circuit in which the electrical conductors are printed on an insulating base; frequently used to describe an etched circuit, where conducting paths are produced on a copper clad insulating base by acid etching and removal of copper not required for conductors.

PRINTER (automation) print' er: A computer output device which prints the characters.

"PRINT FREE" (paint. and dec.) "print free": Paint sufficiently dry so that no imprint is left when something is pressed against it.

PROBE (elec.) probe: A pointed metal end of a test lead, to contact specific points in a circuit to be measured.

PROCESS (automation) proc' ess: A series of operations intended to produce a desired result or product.

PROCESS COLOR INK (graphics) proc'- ess col' or ink: Special inks used in process color printing. Made in primary colors of red, yellow and blue.

PROCESS CONTROLLER (automation) proc' ess con trol' ler: An automatic instrument for feedback control of a continuous process.

PROCESS INDUSTRIES (automation) proc' ess in' dus tries: Common name for petroleum and chemical industries which use continuous operations.

PROCESSING (automation) proc' es sing: Manufacturing by a continuous series of operations.

PROFILE (draft.) pro' file: A line showing the relative elevation of every point on the line. It may be prepared from a contour map.

The outlined view of an object; the projection on the profile or P plane; the side view.

PROGRAM (automation) pro' gram: Instructions to a machine (what to do and how to do it).

PROGRAM (automation) pro' gram: A list of instructions for a computer.

PROGRAM (space) pro' gram: To set a sequence of operations into an electronic sequencer. To provide for a series of events during a flight or other action.

PROGRAM LEVEL (elec.) pro' gram lev' el: Refers to the audio signal level in a system expressed in VU.

PROGRAM LOG (elec.) pro' gram log: A record kept at master control of a radio station showing all programs, sponsors and type of entertainment.

PROGRAMMERS (automation) pro'- gram mers: Personnel who prepare programs for computers.

PROGRAMMING (automation) pro'- gram ming: Instructions to a machine which give step-by-step operations necessary for automatic control.

PROGRESSIVE STAMPING (automation) pro gres' sive stamp' ing: The process of making a part by advancing the part through a series of stamping dies. Each stroke of the press represents a progressive stage toward completion.

PROJECT (draft.) pro ject': To extend from one point to another; protrude; to stick out.

PROJECT ENGINEER (automation) pro'- ject en gi neer': The responsibility of coordinating investigation, planning and design of a product.

PRONY BRAKE (auto.) pro' ny brake: A device for measuring power, consisting of a brake drum and a brake with an arm resting on a spring scale.

PROOF (graphics) proof: A printed impression of a job for purposes of correction and inspection.

PROOF PAPER (graphics) proof pa' per: Paper used to pull a proof.

PROOF PRESS (graphics) proof press: A special press for pulling proofs.

PROOFREADER (graphics) proof' reader: One who reads proofs and makes corrections.

PROOF (SPIRIT) (paint and dec.) proof: Indication of percentages of water and grain alcohol; a mixture which is 100 proof would be 50% water, 50% alcohol by volume. A mixture which is 120 proof would contain 60% alcohol.

PROPAGATION (elec.) prop a ga' tion: The movement of electromagnetic or sound waves in space.

PROPELLANT (space) pro pel' lant: The oxident and fuel expanded to obtain propulsion or thrust.

PROPULSION SYSTEM (space) pro- pul' sion sys' tem: A major system of a missile or other vehicle that includes the engines, booster tanks and all necessary equipment to insure desired ground and in-flight operation.

PROSPECTORS PICK (crafts) pros' pec tors pick: A metal pick with handle for breaking small rocks. One end is chisel shaped for digging in crevices of rock and breaking out samples of ore.

PROPELLER SHAFT (auto.) pro pel' ler shaft: A shaft which connects the transmission to the rear wheel final drive.

PROTON (elec.) pro' ton: Positively charged particle.

PROTOTYPE (space) pro' to type: A model that is suitable for complete evaluation of form, design and performance.

PROTRACTOR (draft.) pro trac' tor: A flat semi-circular gauge for measuring or laying off angles.

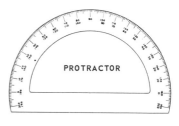

PROTRACTOR

PROTRACTOR ANGLE (draft.) pro- trac' tor an' gle: A combination triangle and protractor used in drafting.

PROXIMITY EFFECT (elec.) prox im' - i ty ef fect': The change in current distribution in a conductor due to the action of an ac current in a nearby conductor.

PROXIMITY MEASUREMENTS (automation) prox im' i ty mea' sure ments: Measurements made by transducers that develop electrical signals in proportion to dimensions without actual contact.

PRUSSIAN BLUE (metal) prus' sian blue:

An intensely blue pigment made of potassium ferrocyanide used for dyes and lay-out ink in the machine shop.

PRUSSIAN BLUE (Ferric Ferrocyanide) (paint. and dec.) prus' sian blue: Pigment which is deep in color and has great strength; dark blue color.

PSYCHROMETER (elec.) psy chrom' e-ter: An instrument used to measure moisture content of air by comparison of readings on dry bulb and wet bulb thermometers.

P TRAP (plumb.) p trap: A trap shaped like the letter P.

PUDDLE (const.) pud' dle: To make a thick mixture of sand, clay and water; clay, worked when wet, to make it impervious to water.

PUDDLE (weld.) pud' dle: Portion of a weld that is molten at the place the heat is supplied.

PUDDLING (weld.) pud' dling: The act of maintaining a small pool of molten metal by a welding flame across the surface of the work.

PUFFING AGENT (paint. and dec.) puff'-ing a' gent: A synthetic organic product used to produce increased viscosity in varnishes and paints.

PUGGING (const.) pug' ging: An insulating and sound deadening mortar laid on the boarding between floor joists; the mixing of clay to make bricks and pottery.

PULL BOX (elec.) pull box: A metal box at a sharp corner in a conduit, to facilitate pulling wires through the conduit.

PULLEY (metal) pul' ley: A wheel used

to transmit power by means of a belt which travels over its face.

PULL-OUT (graphics) pull-out: Anything pulled out of the form by suction from the press rollers.

PULSATING CURRENT (elec.) pul sa' - ting cur' rent: A varying direct current; a direct current in which the amplitude is not constant.

PULSE (elec.) pulse: The sudden rise and fall of a voltage or current.

PULSE (elec.) pulse:

CODE, a train of pulses used to transmit information.

DECAY TIME, the time required for a pulse to drop from 90 percent to 10 percent of its maximum amplitude.

DROOP, a slight decrease in amplitude of flat top square pulse; a form of square wave distortion.

DURATION, the time interval between the first and last instants at which the instantaneous amplitude reaches a stated fraction of the peak pulse amplitude.

MODULATION, use of pulse code to modulate a transmitter.

REPETITION PERIOD, the reciprocal of the repetition frequency.

REPETITION RATE, the frequency of the periodic pulse train.

RISE TIME, the time required for a pulse to rise from 10 percent to 90 percent of its maximum amplitude.

SPIKE, an unwanted pulse of relatively short duration superimposed on a main pulse.

SYNC, a pulse sent by a TV transmitter to synchronize the scanning of the receiver with the transmitter; a pulse used to maintain predetermined speed and/or phase relations.

PULSEJET (space) pulse' jet: A jet-propulsion engine, containing neither compressor nor turbine which produces thrust intermittently.

PUMICE (crafts) pum' ice: Fine ground volcanic rock used as a polishing abrasive.

PUMICE STONE (paint. and dec.) pum'-ice stone: A stone of volcanic origin which is pulverized to produce a soft abrasive used extensively in rubbing finishing coats of fine wood finishes.

PUMP (metal) pump: A machine which forces a liquid or gas into a tank or system or draws it out by means of suction. A common variety of pump would be a piston operating in a closed cylinder with appropriate valves at the output end of the cylinder.

PUNCH (wood.) punch: A piece of metal shaped to use as a driver or marker. It is held in the hand and driven with a hammer.

PUNCH (wood.) punch:

HAND, a punch with a round tapered point for general work.

CENTER, a punch with a conical point for making a small mark on wood or metal to locate a position or the center of a hole.

PIN, a punch with a round point of specified diameter used for driving pins or bolts out of a hole.

PRICK, a punch with a tapered pointed point for marking sheet metal.

TAPERED, a longer and heavier type of hand punch used for driving large pins and shafts.

PUNCH CARD (automation) punch card: A card suitable for punching in a pattern, coded information which has meaning and can be mechanically handled.

PUNCHED TAPE (automation) punched tape: Tape punched with a pattern of holes to represent information.

PUNCH PRESS (metal) punch press: An industrial machine for punching and shaping metal by extreme pressures. A hydraulic or mechanical ram moves a punch against a die held on the bed of the machine.

PUNCH-THROUGH VOLTAGE (elec.) punch-through volt' age: The voltage applied to a transistor which effectively short circuits the base region and the transistor is inoperative.

PUNCTURE (elec.) punc' ture: The break through of an insulation by an applied high voltage.

PURGING (air cond.) purg' ing: The process of blowing-out and cleaning a refrigeration system to remove non-condensibles.

PURITY (elec.) pu' ri ty: The condition in color TV when the individual color fields are uniform.

PURLINS (const.) pur' lins: Timbers used to prevent rafters from sagging.

PUSH-PULL AMPLIFIER (elec.) push-pull am' pli fi er: Two tubes used to amplify a signal in such a manner that each tube amplifies one half cycle of the signal. Tubes operate 180° out of phase; two amplifiers with grids connected in phase opposition and plates in parallel to a common load.

PUSH ROD (auto.) push rod: A mechanical link, in the form of a rod, between the valve lifter and valve rocker arm in an I head engine.

PUTLOGS (const.) put' logs: Horizontal supports for the flooring of a scaffold.

PUTTY (const.) put' ty: A plastic compound of powdered whiting and linseed oil; lime slacked with water to the consistency of cream and then left to dry by evaporation.

PUTTY (paint. and dec.) put' ty: A dough-like mixture of pigment and oil (usually whiting and linseed oil - sometimes mixed with white lead). Used to set glass in window frames, fill nail holes and cracks.

"PUTTY COAT" (paint. and dec.) "put' ty coat": Final smooth coat of plaster.

PYROMETER (metal) py rom' e ter: An instrument for measuring temperatures.

PYROXYLIN (paint. and dec.) py rox'- y lin: See cellulose nitrate.

Q (elec.): Quality; figure of merit; the ratio between the energy stored in an inductor during the time the magnetic field is being established to the losses during the same time.

$$Q = \frac{X_L}{R}$$

Q (elec.): Letter representation for quantity of electricity (coulomb).

Q DEMODULATOR (elec.) q de mod' u- la tor: In color TV, it is the demodulator circuit which converts one of the two quadrature chrominance carriers back into the Q subcarrier.

Q FACTOR (elec.) q fac' tor: Figure of merit of a circuit; it expresses the ability of a tuned circuit to increase the value of induced voltage at resonance.

Q MULTIPLIER (elec.) q mul' ti pli er: A filter device used with a communications receiver in the IF sections to provide sharply peaked response or rejection.

Q-SIGNAL (elec.) q-sig' nal: In TV. The color TV signal containing the green or purple picture information.

Q SIGNALS (elec.) q sig' nals: An international system of abbreviations of words and sentences used in radio communications. Ex: QRT means STOP SENDING.

QSL CARD (elec.) qsl card: A postal card used by the radio amateur to confirm a radio contact.

QUAD (elec.) quad: Shortening of word QUADRUPLE meaning fourfold.

QUADRANT (draft.) quad' rant: A quarter of a circle.

QUADRATURE (elec.) quad' ra ture: A 90 degree difference between two a-c waveforms.

QUADS (graphics) quads: Blocks of type metal, cast to point sizes of body, and in multiples of the square of the body, less than type-high used for spacing material in setting type. A one-em quad is just as wide as it is thick; a two-em quad is twice as wide as it is thick; a three-em quad is three times as wide as it is thick.

QUALITATIVE ANALYSIS qual' i tative a nal' y sis: That branch of chemistry concerned with the determination of the elements or ingredients of a compound.

QUANTA (elec.) quan' ta: A definite amount of energy required to move an electron to a higher energy level.

QUANTITATIVE ANALYSIS quan' ti tative a nal' y sis: That branch of chemistry concerned with the determination of quantity of each element or ingredient in a compound.

QUANTUM (automation) quan' tum: The numerical value of the smallest unit measure used in a system.

QUANTUM (elec.) quan' tum: Discrete quantities of any physical property such as momentum, energy, mass, etc.

QUARRY-FACED MASONRY (const.) quar' ry-faced ma' son ry: Face stone used in building, left in an unfinished surface as it comes from the quarry.

QUARTER-PHASE (elec.) quar' terphase: Two voltages one quarter of a cycle out of phase; two phase.

QUARTERSAW (wood.) quar' ter saw: To saw a log first into quarters. Each quarter is then sawed into boards at

RADIAL QUARTER CUT

right angles to the annual rings and parallel to the medullary rays. This method produces beautiful grain patterns.

QUARTZ (elec.) quartz: A mineral; silicon oxide.

QUATERNARY STEEL (metal) qua ter'na ry steel: Steels which contain two other special elements with the iron and carbon.

QUENCH (metal) quench: Rapid cooling by immersion.

QUENCH VOLTAGE (elec.) quench volt'-age: A low frequency r-f voltage used to interrupt oscillations in a super-regenerative receiver.

QUICK-BEAD (const.) quick-bead: A bead molding applied directly to the surface.

QUICK CHANGE GEARS (metal) quick change gears: The gear box on a lathe and other machine tools for changing the speed relationship between the spindle and the lead screw.

QUICK-CHARGE (elec.) quick-charge: Recharging storage battery rapidly by increasing the rate of charge.

QUICK DRYING (paint. and dec.) quick dry' ing: A material with a relatively short drying time.

QUICK LIME (const.) quick lime: Unslaked lime made from pure limestone.

QUICKSILVER quick' sil ver: Mercury; an amalgam of tin used on the backs of mirrors.

QUIESCENT (elec.) qui es' cent: At rest. Inactive.

QUILL (metal) quill: A hollow spindle which revolves on a shaft. It may carry pulleys and gears.

QUOIN (graphics) quoin: A wedge-shaped

block of wood or metal used to lock up type in a galley or form.

QUOIN KEY (graphics) quoin key: A key for tightening quoins.

QUOINS (const.) quoins: Members forming corner of building which are of different material from adjoining surfaces. Example: Stone blocks set at corner of brick wall.

RABBET (wood.) rab' bet: A groove cut in wood along the edge of a board; a continuous recess having a right angle included between its sides, cut along the edge of a board; a rebate.

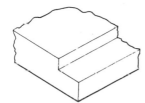

RABBET JOINT (wood.) rab' bet joint: Wood joint assembled as shown.

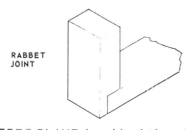

RABBET
JOINT

RABBET PLANE (wood.) rab' bet plane: A plane with necessary stops and adjustments to cut rabbets.

RACE CAM (auto.) race cam: Type of camshaft for race cars, which increases valve lift and speed of valve opening and closing.

RACES (auto.) races: Hardened steel surfaces on which ball bearings or rollers operate.

RACEWAY (elec.) race' way: An elec-

trical conduit; an enclosure for electrical conductors.

RACK (wood.) rack: A shelf type piece of furniture.

(elec.) A metal frame and enclosure in which electronic equipment may be mounted.

(metal) A flat straight piece of metal on which gear teeth have been milled. Used with a gear called a pinion.

RACK FEED (metal) rack feed: A tool feed mechanism employing a rack and pinion. Ex: machine lathe.

RADAR (elec.) ra' dar: A transmitting system employing bursts of energy of required frequency and duration and radiated in a specific direction. The echo is used to determine range and bearings of objects.

RADAR MILE (elec.) ra' dar mile: The distance of travel of a radar pulse to target one mile out and back. Pulse requires 10.75×10^{-6} sec. to travel a radar mile.

RADIAL DRILL (metal) ra' di al drill: A drill press with spindle mounted in radial arm supported on a column, permitting greater convenience and increased production.

RADIAL ENGINE (auto.) ra' di al en'gine: An engine constructed with cylinders in a radial pattern and all connecting rods attached to one crank pin on the crankshaft at center of engine.

RADIAL FACING (metal) ra' di al fac'ing: The process of truing the face of work held on faceplate or in a chuck.

RADIALS (elec.) ra' di als: Ground wires extending like spokes from the base of an antenna.

RADIAL SAW (wood.) ra' di al saw: A machine for sawing lumber on which the saw and driving motor are mounted on an arm above the work. The saw blade is pulled through the work. The radial arm may be turned at various angles for miter cutting. The saw may also be turned at an angle for compound angle cutting. One important advantage of this machine is that the work remains stationary, and long and heavy boards may be cut with ease if properly supported.

RADIAN (elec.) ra' di an: An angle, with its vertex at the center of a circle, will intercept an arc of the circumference equal to the radius of the circle. The circumference of a circle is equal to 2π radians and a radian approximates 57 degrees.

RADIATION (air cond.) ra di a' tion: The transmission of heat by wave motion of air.

RADIATION (elec.) ra di a' tion: The emission and propagation of electromagnetic waves into space.

RADIATION LOSS (elec.) ra di a' tion loss: Losses in transmission lines due to radiation of electric and magnetic fields.

RADIATION RESISTANCE (elec.) ra di a' tion re sis' tance: The apparent resistance of an antenna as a result of energy radiated from antenna.

RADIATOR (auto.) ra' di a tor: A device for cooling liquid. A container made up of hollow ribs and fins through which liquid to be cooled is circulated. Air is passed around and through the outside of the radiator to absorb the heat.

RADIO (elec.) ra' di o: The study of or the equipment used in wireless communication.

RADIOACOUSTICS (elec.) ra di o a-cous' tics: The study of the transmission, production and reproduction of sound waves.

RADIOACTIVITY (elec.) ra di o ac-tiv' i ty: The emission of rays or particles from an unstable nucleus as it decays to a more stable state.

RADIO CHANNEL (elec.) ra' di o chan'-nel: A band of radio frequencies allocated for radio transmission.

RADIO COMPASS (elec.) ra' di o com'-pass: A navigational instrument used to detect the direction of a radio wave.

RADIO DIRECTION FINDER, (RDF) (elec.) ra' di o di rec' tion find' er: A radio receiver designed to determine the direction from which a radio signal is transmitted. It is used in navigation.

RADIO FREQUENCY (elec.) ra' di o fre' quen cy: Those frequencies used in radio communications generally classified from 30,000 cps to 30,000,000 cps.

RADIO FREQUENCY CHOKE, (RFC) (elec.) ra' di o fre' quen cy choke: A coil which has a high impedance to rf currents.

RADIOGRAPH (weld.) ra' di o graph: A photograph obtained by passing X rays or gamma rays through the object to be photographed and recording the variations in density on a photographic film.

RADIOGRAPHY (elec.) ra di og' ra phy: X ray; the science of photography in which an object is examined by exposure to X rays and the shadow of its internal structure is produced on film.

RADIOSONDE (space) ra' di o sonde: A balloon-borne instrument and transmitter for measurement of meteorological data.

RADIOISOTOPE (elec.) ra di o i' sotope: A radio active isotope.

RADIOMETALLOGRAPHY (metal) radi o met al log' ra phy: The process of examining the structure and characteristics of metal by X rays.

RADIOPAQUE (elec.) ra' di o paque: Impervious to radiation.

RADIO RANGE (elec.) ra' di o range: A directional radio transmitter, located on the ground, which emits a radio beam of a specific compass bearing by which aircraft can locate their positions and compass headings.

RADIOSONIC (elec.) ra di o son' ic: Using radio waves for sounding purposes.

RADIO SPECTRUM (elec.) ra' di o spec' trum: The division of the electromagnetic spectrum used for radio.

RADIOTELEGRAPHY (elec.) ra' di o te leg' ra phy: Radio communication by means of interrupted continuous waves conforming to the dots and dashes of the Morse Code.

RADIOTELEPHONY (elec.) ra' di o te leph' o ny: Radio communication by voice.

RADIO TELESCOPE (elec.) ra' di o tel' e scope: An extremely sensitive radio receiving system for detection of radio waves from outer space. Usually employed with a high gain antenna which can collect and focus incoming signals.

RADIO TELESCOPE (space) ra' di o tel' e scope: A radio receiving station for detecting radio waves emitted by celestial bodies or by space probes in space.

RADIO WAVE (elec.) ra' di o wave: A complex electrostatic and electromagnetic field radiated from a transmitter antenna.

RADIUS (draft.) ra' di us: The straight line distance from the center to the circumference of a circle.

RADIUS ROD (auto.) ra' di us rod: Steel brace rods underneath an automobile which hold the wheels in proper alignment.

RAFFIA (crafts) raf' fi a: Fibers from the leaves of a Madagascar palm tree, used in making woven baskets and furniture.

RAFTER (const.) raft' er: The joists which form the roof and to which the roof boards are nailed.

COMMON RAFTER, a full length rafter running from ridge to top plate of exterior wall.

CRIPPLE-JACK, a short rafter between the hip and valley rafter.

HIP RAFTER, a supporting rafter at the intersection of an external roof angle.

JACK RAFTER, a short rafter between the top plate and the hip rafter; a short rafter between the ridge and a valley rafter.

VALLEY RAFTER, a supporting rafter at the intersection of an internal roof angle.

RAFTER TABLES (wood.) raft' er ta' bles: Tables usually found on the carpenter's steel square which are used to determine the lengths of rafters and their cutting angles.

RAG CONTENT PAPER (graphics) rag con' tent pa' per: Paper made from materials in which rags are used.

RAIL (const.) rail: A horizontal timber betweem posts in a fence; in joinery, the horizontal pieces of framing are called rails.

RAILROADING (graphics) rail' road ing: The marking over of words at the ends of successive lines.

RAINBOW GENERATOR (elec.) rain' bow gen' er a tor: A generator used in servicing color TV which produces the entire color spectrum on the picture tube.

RAISING (crafts) rais' ing: Similar to hollowing, except that the bowl is formed from the outside over a stake.

RAKE (metal) rake: The angle made by a cutting tool and a plane perpendicular to the surface being worked.

RAKE JOINT (const.) rake joint: A type of mortar joint, where the mortar is raked out to a specified depth before the mortar has hardened.

RAMJET (space) ram' jet: A ramjet engine. A kind of jet engine consisting essentially of a tube open at both ends in which fuel is burned continuously to create a jet thrust.

RAMMER (metal) ram' mer: A wood ram used to pack molding sand in the mold.

RAMP (const.) ramp: A sloping roadway or passage; the concave bend in the hand rail of a staircase where it changes direction, such as at a landing.

RANDOM WORK (const.) ran' dom work: Stones fitted together in a wall and joined with mortar, disregarding any attempt at laying them in courses.

RANGE CORD (elec.) range cord: A heavy duty three wire insulated cord to provide a semi-flexible electrical connection between an electric range and its wall receptacle.

RANGE RECEPTACLE (elec.) range re cep' ta cle: A heavy-duty, flush mounted, receptacle for an electric stove connection.

RANGE WORK (const.) range work: Ashlar stone laid in horizontal courses.

RAPID TRAVERSE (metal) rap' id tra'- verse: A rapid power movement of table of a machine tool to bring work up to cutting tool and return tool to starting position at finish of cut.

RASP (const.) rasp: A coarse file for rough work.

RASTER (elec.) ras' ter: The area of light produced on the screen of a TV picture tube by the electron beam. It contains no picture information.

RATCHET (metal) ratch' et: A gear and pawl mechanism used either for intermittent motion or as a locking device.

RATING (elec.) rat' ing: The capacity of a machine or device in power, watts, volts, etc.

RATIO ARMS (elec.) ra' tio arms: The arms or branches of a Wheatstone Bridge whose resistances are known and form the bridge ratio.

RATIO DETECTOR (elec.) ra' tio detec' tor: A type of FM detector.

RATIO OF COMPRESSION (air cond.)
ra' tio of com pres' sion: The ratio
between pressures before and after
compression.

RAT-TAIL FILE (metal rat-tail file:
Name for smaller sizes of round files.

RAT-TAIL SPLICE (elec.) rat-tail
splice: A wire splice made by twisting
two conductors tightly together; also
called a pig-tail splice.

"RAW" (paint. and dec.) raw: Raw linseed oil.

RAW OIL (paint. and dec.) raw oil: Oil
as received from the press or separated from the solvent in the solvent
extraction process.

RAW SIENNA (paint. and dec.) raw
si en' na: See Sienna.

RAZE (const.) raze: To tear down; to
demolish.

RC TIME CONSTANT (elec.) rc time
con' stant: See TIME CONSTANT.

REACTANCE (X) (elec.) re act' ance:
The opposition to an alternating current
as a result of inductance or capacitance.

REACTANCE TUBE (elec.) re act' ance
tube: A tube operated so that its reactance varies with a modulating signal.

REACTIVE LOAD (elec.) re ac' tive
load: A load on a power source which
causes the current to lag the applied
voltage; a load consisting of inductive
reactance.

REACTIVE POWER (elec.) re ac' tive
pow' er: The power apparently used
by the reactive component of a circuit.

REACTOR (elec.) re ac' tor: A device
in which nuclear fission is controlled
and sustained.

REACTOR, SATURABLE (elec.) re-
ac' tor, sat' u ra ble: A transformer
type device in which a direct current
is passed through one set of windings.
The d-c current can control the degree of magnetic core saturation and
therefore control the a-c output of
transformer.

READ (automation) read: The act of
sensing the input information in the
form of characters.

READ (automation) read: To acquire
information from storage in a computer system.

REAM (graphics) ream: A quantity of
paper; 500 sheets.

REAMER (metal) ream' er: A tool used
for enlarging or finishing a hole previously drilled or bored, to give a good
finish and accurate dimension.

REAMING (metal) ream' ing: Using a
reamer for smoothing and sizing holes
in metal.

REAR AXLE (auto.) rear ax' le: A term
referring to housings, shafts, gears and
all other assemblies associated with
the rear wheel support and drive of an
automobile.

REBATE (const.) re' bate: See RABBET.

RECALESCENT POINT (elec.) re ca-
les' cent point: A point in the cooling
of hot iron or steel when there is a
sudden and temporary increase in temperature.

RECEIVER (elec.) re ceiv' er:

    DUAL CONVERSION, a communications radio receiver which employes two IF frequencies. Advantages include greater selectivity and image rejection.

FM, a receiver for frequency modulated signals.

SUPERHETERODYNE, a receiver in which the incoming signal is mixed with a local oscillator frequency to produce an intermediate frequency. The IF is further amplified and then detected.

TUNED RADIO FREQUENCY, (TRF), a receiver in which the incoming signal is selected and amplified by tuned stages before detection.

RECEPTACLE (elec.) re cep' ta cle: A female type connector, usually mounted in a box or on a panel. Power supplied to the receptacle can rapidly be connected to other equipment by means of a plug; sometimes called a convenience outlet.

RECESS (const.) re cess': A hollowing out or cavity in a wall; a niche.

RECIPROCAL re cip' ro cal: The reciprocal of a number is one divided by the number.

RECIPROCATING MOTION (auto.) re- cip ro cat' ing mo' tion: Up and down or straight line motion.

RECORDER (elec.) re cord' er: Any device which makes a record of electrical signals or changing physical or electrical conditions of an apparatus or equipment. Ex: a tape recorder makes a record of sound entering a microphone by transforming the sound to electrical signals which are stored on a magnetic tape.

RECORD STRIP (draft.) re cord' strip: Similar to the title block on a drawing, giving such information as the name of

the drawing, manufacturer, date, scale, number and other information.

RECOVERY (space) re cov' er y: The act of retrieving a portion of a launched missile or satellite which has survived reentry.

RECTANGLE (draft.) rec' tan gle: A geometric figure having four sides and four right angles.

RECTANGULAR COORDINATE GRAPH (draft.) rec tan' gu lar co or' di nate graph: A graph paper ruled with equispaced horizontal and vertical lines, forming small rectangles.

RECTANGULAR COORDINATES (draft.) rec tan' gu lar co or' di nates: The description of a vector in terms of two sides of a right triangle, the hypotenuse of which is the vector.

RECTIFIER (air cond.) rec' ti fi er: An externally cooled heat exchange unit in the high side of the absorption system in a refrigerator unit. Its purpose is to condense and separate the absorbent from the refrigerant before feeding into the condenser.

RECTIFIER (elec.) rec' ti fi er: A component or device used to convert ac into a pulsating dc.

RECTIFIERS, TYPES OF (elec.) rec' ti- fi ers, types of:

COPPER OXIDE, a unidirectional conductor made by the barrier between copper and cuprous oxide.

FULL WAVE, a rectifier circuit which converts both the positive and negative halves of the ac cycle into pulses of direct current.

HALF WAVE, a rectifier circuit

which converts only one half of the input ac wave into direct current.

MERCURY VAPOR, a diode rectifier which uses mercury vapor in place of vacuum. Conduction in diode is the result of ionization of the mercury vapor.

SELENIUM, a unidirectional conductor used in rectification consisting of an iron disk coated with a layer of selenium.

VACUUM TUBE, a rectifier which uses a vacuum tube diode.

RED LEAD (const.) red lead: A primer and protective coat for metal.

RED LEAD (paint. and dec.) red lead: A compound formed by roasting lead or litharge. It is used extensively in paints for protecting iron and steel against corrosion.

RED-SHORTNESS (metal) red-short'-ness: A characteristic of some steels to retain their hardness at dark red heat.

REDUCER (graphics) re duc'er: A liquid to lessen the stickiness and adhesiveness of ink.

REDUCER (paint. and dec.) re duc'er: Volatile ingredients used to thin or reduce viscosity of a finishing material.

REDUCER (plumb.) re duc'er: A short internally threaded fitting with a different size on each end. Used for joining pipes of different sizes.

REDUCING FLAME (weld.) re duc'ing flame: An oxygen-fuel gas flame with a slight excess of fuel gas.

REDUCTION OF AREA (weld.) re duc'-tion of a're a: Difference in cross

sectional area of a specimen after fracture, as compared to original cross sectional area.

REDWOOD (Sequoia Sempervirens) (wood.) red'wood: A wood which is light in weight (28 lbs. to cu. ft.) and soft. Texture is usually fine and even grained. Heartwood is reddish-brown in color. Easy to work, but splits easily. Especially durable and well suited for products exposed to water and moisture.

REED AND PRINCE SCREWDRIVER (metal) reed and prince screw'-dri ver: A screwdriver with a special cross point similar to the Phillips screwdriver but with a sharper joint. Used to drive Reed and Prince screws.

REEDING (wood.) reed'ing: A decorative process by cutting concave reeds on surface of board or table leg.

REED TAPER (metal) reed ta'per: One of the standard taper systems used on the hollow spindles of a machine lathe.

REENTRY NOSE CONE (space) re en'-try nose cone: A nose cone designed especially for reentry, consisting of one or more chambers protected by an outer shield.

REENTRY WINDOW (space) re en'try win'dow: The area at the limit of the Earth's atmosphere through which a space craft on a given trajectory can reenter successfully.

REFACE (auto.) re face': To clean and true up a valve by grinding and turning.

REFERENCE POSITION (elec.) ref'er-ence po si'tion: The angular position of a polar vector or synchro to which reference is made to give meaning to angular measurement.

REFINED SHELLAC (paint. and dec.)

re fined' shel lac': A grade of orange or white shellac from which the wäx has been removed.

REFLECTION (elec.) re flec' tion: The turning back of a wave as it strikes a medium different from the one in which it is travelling.

REFLECTOR (elec.) re flec' tor: A reflecting surface; an antenna element placed behind the radiating element to reinforce the radiation in a certain direction; an antenna element placed behind the receiving element to reinforce received signals and prevent signal pickup from the back or undesired direction.

REFLEX CIRCUIT (e l e c.) re' flex cir' cuit: A radio receiver circuit in which the same tubes are used to amplify the signal before and after detection.

REFRACTION (elec.) re frac' tion: The bending of a wave as it passes through mediums of different densities.

REFRACTION INDEX (elec.) re frac'tion in' dex: The ratio between velocity of wave radiation in free space to the velocity in other materials.

REFRACTIVE INDEX (paint. and dec.) re frac' tive in' dex: Ratio of velocity of light in a certain medium compared with its velocity in air under same conditions.

REFRACTORY (crafts) re frac' to ry: A material resistant to heat; difficult to melt.

REFRIGERANT (air cond.) re frig' er-ant: The medium used for heat transfer in a refrigeration system. It picks up heat by evaporation and pressure at low temperature and gives up heat by condensing at higher temperatures and pressures.

REGAIN (air cond.) re gain': The percentage of moisture absorbed by a material in reference to its weight.

REGELATION (air cond.) re ge la' tion: The refreezing of water which has been melted under pressure.

REGENERATIVE DETECTOR (elec.) re gen' er a tive de tec' tor: A detector in which part of the demodulated signal is fed back in phase with the input signal to the detector. This is a condition of oscillation. However, feedback is limited to just the threshold of oscillation. At this point the detector is most sensitive.

REGENERATIVE FEEDBACK (elec.) re gen' er a tive feed' back: Feedback in phase with input signal so that it adds to input.

REGISTER (air cond.) reg' is ter: A grille covering an air outlet, usually supplied with a control damper.

REGISTER (graphics) reg' is ter: As applied to color printing. To bring together two or more images so they are in agreement in respect to position.

 REGISTRATION MARK

Alignment of colored images, one with another, during printing. Register is achieved by using registration marks which indicate exact position of various images.

REGLET (graphics) reg' let: A flat strip of wood or metal lower than the type face and used to separate lines of type. Wooden furniture thinner than two picas.

REGULATION (e l e c.) reg u la' tion:

The voltage change that takes place in the output of generator or power supply when the load is changed; maintaining a constant value within a specified range.

REGULATION, PERCENTAGE OF (elec.) reg u la' tion, per cent' age of: The percentage of change in voltage from no-load to full-load in respect to the full load voltage. Expressed as:

$$\frac{E_{no\ load} - E_{full\ load}}{E_{full\ load}} \times 100 = \%$$

REGULATOR, CURRENT-VOLTAGE (elec.) reg' u lator, cur' rent-volt' - age: A combination of relays used with a generator to control its output voltage and current within specified limits. Newer types employ transistors for switching functions. The regulator controls the generator by switching resistance in series with the field circuit.

REGULATORS (weld.) reg' u la tors: See ACETYLENE, OXYGEN.

REINFORCED CONCRETE (const.) re-in forced' con' crete: Concrete work in which iron mesh or bars are added for strength.

REINFORCEMENT OF WELD (weld.) re in force' ment of weld: Excess metal on the face of a weld.

REINHARDT (draft.) rein' hardt: An alphabet of single-stroke Gothic letters universally used on working drawings.

REJECT CIRCUIT (elec.) re ject' cir'-cuit: A parallel tuned circuit at resonance. Rejects signals at resonant frequency.

REL (elec.) rel: The unit of measurement of reluctance.

RELATIVE CONDUCTANCE (elec.) rel' a tive con duc' tance: The relative conductance of a material in reference to silver which is considered as 100 percent.

RELATIVE HUMIDITY (air cond.) rel' - a tive hu mid' i ty: Indication in terms of percentage of amount of water vapor in a given volume of air at a given temperature, compared to total amount of water vapor the air could hold at the given temperature.

RELATIVE RESISTANCE (elec.) rel' a-tive re sis' tance: A numerical comparison of the resistance of a material compared to silver which is assigned the value 1.0.

RELATIVISTIC (space) rel a tiv' is tic: Material moving at speeds which are an appreciable fraction of the speed of light, such as subatomic particles.

RELAXATION OSCILLATOR (elec.) relax a' tion os' cil la tor: A nonsinusoidal oscillator whose frequency depends upon the time required to charge or discharge a capacitor through a resistor.

RELAY (elec.) re' lay: A magnetic switch.

RELAY (elec.) re' lay:

CURRENT, a relay which operates at a predetermined current value.

ELECTRONIC, a precision type of switching relay using vacuum tubes or transistors and associated electronic components.

OVERLOAD, a protective device which opens the circuit if abnormally high currents flow.

PHOTOELECTRIC, a relay circuit which is activated by light energy.

REVERSE CURRENT, sometimes called a cut-out. A relay circuit which permits current flow in one direction only.

TEMPERATURE, a relay activated by a change in temperature.

TIME DELAY, a relay which operates at some specified interval of time after it is energized.

VOLTAGE, a relay which operates at a predetermined voltage value.

RELAY RACK (elec.) re' lay rack: A steel frame in which standard nineteen inch panels containing chassis and equipment are mounted.

RELIEF PRINTING (graphics) re lief' print' ing: Printing from characters or designs which are raised above the surrounding surface.

RELIEVING (metal) re liev' ing: The removing of material in back of the cutting edge of a tool to reduce friction and heat.

RELUCTANCE (elec.) re luc' tance: Resistance to the flow of magnetic lines of force.

RELUCTIVITY (elec.) re luc tiv' i ty: The reciprocal of permeability; resistance to being magnetized.

REMOTE CONTROL (elec.) re mote' con' trol: The operation of equipment, such as a motor, from a distant location by means of electrical circuits and relays.

REMOTE CUTOFF TUBE (elec.) re-mote' cut' off tube: A tube which gradually approaches its cutoff point at a remote bias point, due to special grid construction.

REMOTE PICKUP (elec.) re mote' pick' up: Television and radio programs recorded by special mobile equipment away from the studio.

REMOVED SECTION (draft.) re moved' sec' tion: See DETAIL SECTION.

REMOVERS (paint. and dec.) re mov'-ers: Compositions designed to soften old varnish or paint coats so that they may be easily removed by scraping or washing.

RENDERING (const.) ren' der ing: A first coat of plaster on stone or brick; (draft.) finishing a drawing to give it a realistic appearance; a representation.

RENDEZVOUS (space) ren' dez vous: The event of two or more aerospace vehicles meeting in flight at a pre-conceived time and place.

REPEATER (elec.) re peat' er: A microwave receive-transmit station, where the signal is received, reamplified and retransmitted.

REPLICA rep' li ca: A copy; a reproduction.

REPOUSSE (crafts) re pous se': Ornamentation on metal hammered up in relief from the reverse side.

REPRODUCTION RATIO (graphics) re-pro duc' tion ra' tio: The amount of enlargment or reduction from original copy.

REPULSION (elec.) re pul' sion: The tendency of two like charges, either electric or magnetic, to oppose and force each other apart.

REPULSION-START MOTOR (elec.) re pul' sion-start mo' tor: A motor which develops starting torque by in-traction of rotor currents and a single-phase stator field.

RESAW (wood.) re' saw: To saw again; usually refers to sawing a thick plank into thinner boards.

RESAW GAUGE (wood.) re' saw gauge: The guides and fences attached to the saw table for resawing boards.

RESEAT (auto.) re seat' : The refinishing and shaping of valve seats by reamers and grinding stones.

RESERVE CELL (elec.) re serve' cell: A cell in which the elements are kept dry until ready for use.

RESIDUAL MAGNETISM (elec.) re sid'-u al   mag' ne tism: Magnetism remaining in a material after the magnetizing force is removed.

RESIN (wood.) res' in: An oily gummy substance soluble in alcohol. It is obtained from certain species of trees.

RESIN HARDNESS (paint. and dec.) res'-in hard' ness: Method of indicating hardness of resins. Usually from No. 1 (hardest) to No. 6.

RESINS (paint. and dec.) res' ins: Normally transparent or translucent semisolid or solid substances of either vegetable or synthetic origin which when heated are soluble in drying oils and solvents. Once dissolved they remain in solution.

RESISTANCE (elec.) re sis' tance: The quality of an electric circuit that opposes the flow of current through it.

RESISTANCE WELDING (weld.) re sis'-tance weld' ing: The process of welding materials by using the resistance of the metals to the flow of electricity to produce the heat for fusion of the metals.

RESISTIVITY, SPECIFIC (elec.) re sistiv' i ty, specific: The resistance offered by one cubic centimeter of material to the flow of an electric current, expressed in ohms/centimeter.

RESISTOR (elec.) re sis' tor: A component containing resistance to flow of an electric current.

BALLAST, a variable resistor which increases in resistance with an increase in current. It is used to control voltage; a special type of resistor used to control current in a fluorescent lamp.

BLEEDER, a resistor used across the output of a power supply to discharge filter capacitors after power has been turned off.

CARBON, a resistor made of finely ground carbon particles with a suitable binder formed into a cylindrical shape with a wire lead from each end. They are made in a wide variety of shapes, ohmic values and power ratings.

NONINDUCTIVE, a wire wound resistor which is designed to have reduced inductive effect at high temperatures.

VARIABLE, a resistor whose resistance can be varied. See POTENTIOMETER AND RHEOSTAT.

WIRE WOUND, a resistor using resistance wirewound on a ceramic core.

RESOLUTION (elec.) res o lu' tion: In television. The quality or definition in the reproduced picture. The degree of reproduction of fine detail in a picture.

RESOLVER (elec.) re solv' er: A device to change data from one form of coordinate system to another, such as position data into voltages.

RESONANT FREQUENCY (elec.) res' o- nant fre' quen cy: The frequency at which a tuned circuit oscillates. See TUNED CIRCUIT.

RESONANT LINE (elec.) res' o nant line: A line that has standing waves of voltage and current. It has a finite length and is not terminated in its characteristic impedance.

RESPIRATION res pi ra' tion: Process by which an organism supplies its cells and tissues with oxygen and relieves them of carbon dioxide.

RESPIRATOR res' pi ra tor: A face mask which covers the nose and some- times the mouth. Used to prevent the breathing of dust and fumes.

RESTORATION (elec.) res to ra' tion: See D-C INSERTION.

RETAINING WALL (const.) re tain' ing wall: A wall, usually placed in the side of a hill, to resist lateral pres- sure of earth and prevent slides or cave-ins.

RETARDERS (paint. and dec.) re tard'- ers: Slow drying solvents or extenders added to lacquer to delay drying of the lacquer.

RETENTIVITY (elec.) re ten tiv' i ty: The ability of a material to retain its magnetism after the magnetizing force is removed.

RETICULATE (wood.) re tic' u late: Designing a furniture decorative sur- face to resemble a net; have a net- like form; having veins like a net. Ex: a leaf from a tree.

RETMA (elec.): RADIO ELECTRONICS TELEVISION MANUFACTURER'S AS- SOCIATION.

RETRACE (elec.) re trace': The proc- ess of returning scanning beam to starting point after one line is scanned.

RETROGRADE MOTION (space) ret' ro- grade mo' tion: Orbital motion oppo- site in direction to that normal to spatial bodies within a given system.

RETROROCKET (space) ret ro- rock' et: A rocket that gives thrust in a direction opposite to the direction of an object's motion, used to slow down the speed of an object.

RETURN (const.) re turn' : Continuation of a molding in an opposite direction.

RETURN BEND (plumb.) re turn' bend: A pipe bend shaped like the letter U.

RETURN NOSING (wood.) re turn' nos'- ing: The mitered overhanging end of a stair tread outside of the baluster.

REVEAL (const.) re veal' : Jamb; the part between an opening for a door or window and the frame.

REVERBERATION TIME (elec.) re ver- ber a' tion time: The time for a sound of a given frequency to decrease to one millionth of its initial value, after the sound is stopped.

REVERSE CURRENT CUT-OUT (elec.) re verse' cur' rent cut'-out: A relay which permits current to flow only in one direction.

REVERSE LETTERING (graphics) re- verse' let' ter ing: Lettering which is made so part normally black is white and vice versa. Example: White letter- ing on black background.

REVERSED POLARITY (electrode posi-

tive-anode) (weld.) re versed' po lar'-
i ty: Referring to d-c and causing
electrons to flow from the base metal
to the electrode.

REVISE (graphics) re vise': To compare a marked proof with a proof from
the corrected job.

REVOLUTION (draft.) rev o lu' tion:
The act of turning an object or part of
an object from its fixed natural position to a position parallel to a picture
plane, to improve its representation and
have surfaces and lines appear in natural shape and true dimension.

REVOLUTIONS PER MINUTE rev o-
lu' tions per min' ute: The rate of
speed of a machine or wheel. Abbreviated: rpm.

REVOLVED SECTION (draft.) re volved'
sec' tion: A drafting convention permitting the cutting plane through a part
of an object which is perpendicular to
the projection plane and then revolving
90°, so that the section appears in its
true shape.

RHEOSTAT (elec.) rhe' o stat: A variable resistor, usually inserted in series
with the load, to control the current.

RHO (p) (elec.): Greek letter designation
of specific resistance in ohms per
circular-mil-foot.

RIBBON (const.) rib' bon: A narrow
board cut into wall studs to give additional support.

RIDDLE (metal) rid' dle: In foundry
work, a metal screen for sifting molding
sand.

RIDE (metal) ride: The tendency of a
cutting tool to ride over the work.

"RIDE THE BRUSH" (paint. and dec.):

To bear down on the brush to the extent
that the paint is applied with the sides
of the bristles instead of the flat ends.

RIDGE (const.) ridge: The horizontal
line at the top of the roof formed by
the intersection of roof surfaces.

RIDGECAP (const.) ridge' cap: A wood
or metal cap over the ridge to weatherproof the joint.

RIDGEPOLE (const.) ridge' pole: The
highest horizontal timber in a building.
It ties the rafters together along the
ridge and supports them.

RIDGE ROOF (const.) ridge roof: A
roof whose rafters meet at an apex or
ridge. The end view of the ridge roof
is a triangular gable.

RIDING (graphics) rid' ing: When a
part of a form works up on a crest.

RIFFLER (metal) rif' fler: A small
curved file for filing inside surfaces.

RIGHT ANGLE right an' gle: An angle
equal to 90 degrees.

RIGHT-HAND SCREW (metal) right-hand
screw: A screw which advances when
turned in a clockwise direction.

RIM LOCK (wood.) rim lock: A door
lock which is fastened onto the surface
of a door rather than mortised into
the door.

RING GAUGE (metal) ring gauge: An
accurate gauge shaped like a ring for
checking external diameters.

RING GEAR (auto.) ring gear: A gear
which has no hub or central bore; a
gear mounted on the flywheel of an
automotive engine and used to engage
the starter motor gear when starting
the engine.

RINGING OSCILLATOR (elec.) ring' ing os cil la' tor: A shock-excited oscillator utilizing a parallel-resonant circuit in its cathode circuit.

RING SHIMMY (auto.) ring shim' my: A condition existing at high engine speeds, when oil rings cannot function efficiently and allow oil to get into combustion chamber.

RIPPING (wood.) rip' ping: To saw wood with the grain or longitudinally.

RIPPING BAR (wood.) rip' ping bar: A strong steel bar with a goose neck end. Used for prying boards and pulling large nails.

RIPPING BAR

RIPPING HAMMER (wood.) rip' ping ham' mer: See HAMMER.

RIPPLE FACTOR (elec.) rip' ple fac'- tor: The ratio between the rms value of the ripple voltage in the output of a rectifier to the average d-c value of output voltage.

RIPPLE VOLTAGE (elec.) rip' ple volt' age: The a-c component of the d-c output of a power supply due to insufficient filtering.

RIPRAP (const.) rip' rap: A foundation of loose broken stone. Used in water and on soft ground.

RIP SAW (wood.) rip saw: A saw designed to cut with the grain of the wood.

RISE (const.) rise: The amount of incline expressed in inches per foot run.

RISER (plumb.) ris' er: A vertical water supply pipe extending between stories of a building.

RISER (wood.) ris' er: The vertical board between the steps in a stairway.

RISER (metal) ris' er: A hole in the cope of a sand mold to allow gases to escape.

RISERS (elec.) ris' ers: Wires and cables which run vertically between floors of a building.

RIVET (metal) riv' et: A headed metal pin used to fasten materials together. The pin is placed through mating holes and the end headed-over by pressing or forging.

RIVETING HAMMER (wood.) riv' et ing ham' mer: See HAMMER.

RMA (elec.): Radio Manufacturer's Association.

RMS VALUE (elec.) rms val' ue: ROOT-MEAN-SQUARE value. The same as effective value. ($.707 \times E_{peak}$).

ROCK (elec.) rock: A slang term used in amateur radio meaning a crystal. If a radio transmitter is "rock bound," it cannot vary its frequency.

ROCKER ARM (auto.) rock' er arm: A valve mechanism in which an arm is pivoted in the center. One end is actuated by a pushrod from the camshaft; the other end operates the spring loaded valves. Used in an overhead-valve engine.

RIP SAW TEETH

ROCKET (space) rock' et: A thrust-producing system, or a complete missile which derives its thrust from ejection of hot gases generated from material carried in the system, not requiring intake of air or water.

ROCKET ENGINE (space) rock' et en'-
gine: A rocket propulsive device that
is relatively complicated in its work-
ings, as distinguished from a rocket
motor.

ROCKET SLED (space) rock' et sled:
A sled that runs on a rail or rails
and is accelerated to high velocities by
a rocket engine. This sled is used by
the Air Force in determining G tolerances and for developing crash sur-
vival techniques.

ROCKETSONDE (space) rock' et sonde:
A meteorological rocket.

ROCK HOUND PICK (crafts) rock hound
pick: See PROSPECTORS PICK.

ROCKOON (space) rock' oon: A high-
altitude sounding system consisting of
a small solid-propellant research rocket launched from a balloon.

ROCKWELL HARDNESS (metal) rock'-
well hard' ness: A hardness test for
metals based on the depth of an impression of a steel ball under a load of
100 kilograms. The hardness is read
directly on a scale in Rockwell numbers.

ROCOCO (draft.) ro co' co: See
BAROQUE.

RODMAN (const.) rod' man: The surveyor's assistant who carries and uses
the leveling rod.

ROENTGEN (elec.) roent' gen: The unit
of measurement of exposure to rays or
gamma radiation.

ROLL (space) roll: The rotational or
oscillatory movement along the longitudinal axis of a spacecraft.

ROLLING RESISTANCE (auto.) roll' ing
re sis' tance: The resistance to mov-

ing a vehicle on the road as a result of
irregularities in road and the flexing of
tires.

ROLL-OFF (elec.) roll-off: The gradual attenuation with increase or decrease in the frequency of a signal.

ROMAN (graphics) ro' man: Vertical
element of letters are upright.

ROMANESQUE (draft.) ro man esque':
A period of architecture (1700-1850
AD) characterized by ribbed vaults and
cloistered piers and the beginning of
the use of buttresses.

ROOF (const.) roof: The covering on a
building.

ROOFERS (const.) roof' ers: Boards
used for roof construction which serve
as an undercover to support shingles
or other roofing materials.

ROOFING (const.) roof' ing: Materials
used to make a roof watertight.

ROOF TRUSS (const.) roof truss: Timbers, supports and beams fastened together to support a roof.

ROOT (metal) root: The bottom joining
surfaces of a thread at the minor
diameter.

ROOT DIAMETER (metal) root di am' -
e ter: The diameter of a screw taken
at the bottom of the threads; the diameter of a gear at the bottom of the teeth.

ROOT OF WELD (weld.) root of weld:
That part of a weld farthest from the
application of weld heat and/or filler
metal side.

ROSETTE WELD (weld.) ro sette' weld:
See PLUG WELD.

ROSIN (metal) ros' in: Used as a solder-

ing flux for copper and tin when corrosion cannot be permitted.

ROSIN (paint. and dec.) ros' in: A
resin obtained from pine trees containing principally isomers of abietic
acid. Wood rosin is obtained from
stump or dead wood, using steam distillation. Gum rosin is obtained from
the living tree.

ROTARY CONVERTER (elec.) ro' ta ry
con vert' er: An a-c generator driven
by a d-c motor or a d-c generator
driven by an a-c motor.

ROTARY MOTION (auto.) ro' ta ry mo'-
tion: Circular or revolving motion.

ROTARY PRESS (graphics) ro' ta ry
press: A press which uses a curved
printing plate and a curved impression cylinder.

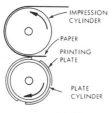

ROTARY PRESS

ROTARY SWITCH (elec.) ro' ta ry
switch: A switch which makes contact
between points by revolution of a shaft.

ROTATING MACHINE (elec.) ro tat' ing
ma chine': Motor or generator.

ROTATING VECTOR (elec.) ro tat' ing
vec' tor: A vector rotating around a
fixed point, used to represent instantaneous values of a sine wave during
one cycle.

ROTOGRAVURE (graphics) ro to gravure': Mass production of gravure
printing using a rotary press.

ROTOR (elec.) ro' tor: The rotating
part of an a-c generator.

ROTTENSTONE (paint. and dec.) rot'-
ten stone: A siliceous limestone which
when finely pulverized, is used in wood
finishing. It has negligible cutting action but is fine for polishing. It is also
known as tripoli.

ROTTENSTONE (wood.) rot' ten stone:
A fine powder made of decomposed
limestone, used for polishing.

ROTUNDA (const.) ro tun' da: A circular room under a dome.

ROUGE (crafts) rouge: See CROCUS.

ROUGHCAST (const.) rough' cast: A
decorative and protective wall finish
accomplished by throwing a mixture
of cement, mortar and stones against
the wall surface to which it adheres.

ROUGHING-IN (plumb.) rough' ing-in:
The installation of drainage and supply
pipes during the construction of the
building. These pipes are installed in
walls and floors and must be in place
before walls are finished.

ROUGHING CUT (metal) rough' ing cut:
A cut to bring the material to approximate dimension.

ROUGH LUMBER (const.) rough lum'-
ber: Unsurfaced lumber; not dressed
to size.

ROUGHNESS (metal) rough' ness: Relatively finely spaced irregularities produced by cutting tools.

ROUND MEASUREMENTS (metal) round
mea' sure ments: Measurement of diameters and radii of work.

ROUND NOSE CHISEL (metal) round
nose chis' el: A type of cold chisel

with a rounded cutting edge for chipping in filleted corners.

ROUTER (wood.) rout' er: A high speed motor to which may be attached a variety of shaped cutters for veining, inlaying, dovetailing mortising and any incise cutting.

ROUTER PLANE (wood.) rout' er plane: A cutting tool fixed in a metal frame with two handles. Used for routing out grooves in the surface of a board.

ROWLAND'S LAW (elec.) row' land's law: A law for magnetic circuits which states that the number of lines of magnetic flux is in direct proportion to the magnetomotive force and inversely proportional to the reluctance of the circuit. $\Phi = \dfrac{F}{R}$

ROWLOCK (const.) row' lock: A course of brick laid on edge called a "rowlock course."

RPM: See REVOLUTIONS PER MINUTE.

RUBBING OIL (paint. and dec.) rub' bing oil: Neutral, medium-heavy mineral oil used as a lubricant for pumice stone in rubbing varnish and lacquer.

RUBBING VARNISH (paint. and dec.) rub' bing var' nish: A hard-drying varnish which may be rubbed with an abrasive and water or oil to a uniform leveled surface.

RUBBLE WORK (const.) rub' ble work: Masonry construction using rough undressed stones.

RUBEN CELL (RM cell) (elec.) ru' ben cell: A mercury cell employing mercuric oxide and zinc. The electrolyte is potassium hydroxide.

RUBRICATION (paint. and dec.) ru brica' tion: The coloring of a background in red; the coloring of a background with enamels or paint.

RULES (graphics) rules: Strips of brass or lead, type high and with one edge prepared to print an impression.

RULING PEN (draft.) rul' ing pen: An adjustable line width pen used for inking drawings.

RUMBLE (elec.) rum' ble: The low frequency mechanical vibration of a turn table which is transmitted to the recorded sound.

RUN (const.) run: The horizontal distance covered by a rafter.

RUN (graphics) run: The number of sheets to be printed.

RUN (plumb.) run: The distance of the straight line direction of a pipe.

RUNIC (graphics) ru' nic: A type face, decorative style.

RUNG (wood.) rung: A round of a chair; crosspiece of a ladder.

RUN-IN (auto.) run-in: The proper final fitting of parts due to slight wear during initial operation.

RUNNING FIT (metal) run' ning fit: Parts mated with sufficient clearance for lubrication and movement.

RUNNING HEAD (graphics) run' ning head: Headlines at the top of each page in a book.

RUNS (paint. and dec.) runs: Also known as "sags." Irregularities of a surface due to uneven flow.

RUPTURE MEMBER (air cond.) rup' -

ture mem'ber: A device which will automatically break at a predetermined pressure.

RUSH (crafts) rush: The stems of marsh growing plants used to weave seats in chairs.

RUST rust: Rusting of metal is generally explained as oxidizing process where oxygen from air combines with iron to form a metallic oxide; water combines with oxide to form rust.

RUST-INHIBITIVE WASHES (paint. and dec.) rust-in hib'i tive washes: Solutions which etch the metal and form a dull gray coating of uniformly fine texture, thus producing rust-inhibitive surface receptive to priming coat.

RUTILE (paint. and dec.) ru'tile: A lustrous dark red mineral, commonly found in prismatic crystals and containing some iron; titanium dioxide.

R-Y SIGNAL (elec.) r-y sig'nal: In color TV, it is one of the three color difference signals.

SABIN (air cond.) sa'bin: A unit of measurement of sound absorptivity. It is equivalent to the absorption of all incident sound energy of one square foot of a material surface.

SADDLE (metal) sad'dle: An H shaped casting, fitted to the V ways of the lathe bed, to carry the cross slide and tool holders.

SADDLE BOARDS (const.) sad'dle boards: Boards nailed along the ridge of a roof to cover roofing and seal joints against the weather.

SADDLE STITCHED (graphics) sad'dle stitched: A booklet in which all leaves inset each other, and then is stitched through to hold the book together.

SAE (auto.): Society of Automotive Engineers.

SAE HORSEPOWER (auto.) sae horse-pow'er: A horsepower measurement developed as a means of comparing all engines uniformly. The formula assumes certain constants such as mechanical efficiency, mean effective pressure and piston speed at full power.

SAFE (plumb.) safe: A pan placed beneath a joint to collect leakage.

SAFE CARRYING CAPACITY (elec.) safe car'ry ing ca pac'i ty: The maximum current a conductor will carry without overheating.

SAFETY VALVE safe'ty valve: A safety device used on a steam or hot water boiler which permits steam or water to escape if the pressures become dangerous.

SAFFLOWER OIL (paint. and dec.) saf'-flow er oil: Oil from seed of thistle-like plant grown mostly in Egypt and India.

SAGGER (crafts) sag'ger: A fire clay enclosure used to protect delicate pieces in a furnace while being fired.

SAGGING (const.) sag'ging: The bending of a joist or timber as a result of its own weight or load.

SAGS (paint. and dec.) sags: See RUNS.

SAL AMMONIAC sal am mo'ni ac: Ammonium Chloride.

SAL AMMONIAC (metal) sal am mo'-ni ac: A flux for cleaning and tinning soldering irons and coppers.

SALINOMETER (air cond.) sal i nom'-e ter: A hydrometer used for measuring salt concentration of a liquid.

SALON (const.) sa lon': A large decorated room for holding exhibitions
and receptions.

SAL SODA sal so' da: Washing soda;
crystallized sodium carbonate.

SALT (paint. and dec.) salt: Substance
that results from reaction between
acid and base.

SAND BLASTING (metal) sand blast'-
ing: A cleaning process by means of
high pressure air carrying suspended
sand.

"SAND DOWN" (paint. and dec.) sand
down: Remove the glass of an old finish and smooth it prior to refinishing.

"SAND FINISH" (paint. and dec.) sand
fin' ish: Rough finish plaster wall.

SAND HOLE (metal) sand hole: An
imperfection in a metal casting, due
to loose sand in the mold breaking
away from the mold cavity during
pouring.

SANDING MACHINE (wood.) sand' ing
ma chine': Machines for sanding wood
surfaces in which the abrasive paper
mounted on a disk, belt or spindle is
power driven.

SANDING SEALER (paint. and dec.)
sand' ing seal' er: A lacquer used as
a seal coat over a filler.

SANDPAPER (wood.) sand' pa per: Paper coated with sharp particles of
sand. It is the most common abrasive
for smoothing wood surfaces.

SANDSTONE (const.) sand' stone: Natural sandstone was formed by fine sand
being cemented together by silica, oxide of iron and carbonate of lime. It is
widely used as a building stone.

SAND TRAP (plumb.) sand trap: A catch

basin designed to catch sand or gritty
material.

SANITARY SEWER (plumb.) san' i tar y
sew' er: Sewers constructed to carry
only sanitary wastes.

SAP (wood.) sap: Juice from plants and
trees.

SAPONIFY (paint. and dec.) sa pon' i-
fy: To convert an oil or fat into soap
by action of an alkali.

SAPONIFICATION NUMBER (paint. and
dec.) sa pon i fi ca' tion num' ber:
Number of milligrams of potassium
hydroxide needed to neutralize the acid
in one gram of substance after it has
been saponified.

SAP STREAKS (wood.) sap streaks:
Streaks of sap wood which show through
the final finish on the wood.

SAPWOOD (wood.) sap' wood: The layers of wood surrounding the heart of a
tree which carry food and moisture to
sustain the growth of the tree.

SASH (const.) sash: The framework
around the glass in a window.

SASH WEIGHT (const.) sash weight: A
weight attached to a window by rope or
metal band to counterbalance the weight
of the sash, to permit easy movement.

SATELLITE (space) sat' el lite: An at-
tendant body that revolves about another
body. A manmade object designed or
expected to be launched as a satellite.

SATELLOID (space) sat' el loid: A
manned vehicle – half airplane, half
satellite – designed to orbit and then
return to Earth.

SATIN FINISH (paint. and dec.) sat' in
fin' ish: Term used in describing dried

film of paint or other finishing material which does not have a full luster, but a dull luster like that of satin.

SATURATED AIR (air cond.) sat' u rat- ed air: A mixture of air and water vapor both at the same temperature.

SATURATION (air cond.) sat u ra' tion: A condition of equilibrium existing when two substances combine to the full extent of their combining capacities with each other.

SATURATION CURRENT (elec.) sat u- ra' tion cur' rent: The current through an electron tube when saturation voltage is applied to plate.

SATURATION TEMPERATURE (elec.) sat u ra' tion tem' per a ture: The cathode temperature in an electron tube, when a further increase in temperature will not increase the plate current.

SATURATION VOLTAGE (elec.) sat u- ra' tion volt' age: The voltage applied to the plate of a vacuum tube so that all emitted electrons are attracted to the plate.

SAW (wood.) saw: A thin flat metal blade with teeth on one edge used for cutting.

SAW GUMMING (wood.) saw gum' ming: Sharpening the teeth of a circular saw and grinding out the gullets.

SAWHORSE (const.) saw' horse: A four legged trestle used to support boards and timbers while sawing.

SAW SET (wood.) saw set: A tool for applying the proper set to the teeth of a saw.

SAWTOOTH GENERATOR (elec.) saw'- tooth gen' er a tor: An electron tube

oscillator producing a sawtooth wave- form.

SAWTOOTH WAVE (elec.) saw' tooth: A wave shaped like the teeth of a saw.

SAWYER (wood.) saw' yer: The man who operates the circular saw in a lumber mill.

SAYBOLT TEST (auto.) say' bolt test: A measure of the viscosity of oil.

SCABBLE (const.) scab' ble: To smooth off rough projections of stone in rubble masonry.

SCAFFOLD (const.) scaf' fold: A tem- porary structure or platform to support workmen and material during con- struction.

SCALE (draft.) scale: A scale with graduations for laying off measure- ments to actual or reduced size.

ARCHITECT'S SCALE, a scale grad- uated in divisions representing a foot.

CIVIL ENGINEER'S SCALE, a scale graduated in decimal parts of an inch.

MECHANICAL ENGINEER'S SCALE, a scale graduated proportionally to give reductions based on inches.

METRIC SCALE, scales using the metric measuring system.

SCALE (metal) scale: A steel graduate ruler, usually six to twelve inches long.

SCALE HEIGHT (space) scale height: A measure of the relationship between density and temperature at any point in an atmosphere.

SCALER (elec.) scal' er: An electronic device which produces an output pulse for a specified number of input pulses.

SCALING (paint. and dec.) scal'ing: Finish condition in which pieces of the dried finishing material come off, exposing the surface below.

SCAN (elec.) scan: The process of sweeping the electron beam across each element of a picture in successive order, to reproduce the total picture in television.

SCANTLING (const.) scant'ling: Small dimension lumber such as 2x4; studding; dimensions of building lumber.

SCARFING (const.) scarf'ing: Joining two timbers together with lap joints so they appear to be one continuous timber.

SCARF JOINT (const.) scarf joint: An end joint made with timbers by notching and lapping the ends. It is held in place by bolts or metal straps.

SCARLET LAKE (paint. and dec.) scar'let lake: Pigment made by precipitation of aniline color upon base of alumina hydrate and barium sulphate.

SCATTER PROPAGATION (elec.) scat'ter prop a ga'tion: The transmission of radio waves beyond the horizon.

SCENOGRAPHIC PROJECTION (draft.) sce no graph'ic pro jec'tion: See PERSPECTIVE PROJECTION.

SCHEMATIC (elec.) sch ma'tic: A diagram of an electrical or electronic circuit showing electrical connections and identification of various components.

SCINTILATION COUNTER (elec.) scin ti la'tion count'er: See COUNTER, SCINTILLATION.

SCLERROSCOPE (metal) scler'ro scope: An instrument used to determine the hardness of a material.

SCONCE (const.) sconce: A candlestick; a projecting or hanging bracket for a candle.

SCORE (const.) score: To scratch along a line; to mark along a cutting line with cuts or notches.

SCORE (crafts) score: The process of cutting a deep line on metal in preparation for a sharp bend.

SCORING (graphics) scor'ing: To crease heavy stock so that it will fold easily without breaking.

SCOTIA (const.) sco'ti a: A concave molding using an irregular curve.

SCRAMBLED SPEECH (elec.) scram'bled speech: See INVERTER.

SCRAPING (metal) scrap'ing: A hand process of pushing off a small chip of metal, using a very sharp tool having no rake.

SCRAP IRON (metal) scrap iron: A term used to describe all kinds and types of salvaged iron.

SCRATCH COAT (const.) scratch coat: The first coat of plaster. It is scratched to provide a good bond for the following coats.

SCREEDS (const.) screeds: Long narrow strips of plaster put horizontally on a wall which serve as guides for plastering the wide intervals between them.

SCREEN (const.) screen: A wire mesh covering for windows; a low wall or partition not reaching to the ceiling.

SCREEN GRID (elec.) screen grid: The second grid in an electron tube between the control grid and plate, to reduce interelectrode capacitance.

SCREW (metal) screw: A cylindrical form on which is cut external grooves conforming to the pattern of a helix; a fastener employing screw threads like a machine bolt.

SCREWDRIVER (metal) screw' dri ver: A steel rod or bar with a handle on one end and the other end flattened to fit the slot in a screw head. They are manufactured in many shapes and sizes to fit special purposes and trades.

SCREW MACHINE (metal) screw ma-chine': A turret lathe.

SCREW-MATE (wood.) screw-mate: The Stanley trade name for a combination drill and countersink.

SCREW PLATE (metal) screw plate: Refers to the handle or stock and the several dies used to cut external threads.

SCREW THREAD MICROMETER (metal) screw thread mi crom' e ter: A micrometer with anvil and spindle shaped to fit screw threads. It measures the pitch diameter of the screw.

SCRIBER (wood.) scrib'er: A steel pencil like tool ground to a long sharp point used for marking on wood and metal surfaces.

SCRIBING (const.) scrib'ing: Fitting woodwork to irregular curves and sur-faces.

SCRIPT (graphics) script: A type face simulating handwriting.

SCROLL SAW (wood.) scroll saw: The same as a jigsaw but with a deeper throat permitting the work to be much larger.

SCROLL WORK (wood.) scroll work: Ornamental woodwork consisting of many curves in its design.

SCRUB (space) scrub: To cancel out a scheduled test firing, either before or during countdown.

SCUTCH (const.) scutch: A small mason's pick with a chisel-like head and used to trim bricks to a particular size.

SEA COAL (metal) sea coal: Finely ground soft coal.

SEALED-BEAM LIGHT (auto.) sealed-beam light: A sealed light consisting of lens, reflector and lamp in a vacu-um. It is widely used in automotive headlights.

SEALER (paint. and dec.) seal'er: A liquid coating composition, usually transparent, such as varnish, that also contains pigment for sealing porous surfaces, such as plaster, preparatory to application of the finish coats. Wood floor sealer is a thin varnish.

SEAM (metal) seam: The line formed when two edges are joined together.

SECONDARY (paint. and dec.) sec'ond-ar y: The colors obtained by mixing the primary colors (red, yellow and blue) together in pairs. Red+yellow=orange), yellow+blue=green, red+blue=purple.

SECONDARY AUXILIARY (draft.) sec'-ond ar y aux il' ia ry: An auxiliary view of a part of an object which is oblique to all principal planes of pro-jection.

SECONDARY BRANCH (plumb.) sec'-ond ar y branch: Any drainage branch other than the main branch.

SECONDARY CELL (elec.) sec' ond-ar y cell: A cell that can be recharged by reversing the chemical action with an electric current.

SECONDARY COLORS (paint. and dec.) sec' ond ar y col'ors: Colors made by combining primary colors. For example, the secondary color orange, is obtained by mixing red and yellow.

SECONDARY EMISSION (elec.) sec' ond- ar y e mis' sion: The emission of electrons as the result of electrons hitting the plate of an electron tube.

SECONDARY FREQUENCY STANDARD (elec.) sec' ond ar y fre' quen cy stand' ard: A highly accurate frequency generator used as a reference for setting up equipment to check alignment and calibration.

SECONDARY WINDING (elec.) sec' ond- ar y wind' ing: The coil which receives energy from the primary winding by mutual induction and delivers energy to the load.

SECOND-CLASS LEVER sec' ond-class le' ver: A lever with the fulcrum at

one end and the force applied to the other. The weight is between the fulcrum and the force applied.

SECOND CUT (metal) sec' ond cut: The spacing of the teeth on a file between bastard and smooth cut.

SECOND HARMONIC DISTORTION (elec.) sec' ond har mon' ic dis tor'- tion: Distortion of a wave by addition of its second harmonic.

SECTION (automation) sec' tion: A ma-

chine on the production line which does a specific operation or a series of operations at a station.

SECTIONAL VIEW (draft.) sec' tion al view: A view of an object obtained by the imaginary cutting-away of the front portion of the object to show the interior detail.

SECTION LINES (draft.) sec' tion lines: Continuous light lines drawn across the face of imaginary cut surfaces to emphasize the contour and detail of the interior. Lines are usually drawn at a 45° angle.

SECTION-LINE SYMBOLS (draft.) sec'- tion-line sym' bols: A system of lines and symbols used instead of section lines, to indicate various kinds of materials.

SEDIMENT BOWL (auto.) sed' i ment bowl: A glass or metal container in the fuel system to collect dirt and water in the fuel.

SEEBECK EFFECT (elec.) see' beck ef fect' : Thermo-electric generation by heating two dissimilar metals in contact with each other; thermocouple.

SEEKER (space) seek' er: A guidance system which homes on energy emanating or reflected from a target or station.

SEGMENT (elec.) seg' ment: A part of a divided object; a commutator bar.

SEIZING (metal) seiz' ing: Freezing or binding two pieces of metal together as a result of heating caused by undue friction.

SELECTIVE FADING (elec.) se lec' tive fad' ing: A condition in radio reception when a signal is received over multiple paths of unequal lengths. The signal may be partially cancelled or out of phase.

SELECTIVITY (elec.) se lec tiv' i ty: The relative ability of a receiver to select the desired signal while rejecting all others.

SELENIUM (elec.) se le' ni um: A nonmetallic element which is photosensitive and is used in photoconductive cells. It is also used in metallic rectifiers.

SELENOCENTRIC (space) sel en o-cen' tric: Relating to the center of the moon.

SELF-BIAS (elec.) self-bi' as: Bias produced by the flow of electrons through a grid resistor.

SELF-CENTERING (metal) self-cen' ter ing: The automatic location of a piece of work in a machine on centers; the automatic locating and marking the centers of a cylindrical piece of work.

SELF-CLEANING (paint. and dec.) self-clean' ing: Term used to describe paint in which rate of chalking is controlled so dirt on surface will be washed away with accumulated chalk.

SELF-EXCITED (elec.) self-ex cit' ed: A generator which uses a part of its output to excite its own field. Initial output is obtained from the residual magnetism of the field poles.

SELF-INDUCTANCE (elec.) self-in duc' tance: An emf is self-induced when it is induced in the conductor carrying the current.

SELF-PRIMING (paint. and dec.) self-prim' ing: Use of the same paint for primer and for subsequent coats. The paint may be thinned differently for the different coats.

SELSYN (elec.) sel' syn: Devices used to transmit and receive angular displacement of a shaft by an electrical signal. Selsyn is a General Electric trade name.

SELVAGES (selvedges) (paint. and dec.) sel' vages: Edges of wallpaper without printing.

SEMIAUTOMATION (automation) semi-au to ma' tion: The development of automatic tool setting, measuring, feeding and surveillance devices as aids to production without displacing the machine operator.

SEMICONDUCTOR (elec.) sem' i con duc tor: A conductor with resistivity somewhere in the range between conductors and insulators.

SEMICONDUCTOR, N type (elec.) sem'-i con duc tor, N type: A semiconductor which uses electrons as the major carrier.

SEMICONDUCTOR, P type (elec.) sem'-i con duc tor, P type: A semiconductor which uses holes as the major carrier.

SEMIDRYING OILS (paint. and dec.) sem' i dry ing oils: Oils which "dry" to a soft tacky film. Principal semidrying oil used in the paint industry is soybean oil.

SEMIFLOATING AXLE (auto.) sem' i-float' ing ax' le: A live axle supported by bearings at the wheel end, but floating at the differential end.

SEMIGLOSS (paint. and dec.) sem' i-gloss: Sheen on dry finish which is about half way between dead flat finish and full gloss.

SEMILOGARITHMIC GRAPH (draft.) sem i log a rith' mic graph: A graph paper ruled by a uniform scale in one direction and a logarithmic scale in the other direction.

SEMI-PRODUCT (automation) sem i-prod' uct: A complete product by itself, but used to complete a larger product.

SEMISATELLITE (space) sem i sat' el-lite: A missile, orbital glider, or other object that attains such velocity as to become subject to some of the conditions of an orbiting body without, however, achieving an orbit itself.

SEMISTEEL (metal) sem' i steel: A high strength cast iron made by adding a portion of steel scrap to the molten pig iron during melting.

SENSIBLE ATMOSPHERE (space) sen'-si ble at' mos phere: That part of the atmosphere that may be felt, i.e. that offers resistance.

SENSITIVE DRILL PRESS (metal) sen'-si tive drill press: A drill press used for drilling small holes with hand feed.

SENSITIVITY (elec.) sen si tiv' i ty: The ability of a circuit to respond to small signal voltages.

SENSITIVITY OF METER (elec.) sen-si tiv' i ty of me' ter: An indication of the loading effect of a meter. The resistance of the moving coil and multiplier divided by voltage for full scale deflection. Sensitivity equals one divided by the current required for full scale deflection.

Ex: A 100 ua meter movement has a sensitivity of,

$$\frac{1}{.0001} \text{ or } 10,000 \text{ ohms/volt.}$$

SENSORS (automation) sen' sors: Devices which convert physical conditions into information which can be understood by the control system.

SEPARATORS (auto.) sep' a ra tors: Thin layers of porous wood, spun glass or rubber used to separate the negative and positive plates in a storage battery.

SEPIA (crafts) se' pi a: Dark reddish brown color.

SEPIA PRINT (graphics) se' pi a print: A photo print with brown backgrounds and masses rather than black.

SEPTIC TANK (plumb.) sep' tic tank: A water tight metal or concrete tank for retention of sewage. Chemical action breaks up the sewage in the septic tank and the liquid flows out into a drainage field.

SEQUENCE (weld.) se' quence: An order in which operations take place.

SEQUENTIAL (automation) se quen'-tial: Arranged in predetermined logical order.

SERIES (graphics) ser' ies: All variations of one type family.

SERIES CELLS (elec.) se' ries cells: A method of connecting cells so that the positive of one cell is connected to negative of the adjacent cell.

SERIES CIRCUIT (elec.) se' ries cir'-cuit: A circuit which contains only one possible path for electrons through the circuit.

SERIES COIL (elec.) se' ries coil: A coil connected in series.

SERIES MOTOR (elec.) se' ries mo' tor: A direct current motor which has its armature and field coils connected in series.

SERIES PARALLEL (elec.) se'ries par'al lel: Groups of series cells with output terminals connected in parallel.

SERIES RESONANCE (elec.) se'ries res'o nance: A series circuit of an inductor, a capacitor and resistor at a frequency when the inductive and capacitive reactances are equal and cancelling. The circuit appears as pure resistance and has minimum impedance.

SERIF (graphics) ser'if: A fine line projecting from a stroke of a letter; fine lines projecting at the top and bottom of Roman type face.

SERRATED (paint. and dec.) ser'rat ed: Notched, or toothed on the edge.

SERRATED PULSE (elec.) ser'rat ed pulse: A longer pulse, used to synchronize the vertical oscillator in a TV. The pulse is divided by serrations of short duration to maintain horizontal synchronization.

SERVICE AREA (elec.) ser'vice a're a: The geographical area around a broadcasting station in which there is satisfactory reception of the station's programs.

SERVICE DROP (elec.) ser'vice drop: Connecting wires from the power lines to the point of entry to building.

SERVICE ELL (plumb.) ser'vice ell: A pipe fitting with either a 45° or 90° bend, which is internally threaded on one end and externally threaded on the other end.

SERVICE ENTRANCE (elec.) ser'vice en'trance: The associated cables, conduit, boxes and meters used to bring electric power from main power line to a building.

SERVICE PIPE (plumb.) ser'vice pipe: A smaller pipe used to convey gas or water from the supply main to the building.

SERVICE TEE (plumb.) ser'vice tee: A T fitting with external thread on one end and internal threads on other ends.

SERVO ASSIST-MANUAL (automation) ser'vo as sist'-man'u al: An operation controlled by the operator, but the operator is provided with a servosystem to act as a force amplifier.

SERVOMECHANISM (elec.) ser'vo-mech a nism: A closed-cycle automatic control system for supplying torque or power in a synchro system.

SERVOMOTOR (elec.) ser'vo mo'tor: The output drive motor in a servo system.

SET (wood.) set: A punch type tool for driving nail heads below the surface of the work; the act of adjusting a cutting tool such as "setting a plane."

SETSCREW (metal) set'screw: A screw used to prevent rotary motion between two parts, such as a pulley and shaft.

SET-POINT (automation) set-point: See SETTING.

SETTING (automation) set'ting: A specific position or point on a manual control.

SETTING UP (paint. and dec.) set'ting up: Initial drying of coating to point where it is no longer able to flow.

SETWISE (graphics) set'wise: Refers to the width of a letter.

SEWAGE (plumb.) sew'age: Liquid and semisolid wastes conducted away from buildings.

SEWER (plumb.) sew'er: A large pipe used to convey sewage.

SEWER AIR (plumb.) sew'er air: A mixture of odors, vapors and gases found in a sewer.

SHACKLE (metal) shac'kle: A metal connecting link.

SHADE (paint. and dec.) shade: Degree of color obtained by adding black to a color or hue.

SHADED POLE MOTOR (elec.) shad'ed pole mo'tor: A motor in which each of its field poles is split to accomodate a short-circuit copper strap called a shading coil. This coil produces a sweeping movement of the field across the pole face for starting.

SHADING (draft.) shad'ing: Producing the effect of solidity by using illumination effects represented by surfaces and lines of varying degrees of darkness.

SHADING LACQUER (paint. and dec.) shad'ing lac'quer: Transparent colored lacquer used in shading. Applied with a spray gun.

"SHADOWING" (paint. and dec.) shad'-ow ing: When preceding coats show through the last coat, the finish is said to be "shadowing."

SHADOW MASK (elec.) shad'ow mask: In a color TV picture tube, it is a perforated metal sheet used for proper color selection. It is placed between the electron gun and the phosphor screen. The holes are so arranged that only the proper phosphor dots are excited at any instant during scanning.

SHAFT (const.) shaft: An open space extending through two or more stories of a building; a slender column.

SHAKE (wood.) shake: A defect in lumber caused by separation of the wood between annual rings.

SHAKES (wood.) shakes: Handsplit shingles.

SHAPER (metal) shap'er: A machine tool used primarily for machining flat surfaces on small work. The cutting tool is supported on a clapper in the head of a ram. The ram reciprocates,

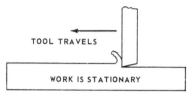

TOOL TRAVELS

WORK IS STATIONARY

moving back and forth in a straight line. The cutter is brought into contact with the work supported on the table of the machine.

SHAPER BLADES (wood.) shap'er blades: Sometimes called moulding cutters. Cutting blades shaped to the contour of the intended cut. See page 223.

SHAPER HEAD (wood.) shap'er head: A metal casting which is attached to a shaper spindle. The head holds the cutting blades.

SHARP LUSTER (paint. and dec.) sharp lus'ter: A very high gloss.

SHAVE HOOK (plumb.) shave hook: A tool used for cutting lead.

SHEAR (metal) shear: A machine for cutting sheet metal. The metal is placed on the table. A sharp knife-like blade is activated by stepping on the foot pedal and cuts the metal along the prescribed line.

SHEAR SPINNING (metal) shear spin'-ning: A process in which a metal blank is clamped between the tailstock of a shear spinning machine and a power driven spinning mandrel. The mandrel is the same shape and size as the finished product. The metal blank is forced to flow onto the mandrel by the action of forming rollers.

SHEATH (elec.) sheath: The outside protective covering of a wire or cable.

SHEATHING (const.) sheath'ing: Boards nailed over studding and rafters to serve as a base for siding or roofing material.

SHEATHING PAPER (const.) sheath'ing pa'per: Building paper applied over sheathing to resist passage of air.

SHEAVE (metal) sheave: A grooved pulley or wheel in a block over which a chain or rope runs.

SHED ROOF (const.) shed roof: See LEAN-TO; a roof with only one slope.

SHELLAC (wood.) shel lac': A material made from the secretion of the lac insect. When dissolved in alcohol, it is called shellac.

SHELL REAMER (metal) shell ream'er: Similar to a machine reamer, but with removable arbor.

SHEPHERD VIOLET TONER (paint. and dec.) shep'herd vi'o let ton'er: A complex manganese phosphate pigment having extreme acid resistance and light fastness.

SHERARDIZING (metal) she rar diz'-ing: The process of coating iron or steel with zinc, to prevent corrosion.

SHERATON (wood.) sher'a ton: A de-sign of furniture developed by Thomas Sheraton in England (1751-1806).

SHIELD (elec.) shield: A partition or enclosure around components in a cir-cuit to minimize effects of stray mag-netic and radio frequency fields.

SHIELD (weld.) shield: An eye and face protector held in the hand. It enables a person to look directly at the electric arc through a special lens without being harmed.

SHIELDED ARC (weld.) shield'ed arc: A form of electric welding in which a heavy flux-coated electrode is used.

SHIELDED CABLE (elec.) shield'ed ca'ble: A wire or cable covered with a braided wire mesh.

SHIMMY (auto.) shim'my: Rapid shak-ing and vibration of front end of car.

SHIMS (auto.) shims: Small pieces of feeler stock used in adjusting the fit of bearings and machined parts.

SHINGLES (const.) shin'gles: Wood shingles. Thin pieces of building ma-terial with one end thicker than other. Used in overlapping rows for roof, wall covering.

SHIP BOTTOM PAINT (paint. and dec.) ship bot'tom paint: Special product de-signed to prevent corrosion and fouling with marine life on the bottom of ships.

SHIPLAP (const.) ship'lap: Boards with rabbeted edges so they will fit together with half-lap joints.

SHOCK ABSORBER (auto.) shock ab-sorb'er: A device to prevent exces-sive or large spring movement and dampen out any tendency to oscillate.

SHOCK EXCITED OSCILLATOR (elec.)

shock ex cit' ed os cil la' tor: A tuned circuit generating a sine wave voltage for the duration of an input gate pulse.

SHOE MOLD (const.) shoe mold: A quarter round mold between the baseboard and flooring.

SHOOTING BOARD (wood.) shoot' ing board: A fixture for holding a plane at a desired angle for making accurate angular cuts.

"SHOP PRIMED OR SHOP COATED" (paint. and dec.) shop primed or shop coat' ed: Said of a prefabricated article that has been primed at the factory.

SHORE (const.) shore: A timber used to brace a wall temporarily during repair.

"SHORT" (paint. and dec.) short: When paint is "short," it is usually due to the absence of easy brushing liquids, and therefore does not have uniform appearance.

SHORT CIRCUIT (elec.) short cir' cult: A direct connection across the source which provides a zero resistance path for the current.

SHORT-OIL VARNISH (paint. and dec.) short-oil var' nish: One made with a relatively low proportion of oil to resin. See LONG OIL VARNISH.

SHORT TON: Two thousand pounds.

SHORT WAVES (elec.) short waves: Radio electromagnetic waves generally considered above 1600 kc.

SHOT EFFECT (elec.) shot ef' fect: Noise produced in an electron tube as a result of a variation in the rate of electron emission from the cathode.

SHOULDER (graphics) shoul' der: The surface of a type face, less than typehigh, which surrounds the printing face.

SHOULDER NIPPLE (plumb.) shoul' der nip' ple: A nipple slightly longer than a close nipple. An unthreaded space of about 1/4 inch exists between threads on each end.

SHRINKAGE (metal) shrink' age: The reduction in size of a metal casting during the process of cooling.

SHRINK FIT (metal) shrink fit: Parts mated by heating the enveloping part to expand it, and then cooling slowly.

SHRINK RULE (metal) shrink rule: A special rule used by the pattern maker when making patterns for molding, which allows for reduction of size due to shrinkage.

SHUNT (elec.) shunt: To connect across or parallel with a circuit or component; a parallel resistor to conduct excess current around the meter moving coil. Shunts are used to increase the range of a meter.

SHUNT COIL (elec.) shunt coil: A coil connected in parallel.

SHUNT PEAKING (elec.) shunt peak' ing: A compensation circuit using a small inductor to create a higher frequency response for an amplifier.

SIAMESE CONNECTION (plumb.) si a-mese' con nec' tion: A Y connection used by firemen, so that two fire hoses can be connected to a single hydrant.

SIDEBANDS (elec.) side' bands: Frequencies above and below the carrier frequency as a result of modulation.

LOWER, Frequencies equal to the difference between carrier and modulating frequencies.

UPPER, Frequencies equal to the carrier plus the modulating frequencies.

SIDE CARRIER FREQUENCIES (elec.) side car' ri er fre' quen cies: Waves of frequencies equal to the sum and difference between the carrier wave frequency and the modulating wave frequency.

SIDE CLEARANCE (metal) side clear'ance: The angle a cutting tool is ground sloping down from its cutting edge to provide relief.

SIDE CUTTING EDGE ANGLE (metal) side cut' ting edge an' gle: The angle which shows the amount the side of the cutting tool has been ground back in reference to the shank of the tool.

SIDE MILLING CUTTER (metal) side mill' ing cut' ter: A circular milling cutter which cuts on its sides as well as by teeth on its periphery.

SIDE OUTLET ELL (plumb.) side out' - let ell: An ell with an outlet on its side at right angle to the water flow.

SIDE RAKE (metal) side rake: The angle a cutting tool slopes back from its cutting edge.

SIDEREAL (space) si der' e al: A measurement of time. A sidereal day, for example, is the time it takes the Earth to make a complete revolution measured from the stars. A sidereal day is four minutes shorter than our day (which is called a solar day).

SIDING (const.) sid' ing: Exterior wall finish of a building.

SIENNA (paint. and dec.) si en' na: A pigment obtained from the earth which is brownish yellow when raw; orange-red or reddish brown when burnt.

SIEVE (const.) sieve: A screen for removing large stones from sand.

SIGHT GLASS (air cond.) sight glass: A glass which indicates the liquid level in a tank.

SIGMA WELDING (weld.) sig' ma weld'ing: See GAS METAL-ARC WELDING.

SIGNAL (automation) sig' nal: Data converted to a usable form for control of a device or machine.

SIGNAL (elec.) sig' nal: The intelligence, message or effect to be sent over a communications system; an electrical wave corresponding to intelligence.

SIGNAL GENERATOR (elec.) sig' nal gen' er a tor: An electronic test instrument which produces a variable radio frequency continuous wave or modulated continuous wave. It is used for servicing and alignment.

SIGNAL TO NOISE RATIO (elec.) sig' - nal to noise ra' ti o: Ratio of signal transmitted by radio equipment to noise generated within the equipment.

SIGNATURE (graphics) sig' na ture: A folded section of a book; small arabic numerals on the first page of each form of pages in a book to indicate order of assembly.

SILENCER (elec.) si' lenc er: A circuit which disables a receiver when no signals are being received.

SILEX (const.) si' lex: A filler made of ground quartz.

SILEX (paint. and dec.) si' lex: A form of silica used extensively in making paste wood fillers; it is chemically inert and does not absorb moisture or shrink.

SILICA (paint. and dec.) sil' i ca: An inert pigment made from quartz rock, which is highly resistant to acids, alkalis, heat and light.

SILICA GEL (air cond.) sil' i ca gel: A drier compound consisting primarily of SiO_2.

SILICATE OF SODA (paint and dec.) sil' i cate of so' da: See W A T E R GLASS.

SILICON CARBIDE (paint. and dec.) sil' i con car' bide: Abrasive crystals are shiny black, very hard and brittle. Made by fusing silica sand and coke in electric furnace.

SILICON DIODE (elec.) sil' i con di' - ode: A semiconductor diode.

SILICONE RESINS (SILICONES) (paint. and dec.) sil' i cone res' ins: Resins derived from silica. Have exceptional resistance to heat and corrosive chemicals, good electrical properties.

SILK SCREEN FINISHING (paint. and dec.) silk screen fin' ish ing: Process of finishing where paint is forced through open meshes of a fabric screen. Parts of the screen are blocked off and do not print, thus producing the design.

SILK SCREEN PROCESS (graphics) silk screen pro' cess: A process of printing in which a stencil is fastened to a fabric screen and stretched on a frame. Ink is forced through the porous screen in the stencil openings with a squeegee.

SILL (const.) sill: The wood timbers which rest on the foundation on which the house is built; wood or stone base support of a door or window.

SILL COCK (plumb.) sill cock: A faucet on the outside of a house for a garden hose connection.

SILO (space) si' lo: A missile shelter that consists of a hardened vertical hole in the ground with facilities either for lifting the missile to a launch position, or for direct launch from the shelter.

SILT (paint. and dec.) silt: Particles so fine that they are scarcely visible to the naked eye, unless finishing material is placed in glass tube and placed before proper light.

SILVER LEAF (paint. and dec.) sil' ver leaf: Thin leaf made of silver, used mostly for lettering on glass.

SILVER SOLDER (metal) sil' ver sol' - der: A high temperature solder made from a compound of silver, copper and zinc.

SIMPLEX CIRCUIT (elec.) sim' plex cir' cuit: A telephone circuit using a center tapped transformer on a balanced telephone line, with a ground return.

SIMPLEX LAP WINDING (elec.) sim' - plex lap wind' ing: A method of winding a generator armature by overlapping coils in slots.

SIMULATION (automation) sim u la' - tion: A training activity in which a real life situation is created by simulating the conditions which make up the situation.

SINAD (elec.) si' nad: The standard method of measuring the sensitivity of a radio receiver. The letters represent Signal plus Noise and Distortion divided by the noise and distortion alone. A receiver is adjusted so that the signal produces fifty percent of the rated output. The number of microvolts of signal applied under these conditions is referred to as 12 db SINAD or usable sensitivity.

SINE BAR (metal) sine bar: A highly finished and accurate chrome steel bar, resting on two cylindrical rollers, the centers of which are either five or ten inches apart. It is used for measuring angles.

SINE WAVE (elec.) sine wave: A wave form of a single frequency alternating current. The graphical representation of all points traced by the sine of an angle as the angle is rotated through 360 deg.

SINGAPORE DAMMAR (paint. and dec.) sin' ga pore dam' mar: A dammar found in the Malay states and adjacent islands. Exported from Singapore.

SINGING (elec.) sing' ing: An undesired self sustained oscillation in the audio frequency range on a transmission line.

SINGLE ENDED AMPLIFIER (elec.) sin' gle end' ed am' pli fi er: An amplifier whose final power stage is a single vacuum tube or transistor.

SINGLE PHASE (elec.) sin' gle phase: Only one alternating current or voltage produced or used.

SINGLE PHASE MOTOR (elec.) sin' gle phase mo' tor: A motor which operates on single phase alternating current.

SINGLE POINT CUTTING TOOLS (metal) sin' gle point cut' ting tools: Cutting tools used in production, such as lathe and boring tools, shaper, planer and slicing tools.

SINGLE-POLE SWITCH (elec.) sin' gle-pole switch: A switch which opens and closes one side of a circuit only.

SINGLE REVOLUTION (draft.) sin' gle rev o ul' tion: The revolution of an object or part about a single axis.

SINGLE ROLL (paint. and dec.) sin' gle roll: A single roll of American-made wallpaper is a roll containing 36 square feet of paper. Wallpaper usually comes in bolts which contain two or three single rolls.

SINGLE SIDEBAND (elec.) sin' gle side' band: A method of radio communication in which the rf carrier wave and one side band wave is suppressed.

SINGLE-STROKE (draft.) sin' gle-stroke: Letters and lines drawn with line width equal to a single stroke of pen or pencil.

SINK (plumb.) sink: A shallow basin-like fixture used in kitchen and bath and for many purposes.

SINKAGE (graphics) sink' age: A blank space at the beginning of a chapter in a book.

SINTERING (metal) sin' ter ing: Pressing metal powders combined with binders into dies or molds under high pressure; pressure compacting of powdered metal.

SINUSOIDAL (elec.) sin u soi' dal: A wave varying in proportion to the sine of an angle.

SIPHONAGE (plumb.) si' phon age: Liquid flow created by suction as a result of pressure below atmospheric pressure.

SISAL FIBER (const.) si' sal fi' ber: A hemp-like fiber of several Central American plants used for making rope.

SIZE (const.) size: Materials used to seal a surface before painting.

SIZE (paint. and dec.) size: Solution of gelatin-type material, such as resin, glue or starch, used to fill or seal pores of surface and prevent absorption of finishing materials.

SIZING (const.) siz' ing: The application of size or coating to plaster or wallboards before painting.

SKELETONIZING (graphics) skel' e-ton iz ing: Taking a job apart and rebuilding it so that selected sections can be printed in different colors.

SKELP (metal) skelp: Steel or iron plate used to make pipe and tubing.

SKETCH (draft.) sketch: A freehand drawing; to draw without instruments.

SKEW (wood.) skew: Not at a right angle; out of square; a chisel with an angular cutting edge used in wood turning.

SKEW BACK SAW (wood.) skew back saw: A handsaw with a curved back to reduce friction and reduce weight.

SKILSAW (wood.) skil' saw: A trade name for an electrical powered hand circular saw.

SKIMCOAT (const.) skim' coat: See WHITE COAT.

SKIMMER (metal) skim' mer: An iron paddle device to hold back dirt on the surface of molten metal and prevent it from entering the mold when pouring.

SKIN (paint. and dec.) skin: A tough layer or skin formed on the surface of a paint or varnish in the container. Caused by exposure to air.

SKIN EFFECT (elec.) skin ef fect': The tendency of an ac current to flow near the surface of a conductor as the frequency of the ac is increased.

SKINTLED (const.) skin' tled: Laying bricks in an uneven manner, some protruding out and others inward; a brick wall laid without jointing so that the squeezed out mortar between the bricks gives a rough effect when hardened.

SKINTLED BRICKWORK (const.) skin'-tled brick' work: Bricks arranged irregularly with variations in projections on outside face-wall. A decorative treatment of a wall.

SKIP (elec.) skip: In radio propagation, it is the result of a sky wave reflected back to the Earth's surface.

SKIP DISTANCE (elec.) skip dis' tance: The distance between the radio transmitter and the point at which the sky-wave returns to earth. It varies with frequency, time of day and geographic location.

"SKIPPY" (paint. and dec.) skip' py: Said of a paint that causes the brush to skip on the surface, leaving some spots uncoated and others too thickly coated.

SKIPS (paint. and dec.) skips: Uncoated spots on finished surface.

SKIRT (wood.) skirt: The horizontal band of wood under a table top or a chair which connects the legs to the top or seat. Sometimes called an "apron."

SKIRTING (const.) skirt' ing: Small boards around a room between wall and floor; baseboard.

SKYLIGHT (const.) sky' light: A glass area in a roof to admit light.

SKY WAVE (elec.) sky wave: Waves

emanating from a radio antenna towards the sky.

SLAB (const.) slab: A flat surfaced stone. (wood.) The outside wood and bark cut from logs during sawing of lumber. (metal) A rectangular block of steel ready to roll into plates.

SLACK (metal) slack: The looseness of mating parts, gears and mechanisms which must first be overcome before power is transmitted by the device.

SLAG (metal) slag: Impurities removed from iron ore during refining.

SLAG INCLUSIONS (weld.) slag in clu'sions: Non-fused, non-metallic substances in the weld metal.

SLAG WOOL (metal) slag wool: An insulating material similar to asbestos, made by blowing a jet stream of steam through molten slag.

SLAKE (paint. and dec.) slake: To produce a chemical change in lime by combining with water.

SLANT (plumb.) slant: A branch connection to a common sewer.

SLASHING (wood.) slash'ing: The branches, tree tops and general debris left after a logging operation.

SLATE FLOUR (paint. and dec.) slate flour: Filler used to considerable extent in asphalt mixtures in roofing mastics, etc.

SLEDGE (metal) sledge: A long handled heavy hammer, used with both hands.

SLEEKER (metal) sleek'er: See SLICK.

SLEEPER (const.) sleep'er: A timber laid horizontally on the ground to support floor joist.

SLICK (metal) slick: A molding tool shaped like a bent double ended spoon.

SLIDE GEAR (metal) slide gear: A gear keyed to a shaft so that it will rotate with shaft, but may slide longitudinally along shaft.

SLIDE REST (metal) slide rest: The parts on the carriage of a lathe above the saddle, which support the compound rest.

SLIDE VALVE (auto.) slide valve: A valve operating with a sliding motion so that certain parts are open at the desired time and others are closed.

SLIDING FIT (metal) slid'ing fit: A running fit.

SLIP (elec.) slip: The difference in speed between the stator field and the rotor to the synchronous speed of a motor.

SLIP FORMING ROLLS (metal) slip form'ing rolls: A machine consisting of rolls which are used to shape sheet metal into a curved surface. Stove pipe is made on a machine of this type.

SLIP JOINT (auto.) slip joint: Two shafts joined with mating splines so that they will rotate together, yet permit longitudinal movement.

SLIP JOINT (plumb.) slip joint: A joint between two pipes when one pipe slides inside another. The joint is sealed with calking compound or a gasket.

SLIPPED COAT (const.) slipped coat: See WHITE COAT.

SLIP RINGS (elec.) slip rings: Metal rings connected to rotating armature windings in a generator. Brushes sliding on these rings provide connections for the external circuit.

SLIP STONE (wood.) slip stone: A very fine wedge-shaped sharpening· stone with rounded edges used to whet gouges and other irregular tools.

"SLIP UNDER THE BRUSH" (paint. and dec.): When coating materials are easy to apply, this is sometimes said of them.

SLITTING SAW (metal) slit' ting saw: A relatively thin milling cutter.

SLOPE (elec.) slope: The ratio between the vertical rise of a curve to the horizontal distance.

SLOPE DETECTOR (elec.) slope de-tec' tor: A process of detecting an FM signal when it falls on the sloping side of an r-f response curve and frequency variations are converted into equivalent amplitude variations.

SLOPE LINE (draft.) slope line: A guide line to insure correct slope of letters on a drawing.

SLOT FORGE (metal) slot forge: A gas fired forge in which the work is heated in an oblong shaped furnace enclosure.

SLOYD KNIFE (crafts) sloyd knife: The knife used in the Swedish Sloyd system of woodwork and crafts.

SLUDGE (air cond.) sludge: A decomposition product formed in a system due to moisture and i m p u r i t i e s in lubricants.

SLUG (elec.) slug: A small magnetic core.

SLUGS (graphics) slugs: Pieces of lead used as spacing material between lines of type; a bar of metal with type molded on it by the Linotype machine.

SMALL CAPS (graphics) small caps: Small capital letters.

SMALL PICA (graphics) small pi' ca: Eleven point type.

SMALT (paint. and dec.) smalt: Deep blue pigment prepared by fusing together potash, silica and oxide of cobalt and reducing to powder the glass thus formed. Smalt is sometimes applied to freshly coated surfaces to provide unusual decorating effect.

SMASH (graphics) smash: To compress the signatures of a book in preparation for binding.

SMELTING (metal) smelt' ing: The process involved in obtaining metals from ores by heating.

S METER (elec.) s me' ter: A meter on a radio receiver which indicates a comparative value of the transmitted radio signal.

SMOKE smoke: Gaseous product formed by burning materials containing carbon. Smoke is made visible by small particles of carbon.

SMOKE CHAMBER(const.) smoke cham'-ber: A chamber in a fireplace flue directly above the damper.

SMOKING (crafts) smok' ing: The first stage in firing green clay during which the moisture is removed.

SMOOTHING TROWEL (const.) smooth'-ing trow' el: A larger trowel used by the mason or plasterer for finishing the surface of his work.

SMOOTH PLANE (wood.) smooth plane: A plane usually 6 to 10 inches long designed for smoothing surfaces of wood.

SNAGGING (metal) snag'ging: Removing fins, sprues and gates from a casting by using a grinding wheel.

SNAKE (elec.) snake: A flexible wire used to push or pull wires through a conduit, a partition, or other inaccessible places.

SNAP GAUGE (metal) snap gauge: A preset gauge for determining correct sizes in production work.

SNAP RING (metal) snap ring: A hardened metal broken ring, which acts as a retainer or stop. The ring may fit into a groove on a shaft.

SNARLING IRON (crafts) snarl'ing iron: A special tool used in craft work for raising or pushing up necessary metal so that a design may be modeled in relief.

SNIPS (metal) snips: A short name for sheet metal shears.

SNOW (elec.) snow: Interference in a TV picture from noise or resulting from a weak signal. It appears as white specks on the picture.

SNUBBER (auto.) snub'ber: A heavy fabric strap coiled around a spring loaded spool. It is used to prevent violent rebound or bouncing of a car on a rough road.

SNUG FIT (metal) snug fit: The closest fit that can be assembled by hand pressure.

SOAKING CHARGE (elec.) soak'ing charge: A low slow charge of a storage battery to remove plate sulfation.

SOAKING PIT (metal) soak'ing pit: A

furnace used to heat ingots in preparation for rolling.

SOCKET (elec.) sock'et: A device for holding a lamp or electron tube.

SOCKET (elec.) sock'et:

PHONO PLUG, special type of socket used to interconnect audio equipment.

SOCKET PLUG (plumb.) sock'et plug: A type of pipe plug with a recess in its end face for a special wrench.

SOCKET WRENCH (auto.) sock'et wrench: Wrench with a hollow end which fits a bolt head or nut.

SOFFIT (const.) sof'fit: The underside of a structural member of a building; the lower horizontal face of a beam; the underside of an arch.

SOFT (crafts) soft: Glazes and clays which can be satisfactorily fired at low temperatures.

SOFT DRAWN (elec.) soft drawn: This term applies to annealed copper wire which is very soft.

SOFT LANDING (space) soft land'ing: A landing on the Moon or other spatial body at such slow speed as to avoid a crash or destruction of the landing vehicle.

SOFT SOLDER (elec.) soft sol'der: A term which applies to a variety of low temperature solders of varying percentages of lead and tin.

SOFT TUBE (elec.) soft tube: A gaseous tube.

SOFT WOOD (wood.) soft wood: Wood from trees that bear cones and needles.

SOIL PIPE (plumb.) soil pipe: Cast

iron pipe with bell and spigot ends used for waste and sewer lines.

SOIL STACK (plumb.) soil stack: A vertical soil pipe used in waste drainage systems.

SOIL VENT (plumb.) soil vent: The part of the soil stack above the highest waste connection.

SOLAR WIND (space) so' lar wind: A stream of protons constantly moving outward from the sun.

SOLDER (elec.) sol' der: An alloy of tin and lead used to bond wires electrically.

SOLDER (metal) sol' der: The process of joining metals together by fusing surfaces together with solder.

SOLDERING COPPER (metal) sol' dering cop' per: A tool, usually called a soldering iron, consisting of a wedge shaped copper head with a handle. It is used to apply heat to a joint to be soldered.

SOLDERING FLUX (elec.) sol' der ing flux: A compound used to dissolve oxides during soldering to assure a good joint.

SOLDERING FURNACE (metal) sol' dering fur' nace: A bench type gas furnace for heating soldering coppers.

SOLDERING GUN (elec.) sol' der ing gun: A gun shaped soldering tool, with a fast heating resistance element at its tip. The tip is heated by the step down action of a transformer, which provides a low voltage-high current in the tip.

SOLDERING IRON (elec.) sol' der ing iron: A soldering tool, usually with a resistance heated copper tip, used to heat joints for soldering.

SOLDERING PASTE (elec.) sol' der ing paste: A flux in paste form.

SOLDIER COURSE (const.) sol' dier course: A course of bricks in which the bricks stand on end.

SOLDIERS (const.) sol' diers: Bricks set on end.

SOLENOID (elec.) so' le noid: A coil of wire carrying an electric current possessing the characteristics of a magnet.

SOLENOID VALVE (air cond.) so' le-noid valve: A valve which is usually closed by spring action or pressure, but opened by an electrically operated magnetic solenoid.

SOLE PLATE (const.) sole plate: The horizontal member, usually a 2 x 4, on which partition or wall studs rest.

SOLID MATTER (graphics) sol' id mat' ter: Type set without leads or slugs between the lines.

SOLID PROPELLANT (space) sol' id pro pel' lant: A rocket propellant in solid state consisting of all the ingredients necessary for sustained chemical combustion.

SOLUBILITY (paint. and dec.) sol u-bil' i ty: Quality or state of being soluble or dissolved.

SOLUBLE OIL (metal) sol' u ble oil: Oils which form an oil-water emulsion when water is added.

SOLVENT (paint. and dec.) sol' vent: A liquid capable of dissolving a material is said to be a solvent for the material.

SONAR (Sound Navigation and Ranging) (elec.) so' nar: A device which transmits ultrasonic waves in water and registers waves reflected back from the object.

SONIC BOOM (space) son' ic boom: An explosion-like sound heard when a shock wave, generated by an aircraft flying at supersonic speed, reaches the ear.

SONIC SPEED (space) son' ic speed: The speed of sound.

SORBITE (metal) sor' bite: Structural element of steel softer than Troostite.

SORTS (graphics) sorts: Individual type characters, not obtained in fonts.

SOUNDER (elec.) sound' er: A part of a sounder electromagnet in a telegraph system, arranged so that its armature will make an audible click when current flows through the coil.

SOUNDER MAGNET (elec.) sound' er mag' net: The electromagnet in a telegraph sounder.

SOUND WAVE (elec.) sound wave: A wave considered to be alternate condensation and rarefactions of air which produce the human sensation of sound.

SOURCE OF SUPPLY (elec.) source of sup ply' : The device attached to the input of a circuit which produces the electromotive force. It may be a generator, battery or other device.

SOYBEAN OIL (paint. and dec.) soy' - bean oil: Made from seed of soybean, a leguminous annual plant.

SPACE AGE (space) space age: A historical age in which man has achieved in some degree, power to project missiles or vehicles into space.

SPACE BAND (graphics) space band: A thin metal wedge used for justifying

the line of composed matrices on the Linotype.

SPACE CHARGE (elec.) space charge: The cloud of electrons around the cathode of an electron tube.

SPACE ENVIRONMENT (space) space en vi' ron ment: The environment encountered by vehicles and living creatures upon entry into space.

SPACE PLATFORM (space) space plat' form: Large satellite with both scientific and military applications, conceived as a habitable base in space. The proposed space platforms would contain such things as housing facilities, power supplies, gravity simulation, provisions for transferring personnel and cargo to and from other space vehicles, scientific instruments, weapon systems, controlled atmosphere, and communications systems.

SPACE PROBE (space) space probe: An instrumented vehicle, as a test sphere or Earch satellite, that is rocketed into space (sometimes into proximity with a spatial body), in order to obtain new knowledge on conditions detected by the instruments of the vehicles.

SPACER (const.) spac' er: Short pieces of wood set at intervals in a concrete form to hold forms at a constant distance apart.

SPACE SATELLITE (space) space sat' - el lite: A man-made satellite body that orbits the Earth, Moon, or other spatial body.

SPACE STATION (space) space sta' - tion: A facility put into orbit by means of which space travel or space exploration may be further effected.

SPACECRAFT (space) space' craft: A

vehicle designed to fly primarily in space.

SPACING (graphics) spac' ing: Putting the proper amount of material between words, lines, etc.

SPACISTOR (elec.) spa cis' tor: A four element semiconductor, similar to a transistor. It uses a space charge region. Its main advantage is its adaptability to ultra high frequencies.

SPACKLING COMPOUND (paint. and dec.) spack' ling com' pound: Kind of plaster which is used to fill surface irregularities and cracks in plaster.

SPAGHETTI (elec.) spa ghet' ti: Flexible tubular insulation which can be slipped over wires.

SPALL (const.) spall: Broken brick; chips of stone.

SPAN (const.) span: The distance between supports of a beam or girder.

SPANDREL (const.) span' drel: The triangular space between the curve of an arch and the rectangular frame above the arch.

SPANNER (metal) span' ner: A flat wrench shaped like a half circle with projecting pins on its sides, which fit matching holes in a round nut or collar.

SPARK COIL (elec.) spark coil: An induction coil used to produce high voltages and cause a spark to jump a gap.

SPARK GAP (elec.) spark gap: A device which permits a high voltage current to jump a gap.

SPARK PLUG (auto.) spark plug: A spark gap device inserted in the combustion chamber of a cylinder where the air-fuel charge is fired by the high tension spark across the electrodes of the plug.

SPARK TEST (metal) spark test: A method of identifying types of iron and steel by observing the sparks when held against a grinding wheel.

SPAR VARNISH (paint. and dec.) spar var' nish: A very durable varnish designed for severe service on exterior surfaces. Such a varnish must be resistant to rain, sunlight and heat. Named from its suitability for the spars of ships.

SPATIOGRAPHY (space) spa ti og' ra- phy: The "geography" of space.

SPATTER FINISH (paint. and dec.) spat'- ter fin' ish: Finish which provides a spattered or speckled effect.

SPATULA (crafts) spat' u la: A flexible knife-like tool for mixing small quantities of chemicals, colors, compounds, etc.

SPECIFICATIONS (draft.) spec i fi ca'- tions: A written set of instructions with a proposed set of plans, giving all necessary information not shown on blueprints such as quality, manufacturers names and types, quantities and manner in which work is to be conducted.

SPECIFIC GRAVITY (air cond.) spe- cif' ic grav' i ty: The ratio between the weight of a given volume of substance to an equal volume of air or water at a given temperature and pressure.

SPECIFIC HEAT (air cond.) spe cif' ic heat: Ratio of quantity of heat needed to raise temperature of a body one degree to that required to raise temperature of equal mass of water one degree.

SPECIFIC PRODUCT MACHINE (auto-

mation) spe cif' ic prod' uct ma_
chine': A custom designed transfer
machine for making a single product.

SPECIFIC RESISTANCE (elec.) spe_
cif' ic re sis' tance: The resistance
in ohms of one MIL_FOOT of a con_
ductor of a given substance.

SPECIFIC RESISTIVITY (elec.) spe cif'_
ic re sis tiv' i ty: Another term for
specific resistance.

SPECTRAL COLORS (paint. and dec.)
spec' tral col' ors: Bands of colors
produced when ray of sunshine is bent
by glass prism.

SPECTRUM (elec.) spec' trum: The ar_
rangement of waves according to fre_
quency.

SPEEDBALL (draft.) speed' ball: A
special lettering pen with a patented ink
reservoir.

SPEED INDICATOR (metal) speed in' di_
ca tor: A gauge which registers the
speed of revolving machines, wheels or
shaft in revolutions per minute.

SPEED LATHE (metal) speed lathe: A
lathe in which the cutting tool is actuated
by hand. The tool may be supported on a
T rest or on a cross slide and carriage.

SPEED OF SOUND (space) speed of
sound: The velocity at which sound
travels. The speed of sound varies with
the static temperature of the surround_
ing medium. In air on a standard day,
the speed of sound is 1108 feet per
second or 756 miles per hour. A
standard day is 59° F. at sea level.

SPEEDOMETER (auto.) speed om' e ter:
A device which indicates the speed of a
car in miles per hour.

SPEED REGULATION (elec.) speed reg_

u la' tion: The ability of a motor to
maintain its speed when a load is
applied.

SPELTER (metal) spel' ter: A com_
pound of copper and zinc.

SPHERE GAP (elec.) sphere gap: A
spark gap which uses spherical elec_
trodes.

SPHEROIDIZING (metal) sphe roid iz'_
ing: A prolonged heating of steel about
its critical temperature, followed by
slow cooling.

SPIDER (elec.) spi' der: A flexible disc
which holds the voice coil of a dynamic
speaker in place.

SPIEGELEISEN (metal) spie' gel ei sen:
Pig iron manufactured from ores high
in manganese.

SPIGOT (plumb.) spig' ot: The end of
a piece of soil pipe that fits into the
bell of another piece; a faucet.

SPINDLE SANDER (wood.) spin' dle
sand' er: A sanding machine in which
the sanding is done by a rotary and
usually reciprocating sleeve on a spin_
dle projecting through the work table.

SPINDLE SHAPER (wood.) spin' dle
shap' er: A woodworking machine de_
signed to cut molding, decorative edges
and irregular patterns. The cutting is
done by a high speed rotary cutter which
projects vertically through the work
table surface. Necessary guides, fences
and safety guards are provided.

SPIRAL OF ARCHIMEDES (draft.)
spi' ral of ar chi me' des: A spiral
curve generated by a point moving
uniformly around and away from a
fixed center point.

SPIRIT STAIN (paint. and dec.) spir' it

stain: A stain made by dissolving a dye in an alcohol.

SPIRIT VARNISH (paint. and dec.) spir' it var' nish: A varnish made by dissolving a resin in a solvent. It dries primarily by evaporation rather than by oxidation.

SPLASH LUBRICATION (auto.) splash lu bri ca' tion: A lubrication system in which moving parts pass through a reservoir of oil and lubricate themselves as well as splashing lubricant upon other moving parts.

SPLAT (wood.) splat: The broad flat upright member in the back of a chair.

SPLAYED (const.) splayed: Beveled or sloping; surfaces at an oblique angle to each other.

SPLICE (elec.) splice: Connecting two wires together.

SPLICING COMPOUND (elec.) splic' ing com' pound: Rubber tape to fill in insulation around joint.

SPLINE (metal) spline: A long keyway to permit a sliding gear.

SPLINE (wood) spline: A thin piece of wood inserted in a joint to increase its strength.

SPLINE
JOINT

SPLIT NUT (metal) split nut: A nut which has been split longitudinally to permit fast movement along a threaded shaft or screw.

SPLIT PHASE (elec.) split phase: Dividing a single phase current into currents of different phases. This principle is used to start single phase AC motors.

SPLIT-PHASE MOTOR (elec.) split-phase mo' tor: A single-phase induction motor, which develops starting torque by a phase displacement between its field windings.

SPOKESHAVE (wood.) spoke' shave: A cutting blade mounted in a frame between two handles. Used for shaping and smoothing edges. It was originally used for shaping wagon wheel spokes.

SPONGE LEAD (elec.) sponge lead: Porous lead used as the negative plates in a storage battery.

SPOT FACE (metal) spot face: The machining of a circular spot around a hole to furnish a bearing for the head of a bolt or nut.

SPOTTING OUT (graphics) spot' ting out: Marking out and patching on a make-ready sheet.

SPOT WELD (weld.) spot weld: A resistance type weld where the base metals are clamped between two electrodes and a momentary electric current produces the heat for welding at the contact spot.

SPRAY ARC (weld.) spray arc: Gas metal arc process which has an arc voltage high enough to continuously transfer the electrode metal across the arc in small globules.

SPREADING (metal) spread' ing: A process of widening a piece of stock in a crosswise direction.

SPREADING RATE (paint. and dec.) spread' ing rate: Amount of area a given volume of coating material can be spread over by spraying, brushing or other method of application. Spreading rate is generally indicated by square feet covered per gallon.

SPRING LEAF (auto.) spring leaf: One of the flat steel leaves in an automobile or wagon spring.

SPROCKET (metal) sprock' et: A wheel with teeth on its periphery to engage a chain belt.

SPRUE (metal) sprue: An opening in a sand mold through which the molten metal is poured.

SPRUE CUTTER (metal) sprue cut' ter: In foundry work, a metal tube used to make a hole in a sand mold so that hot metal can be poured into the mold cavity.

SPUD (plumb.) spud: A short piece of pipe, used in the connection of a meter to the supply line.

SPUTNIK (space) sput' nik: The Russian name for its man-made moons or satellites.

SPY (crafts) spy: A small peep hole in a ceramics kiln through which temperature cones may be observed.

SQC (automation) sqc: Statistical Quality Control.

SQUARE (draft.) square: A geometric figure having four equal sides and four right angles.

SQUARE (metal) square: To machine or cut at right angles to a given surface or edge.

SQUARE (wood) square: To make edges or surfaces of lumber at right angles to each other.

SQUARE LAW DETECTOR (elec.) square law de tec' tor: A detector whose output voltage is proportional to the square of the effective input voltage.

SQUARE LAW SCALE (elec.) square law scale: A meter scale in which the deflection is proportional to the square of the current.

SQUARE MIL (elec.) square mil: The cross sectional area of a conductor one mil square.

SQUARE WAVE (elec.) square wave: A wave which alternately assumes two fixed values for equal lengths of time.

SQUARING (metal) squar' ing: Used to describe facing operations in some shops.

SQUARING SHEARS squar' ing shears: Power or foot operated shears for cutting sheet metal to size.

SQUEALING (elec.) squeal' ing: The shrill squeal produced in a radio by interference from other radio stations.

SQUEEGEE (graphics) squee' gee: A rubber blade and handle used to force ink through a silk screen.

SQUELCH (elec.) squelch: To automatically quiet a radio receiver by reducing its gain when its input signal is below a specified value.

SQUIB (space) squib: A small pyrotechnic device which may be used to fire the igniter in a rocket.

SQUIRREL CAGE ROTOR (elec.) squir'-rel cage ro' tor: A rotor used in an induction motor made of bars placed in slots of the rotor core and all joined together at the ends.

SQUIRT WELDING (weld.) squirt weld'-ing: Another name for "submerged arc welding."

S.S. GLASS (const.) s.s. glass: Single

Strength Glass. Used in small window panes.

STABILITY (elec.) sta bil' i ty: The ability to stay on a given frequency or in a given state without undesired variation.

STACK (plumb.) stack: Any vertical system of drainage pipes.

STACK VENT (plumb.) stack vent: The extension of the soil stack to above the roof of a building.

STAGE (elec.) stage: A section of an electronic circuit, usually containing one electron tube and associated components.

STAGE (space) stage: A propulsion unit of a rocket. Usually one unit of a multi-stage rocket.

STAGGERED SPLICE (elec.) stag' gered splice: Splicing wires at staggered intervals to minimize bulkiness.

STAGING (const.) stag' ing: Timber and lumber assembled to provide support and working space for material and workmen around and in a building.

STAIN (wood.) stain: Finish for wood containing dye or pigment. Transparent stain is one that dissolves in the solvent and is carried into fibers of wood coloring like a dye. Dye stains come in water, alcohol and oil-soluble types. Pigment stains contain finely ground color pigments in solution with linseed oil, turpentine, varnish, etc.

STAINLESS STEEL (metal) stain' less steel: An alloy of steel and nickel or chromium which is highly resistant to corrosion.

STAIN WAX (Penetrating) (paint. and

dec.) stain wax: Wood finish which produces color of penetrating stain with luster of wax.

STAIRCASE (const.) stair' case: A complete set of stairs with landings, balusters, handrails and newel posts.

STAIRCASE WAVEFORM (elec.) stair'-case wave' form: A multi-segmented wave produced by the addition of a number of square or rectangular waves.

STAIR GAUGE (wood.) stair gauge: Small clamp fixtures which may be fastened to a carpenter's steel square. They form a gauge for laying out stair stringers and rafters.

STAKE (crafts) stake: A metal anvil of a variety of sizes and shapes, used in forming metal.

STAMP (graphics) stamp: To impress or imprint with some mark or design.

STAMPING (metal) stamp' ing: The process of forming sheet steel into various shapes by forcing the metal into impressions in dies, at room temperature.

STANDARD TIME (metal) stand' ard time: The time required for an average worker to accomplish a task.

STAND-BY (elec.) stand-by: Equipment held in reserve or ready for use.

STANDING WAVE (elec.) stand' ing wave: A wave in which the ratio of the instantaneous value at one point to that at another point does not vary with time: Waves appearing on a transmission line as a result of reflections from the termination of the line.

STANDING WAVE RATIO (elec.) stand'-ing wave ra' tio: The ratio of the effective voltage at a loop of a standing wave to the effective voltage at a node. It may also be expressed by effective current. Also the ratio of the characteristic impedance to the load impedance.

STAND OIL (paint. and dec.) stand oil: Heat-thickened vegetable oil (or combination of vegetable oils, such as linseed and tung).

STANDPIPE (plumb.) stand' pipe: A vertical pipe used for water storage.

STARCH COATING (paint. and dec.) starch coat' ing: Protective coating for surfaces coated with flat paint, also wallpapers made with colors that do not smear when wet. Starch coating is made by soaking ordinary laundry starch in small quantity of cold water to break up lumps. Boiled water is then poured on to cool starch and make it transparent. Mix to consistency of cream, let it cool, and apply with large paint or calcimine brush. Coating should be stippled while still wet, to remove brush marks. It may be removed by using water and sponge.

STAR CONNECTION (elec.) star connec' tion: Sometimes called the Y connection; when one end of each phase of a three-phase circuit or machine is connected at a common point.

STAR DRILL (const.) star drill: A tool with a star shaped head and used to drill masonry and stone. It is usually driven with a hammer, but industrially it is driven by pneumatic hammers.

STARTER (elec.) start' er: A thermal switch used with fluorescent lamps. When the light is turned on, current flows through the starter and the filaments of the lamp. A resistance unit in the starter heats and a bimetal thermo-

static switch opens the filament circuit at a specified time.

STARTING MOTOR (auto.) start' ing mo' tor: The motor used to crank the automotive engine.

STAR TRACKER (space) star track' er: A telescopic instrument on a missile or other flightborne object that locks onto a celestial body and gives guidance to the missile or other object during flight. A star tracker may be optical or radiometric.

STATIC CHARACTERISTICS (elec.) stat' ic char ac ter is' tics: Characteristics of a tube taken with a constant plate voltage.

STATIC CHARGE (elec.) stat' ic charge: A charge on a body either negatively or positively.

STATIC ELECTRICITY (elec.) stat' ic e lec tric' i ty: Electricity at rest as opposed to an electric current.

STATIC TESTING (space) stat' ic test' ing: The testing of a device in a stationary or hold-down position as a means of testing and measuring it dynamic reactions.

STATION (automation) sta' tion: The position or location of a machine.

STATION POINT (draft.) sta' tion point: The point from which the object is observed.

STATOR (elec.) sta' tor: The stationary coils of an a-c generator.

STEADY REST (metal) stead' y rest: rest for supporting the center of long thin work while being turned in a lathe.

STEADY STATE (elec.) stead' y state: A fixed nonvarying condition.

STEAM (air cond.) steam: Water vapor.

STEAM DISTILLED WOOD TURPEN-
TINE (paint. and dec.) steam dis tilled'
wood tur' pen tine: Turpentine made
from pine tree stumps by treating
shredded chips with live steam to produce a distillate which is fractionated
to yield turpentine, pine oil and solid
residue.

STEATITE (elec.) ste' a tite: Magnesium silicate; soapstone; an insulating
material made from sintered talc.

STEEL, Classes based upon form (metal)
steel:

STRIPS – Less than 1/4" thick and
less than 24" wide.
SHEETS – Less than 1/4" thick and
over 24" wide.
PLATES – 1/4" and over in thickness and over 6" wide.
BARS – 1/4" and over in thickness and 6" or under in
width.

STEEL SQUARE (wood.) steel square:
A flat steel square used by the carpenter in framing a building. The body
of the square is usually 24 inches long
and the tongue 16 inches long. Both the
body and tongue are marked in one
inch intervals and fractions of an inch.
Tables frequently used by the carpenter
may be engraved on both sides of the
body and tongue. Ex: Essex Board
Measure, and Brace Table.

STEEL WOOL (paint. and dec.) steel
wool: Steel in fine strands. Comes in
grades 3, 2, 1, 0, 2/0, 3/0, and 4/0
(finest).

STEEPLE JACK (const.) stee' ple jack:
One who works on and climbs towers,
steeples, etc.

STEERING COLUMN (auto.) steer' ing

col' umn: The column and shaft between the steering wheel and the steering mechanism in an automobile.

STEERING GEAR (auto.) steer' ing gear:
The entire steering assembly and mechanism from the wheel to the front axle
of an automobile.

STELLITE (metal) stel' lite: A nonferrous metal consisting of cobalt,
tungsten and chromium with small percentage of carbon.

STENCILING (paint. and dec.) sten' cil-
ing: Placing design on surface by applying finish through template cut out
of thin paper or metal.

STEP BLOCK (metal) step block: A
block of steel, with machined steps of
various heights, used as a clamping
block, when fastening work to the table
of a machine.

STEP DOWN (elec.) step down: To reduce from higher voltage to lower voltage as in a step down transformer.

STEP UP (elec.) step up: To increase to
a higher voltage as in a step up transformer.

STEREOPHONIC SOUND (elec.) ster e-
o phon' ic sound: Three dimensional
sound; sound recorded from microphones placed at spaced intervals, usually right and left locations before the
source. Music is reproduced by spaced
speakers, each with a different audio
signal similar to original recording.

STEREOTYPE (graphics) ster' e o type:
Printing plate cast in type metal from
matrix mold of printing surface.

STERLING SILVER (crafts) ster' ling
sil' ver: An alloy of silver (92.5%)
and copper (7.5%).

STET (graphics) stet: A proofreading mark meaning "do not remove that part marked out, let it stand."

STICK (graphics) stick: A tool used in hand typesetting; the tray on a Linotype into which the finished line is delivered.

STICK SHELLAC (wood.) stick shel lac': Shellac in stick form used in furniture repair and refinishing to fill cracks and scratches.

STILE (const.) stile: The vertical parts of a panel; vertical sides of a panel door.

STILLSON WRENCH (plumb.) still' son wrench: See PIPE WRENCH.

STILTED (const.) stilt' ed: Raised above its usual level.

STIPPLE (crafts.) stip' ple: To draw or engrave by dots or points instead of lines.

STIPPLE FINISH (paint. and dec.) stip'- ple fin' ish: Finish obtained by tapping surface with stipple brush, before paint is dry.

STL (elec.): STUDIO TRANSMITTER LINK. A radio link between studio and transmitter.

STOCKS AND DIES (metal) stocks and dies: The handles and dies for cutting external male threads.

STOICHIOMETRIC (space) stoich i o- met' ric: Combustible mixture having exact proportions for complete combustion.

STONE (graphics) stone: Work table used in letterpress printing. Top surface used to be stone, now it is usually steel.

STONE-HAND (graphics) stone-hand: A workman who imposes and locks up forms.

STOOL (const.) stool: An inside window sill.

STOOP (const.) stoop: A seat or bench beside a door, sometimes on a small porch.

STOP and WASTE COCK (plumb.) stop and waste cock: A stop valve with a drain, so that when water is shut off, the pipe on the down stream side of the valve is drained to waste.

STOP CHAMFER (wood.) stop cham' fer: To chamfer the edge of board partially, so that the end portions remain sharp.

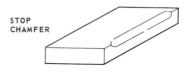

STOP CHAMFER

STOPCOCK (plumb.) stop' cock: A small ground key valve.

STOPPED MITER (wood.) stopped mi' ter: A combination miter and butt joint. See illustration, page 317.

STORAGE (automation) stor' age: The section of a computer in which directions and information are stored for use in calculations.

STORAGE BATTERY (auto.) stor' age bat' ter y: An electrochemical device providing a source of electric current for operation of an automobile.

STORM SEWERS (plumb.) storm sew'- ers: Sewers constructed to carry only storm water to a natural drainage area.

STORY (const.) sto' ry: A floor of a

building; the space between one floor and the floor above it.

STOVE BOLT (metal) stove bolt: A name given to machine screws when supplied with nuts.

STRADDLE MILL (metal) strad' dle mill: Two or more side milling cutters mounted on an arbor.

STRAIGHT ANGLE (draft.) straight an'- gle: An angle of 180°.

STRAIGHTEDGE (const.) straight' edge: A board with a straight side used for leveling and measuring.

STRAIGHT POLARITY (Electrode negative-cathode) (weld.) straight po- lar' i ty: Connecting DC to cause elec- trons to flow from the electrode to the base metal.

STRAIGHT SHANK DRILL (metal) straight shank drill: A drill with a round uniform shank used with self- centering chucks.

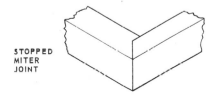

STOPPED
MITER
JOINT

STRAIGHT TURNING (metal) straight turn' ing: The operation of turning work in the lathe when the diameters of the work are equal everywhere. The finished piece is a cylinder.

STRAIN (metal) strain: A change in size, length or form.

STRAIN (weld.) strain: Reaction of an object to a stress.

STRAIN GAUGE (elec.) strain gauge: A

sensitive instrument usually employ- ing a bridge circuit, used to measure strain or distortion of metal parts during operation of a device.

STRAIN INSULATOR (elec.) strain in'- sul a tor: An insulator with both high insulation and tensile strength used to support the entire weight and strain of a wire or cable. It is used in guy wires for towers.

STRANDED CONDUCTOR (elec.) strand' ed con duc' tor: A conductor of several strands of solid wire twisted together. Standard cables have 7, 19, and 37 strands.

S TRAP (plumb.) s trap: A trap bent like the letter S.

STRAP (const.) strap: An iron plate used to connect two timbers together. It is screwed or bolted to both timbers.

STRATOSPHERE (space) strat' o- sphere: A calm region of the upper atmosphere characterized by little or no temperature change in altitude.

STRAY FIELD (elec.) stray field: Mag- netic lines of force outside of the magnetic path.

STRAYS (elec.) strays: Electromagnetic disturbances in radio reception which are not associated with the transmis- sion.

STREAMLINING (auto.) stream' lin ing: The rounding and contouring of the shape of a vehicle to reduce air resistance.

STREET ELL (plumb.) street ell: See SERVICE ELL.

STRENGTH (metal) strength: The ability of a material to resist deformation.

STRESS (metal) stress: A force applied

to a body which tends to change its shape.

STRESS (weld.) stress: Load imposed on an object.

STRESS RELIEVING (weld.) stress reliev' ing: Even heating of a structure to a temperature below the critical temperature followed by a slow, even cooling.

"STRETCH" (paint. and dec.) stretch: The width of the area on which a painter will normally apply paint across a ceiling or down a side wall.

STRETCHER (const.) stretch' er: A brick or block laid lengthwise in a wall.

STRIKING IN (paint. and dec.) strik' ing in: Materials used in finishing are said to "strike in" when they soften undercoats and sink into them.

STRIKING POTENTIAL (elec.) strik' ing po ten' tial: See IONIZATION POTENTIAL.

STRIKING THE ARC (weld.) strik' ing the arc: The process of starting the electric arc when electric welding. Correct feeding of the electrode into the weld maintains the arc and produces a good weld.

STRINGBOARD (const.) stringboard: A board used in the well hole to terminate a flight of stairs.

STRINGERS (const.) string' ers: The sides of a flight of steps; see CARRIAGE.

STRINGPIECE (const.) string' piece: Supports placed under the treads and risers of steps.

"STRIP" (paint. and dec.) strip: Com-

plete removal of an old finish with paint removers.

STRIPPER (elec.) strip' per: A tool for removing insulation from wire.

STROBOSCOPE (elec.) strob' o scope: An instrument used to measure the speed of a rotating machine or examine its operation. It consists of a variable speed flashing light which can be synchronized with the rotating machine. At synchronized speed the rotating parts appear stationary.

STROBOTRON (elec.) stro' bo tron: A neon light with reflector used in a stroboscope. It produces a brilliant light when energized by accurately timed voltage pulses.

STROKE (auto.) stroke: The maximum movement of piston from top to bottom dead center.

STRUT (const.) strut: A brace used to support a rafter.

STUB'S GAUGE (metal) stub's gauge: A gauge for measuring the size of wire; also called the "Birmingham Gauge."

STUCCO (const.) stuc' co: A plaster type material used to surface the exterior walls of a building.

STUD (auto.) stud: A bolt threaded on both ends.

STUD (const.) stud: Small timbers usually 2x4 used in framing walls and partitions.

STUFFING BOX (metal) stuff' ing box: An enclosure around a piston rod or valve in a steam engine filled with packing to prevent leakage.

STUNT (crafts) stunt: A term describing the cracking of ceramic pottery when cooling.

STYLUS (elec.) sty' lus: A phonograph needle or jewel, which follows the grooves in a record.

STYLUS DRAG (elec.) sty' lus drag: The force of friction between the stylus and the record grooved surface.

STYLUS FORCE (elec.) sty' lus force: The vertical force exerted on the record by the stylus in operating position.

STYRENE-BUTADIENE RESIN (paint. and dec.) sty' rene-bu' ta di ene res'-in: Synthetic rubber resin; liquid styrene and butadien gas are copolymerized to form chemical resistant product with excellent film-forming properties.

STYROFOAM (crafts) sty' ro foam: A foam type plastic.

SUBASSEMBLY (draft.) sub as sem'-bly: A group of assembled parts which are a part of a larger machine.

SUBATOMIC (elec.) sub a tom' ic: A particle of an atom.

SUBAUTOMATION (automation) sub-au to ma' tion: A group of auxilliary production practices which contribute to the final goal of production but do not in themselves permit production without human intervention.

SUBCARRIER (elec.) sub car' ri er: A carrier wave used to modulated another carrier wave.

SUBFLOOR (const.) sub' floor: The rough boarding on floor joists to which finish floor is applied.

SUBHARMONIC (elec.) sub har mon' ic: A frequency below the harmonic, usual-

ly a fractional part of the fundamental frequency.

SUBLIMATION (air cond.) sub li ma'-tion: The change in state from a solid to gas without appearance of liquid.

SUBMINIATURE CIRCUITRY (elec.) sub min' i a ture cir' cuit ry: Circuits using very small electronic components.

SUBSATELLITE (space) sub sat' el-lite: An object designed to be carried into orbit inside an artificial Earth satellite, but later ejected to serve a particular purpose.

SUBSONIC (elec.) sub son' ic: A frequency below the audio frequency range; infrasonic.

SUBSTATION (elec.) sub' sta tion: A station in a power transmission system at which electric power is transformed to a conveniently used form. The station may consist of transformers, switches, circuit breakers and other auxilliary equipment.

SUCCESSIVE REVOLUTION (draft.) succes' sive rev o lu' tion: The succession of several single revolutions of an object or part which is oblique to more than one picture plane.

SUCTION SPOTTING (paint. and dec.) suc' tion spot' ting: Spotting of paint job caused by oil in new coat being absorbed by spots or porous areas of surface.

SULFATION (elec.) sul fa' tion: An undesirable condition of a lead acid battery caused by leaving it in a discharged condition or by improper care. Sulfates forming on plates make the battery partially inactive.

SUMMER (const.) sum' mer: The main beam or girder of a floor.

SUMP (plumb.) sump: A pit or receptacle for the collection of water.

SUNDAYS (paint. and dec.) sun' days: Places skipped when applying finishing materials to a surface.

SUN EFFECT (air cond.) sun ef fect': Solar energy transferred into rooms through windows and building walls.

SUNSPOT (space) sun' spot: A relatively dark area on the surface of the sun.

SUNSPOT CYCLE (space) sun' spot: A periodic variation in the number and area of sunspots with an average length of 11.1 years.

SUPERCHARGER (auto.) su' per charger: A blower or air pump to force fuel-air mixture into cylinders to increase volumetric efficiency.

SUPERCONDUCTIVITY (elec.) su per con duc tiv' i ty: A phenomenon of conduction at temperatures near absolute zero at which resistance seems to disappear; see CRYOGENICS.

SUPER CONTROL TUBE (elec.) su' - per con trol' tube: Another name for a REMOTE CUTOFF TUBE; a variable mu tube, a tube in which the amplification factor varies with control grid bias.

SUPERFLUOUS VIEWS (draft.) su per' - flu ous views: Views drawn of an object which are unnecessary to describe the object.

SUPERHETERODYNE (elec.) su per-het' er o dyne: A radio receiver in which the incoming signal is converted to a fixed intermediate frequency before detecting the audio signal component.

SUPERSONIC (elec.) su per son' ic: Frequencies above the audio frequency range.

SUPERSONIC (space) su per son' ic: Of or pertaining to the speed of an object moving at a speed greater than that of sound.

SUPPLEMENTARY ANGLES (draft.) sup ple men' ta ry an' gles: Two angles are supplementary when their sum is 180 degrees.

SUPPRESSOR (elec.) sup pres' or: A device used to eliminate radio interference from automotive ignition systems.

SUPPRESSOR GRID (elec.) sup pres' - sor grid: A third grid in an electron tube, between the screen grid and plate to repel or suppress secondary electrons from the plate.

SURBASE (wood.) sur' base: A molding above the baseboard around a room.

SURFACE ALLOY TRANSISTOR (elec.) sur' face al' loy tran sis' tor: A silicon junction transistor, in which aluminum electrodes are deposited in shallow pits etched on both sides of a thin silicon crystal, forming P regions.

SURFACE BARRIER TRANSISTOR (elec.) sur' face bar' ri er tran sis' - tor: A transistor so constructed that the interfaces performing the collection and emission of carriers are located at the surface of the semiconductor crystal.

SURFACE DRYING (paint. and dec.) sur' face dry' ing: Drying of a finishing material on top while the bottom remains more or less soft.

SURFACE GAUGE (metal) sur' face gauge: An adjustable steel scriber mounted on a base.

SURFACE GRINDER (metal) sur' face grind' er: A machine tool for accurately grinding the surface of metal. The work is attached to a moving table by a vise or magnetic chuck. The table passes beneath the grinding wheel in a reciprocating motion. Accurate controls provide for location and depth of cut.

SURFACE NOISE (elec.) sur' face noise: Noise in a sound recording resulting from rough particles or irregularities left in the grooves of a record after cutting.

SURFACE PLATE (metal) sur' face plate: A cast iron plate of convenient size, accurately machined to a smooth surface, used for layout work.

SURFACE TENSION (paint. and dec.) sur' face ten' sion: Property of finishing material which causes it to try to shrink.

SURFACE WATER (plumb.) sur' face wa' ter: Rainfall which does not soak into the ground and runs off into drainage system.

SURFORM (wood.) sur' form: A trade name of the Stanley Tool Co. for a variety of wood cutting tools employing a specially designed metal surface with sharp cutting edges.

SURGE (elec.) surge: A sudden increase in voltage or current.

SURGE IMPEDANCE (elec.) surge imped' ance: See CHARACTERISTIC IMPEDANCE.

SUSCEPTANCE (Symbol B) (elec.) suscep' tance: The reciprocal of reactance.

SWAGE (metal) swage: Tool used to shape metal. Work is held on swage and struck with hammer.

SWAGE BLOCK (metal) swage block: A heavy specially formed block used in forging.

SWAGES (metal) swages: Forging tools with concave faces for shaping cylindrical parts.

SWARF (metal) swarf: The solid material from grinding wheel and work piece resulting from a grinding operation.

SWASH LETTERS (graphics) swash let'ters: Italic letters with many embellishments and ornamental prolongations.

SWEATING (air cond.) sweat' ing: The condensation of moisture on a surface which is below the dew-point temperature.

SWEAT JOINT (plumb.) sweat joint: Metal pieces are coated with solder, placed together, and heat applied to melt solder and join pieces.

SWEDISH PUTTY (paint. and dec.) swe'dish put' ty: Spackling compound mixed with paste paint.

SWEEP CIRCUIT (elec.) sweep cir' cuit: A periodic varying voltage applied to the deflection circuits of a cathode-ray tube to move electron beam at a linear rate.

SWEEP FITTING (plumb.) sweep fit'ting: A fitting with a long radius curve.

SWEEP GENERATOR (elec.) sweep gen' er a tor: A test instrument employed as a radio frequency generator in which the frequency may be varied above and below a mean frequency. When used with an oscilloscope, the response patterns of tuned circuits may be observed.

SWEEP OSCILLATOR (elec.) sweep os'-

cil la tor: An oscillator used to deflect the beam in a cathode-ray tube.

SWINGING CHOKE (elec.) swing ing choke: A choke coil whose inductance varies as the average current through the coil.

SWITCH (elec.) switch: A device for directing or controlling the current flow in an electric circuit. Switches are manufactured in many types and forms. They may be single pole, three way, four way, etc.; a switch is usually mounted in a metal wall case and is then covered with a switch plate.

SWITCH BOX (elec.) switch box: A metal box used in electric wiring to terminate a line at a switch or convenience outlet.

SWITCH PLATE (elec.) switch plate: A decorative and protective cover for a wall switch.

SWITCH, ROTARY (elec.) switch, ro' ta-ry: A switch which is operated by a rotating action. Frequently several switches are operated in tandem and controlled by a single shaft.

SWITCH, TYPES OF (elec.) switch, types of:

DOUBLE POLE, two single pole switches operated in tandem for opening and closing both sides of a line simultaneously.

DOUBLE THROW, a switch which can be in an open position or closed in either of two other positions. Used to connect a circuit to either of two other circuits.

FOUR WAY, a switch used in lighting circuits in conjunction with three way switches to provide three or more control points.

LIMIT, a switch which is either opened or closed when its activating device has moved through a specified distance.

KNIFE, a hand operated switch in which the circuit is switched by moving a knife-like metal blade in or out of contact with a metal slot.

SINGLE POLE, a simple switch for opening or closing a single wire circuit.

SINGLE THROW, a switch with open or closed positions only.

THREE WAY, a three terminal switch in which a circuit may be switched to either of two paths.

TOGGLE, a small lever operated switch.

SWIVEL JOINT (plumb.) swiv' el joint: A joint made with threaded pipe which permits movement of pipe from normal line of direction.

S WRENCH (metal) s wrench: An open ended wrench shaped like the letter S.

SYMBOL (elec.) sym' bol: A letter, character or schematic design representing a unit or component. Ex: X stands for reactance.

SYMBOLS, HOUSE WIRING (elec.) sym'-bols, house wir' ing: Symbols used by the architect to tell the electrician the placement of outlets, switches, etc. in a home.

SYMMETRICAL AUXILIARY (draft.) sym met' ri cal aux il' ia ry: An auxiliary view which is symmetrical about a center reference line.

SYMMETRICAL MULTIVIBRATOR
(elec.) sym met' ri cal mul' ti vi bra-
tor: A multivibrator producing equal
or symmetrical waves from each tube.
Tubes have equal conduction periods.

SYNCHRO (elec.) syn' chro: An electromechanical device used to transmit the
angular position of a shaft from one
position to another without mechanical
linkage.

SYNCHRO-MESH (auto.) syn' chro-
mesh: A device used in a transmission consisting of a bronze cone on the
shaft contacting a steel cone on the
gear. It acts as a clutch to synchronize
the speeds for easy engagement.

SYNCHRONIZING PULSE (SYNC PULSE)
(elec.) syn' chro niz ing pulse: A pulse
wave used to trigger a circuit or to
synchronize an oscillator.

SYNCHRONOUS (elec.) syn' chro nous:
Having the same period or frequency.

SYNCHRONOUS MOTOR (elec.) syn'-
chro nous mo' tor: A type of a-c motor
which uses separate d-c source of power for its field. It runs at synchronous
speed under varying load conditions.

SYNCHRONOUS VIBRATOR (elec.) syn'-
chro nous vi' bra tor: A vibrator with
additional contact points to switch output circuit so that current is maintained in one direction through the load.

SYNCHRO RECEIVER (elec.) syn' chro
re ceiv' er: Similar to the synchro
transmitter, but converts signal into
mechanical motion.

SYNCHROSCOPE (elec.) syn' chro-
scope: A device used to determine
synchronization by means of lamps;
an oscilloscope that has a sweep of
very short duration generated only when
a synchronizing signal is provided.

SYNCHRO TRANSMISSION SYSTEM
(elec.) syn' chro trans mis' sion sys'-
tem: The complete system of synchros
and other devices used to transmit and
receive angular displacement of a shaft.

SYNCHRO TRANSMITTER (elec.) syn'-
chro trans mit' ter: A transformer
with a rotatable primary that converts
mechanical input into an electrical
signal and transmits the signal to the
receiver.

SYNC LIMITER (elec.) sync lim' it er:
A tube used to limit a sync pulse to a
definite amplitude.

SYNC PULSE (elec.) sync pulse: An
abbreviation for synchronization pulse,
used for triggering an oscillator or
circuit.

SYNC SEPARATOR (elec.) sync sep' a-
ra tor: A tube used to separate the
sync pulses from picture information in
the TV signal.

SYNERGIC CURVE (space) syn er' gic
curve: A curve plotted for the ascent
of a space craft calculated to give the
craft optimum economy in fuel with
optimum velocity.

SYNTHETIC RESIN (paint. and dec.)
syn thet' ic res' in: An artificial resin
or plastic produced by systematic ex-
ploitation of chemical reaction of or-
ganice substances.

SYSTEM (automation) sys' tem: Includes
all the apparatus, interrelationships
and influencing factors necessary to
accomplish an end result.

SYSTEMS ENGINEERING (automation)
sys' tems eng i neer' ing: The designing of complete and complex systems by coordinating all parts of the
system, considering interaction be-

tween elements and individual characteristics of each element.

TABLE SAW (wood.) ta' ble saw: See BENCH SAW.

TABORET (wood.) tab' o ret: A small table or seat. Sometimes used as a plant stand or foot stool.

TACHOMETER (auto.) ta chom' e ter: A device used to measure the rotational speed of an engine, wheel or shaft.

TACK (graphics) tack, the adhesiveness of ink.

TACKINESS (paint. and dec.) tack' i-ness: Stickiness. When a painting material dries out, gels or sets up, it loses tackiness, or stickiness.

TACK RAG (paint. and dec.) tack rag: Cloth impregnated with varnish used in wood finishing to remove abrasive dust from surface of wood, before applying finishing material.

TACK WELD (weld.) tack weld: Small weld used to temporarily hold together components of an assembly.

TAIL BEAM (const.) tail beam: A short beam supported at one end in a wall and by a header at the other end.

TAIL JOIST (const.) tail joist: A floor joist with one end terminated at a header joist.

TAIL LIGHT (auto.) tail light: A red light required by law on the rear of all automobiles. It must be lighted during night driving. Combination tail lights now include a stop light and turn signal lights.

TAIL PIECE (graphics) tail piece: An

ornamental design at the conclusion of a piece of printing.

TAILPIECE (plumb.) tail' piece: A T connection used with a sink drain.

TAIL SCREW (wood.) tail screw: The adjustable screw on the tailstock of a woodturning lathe.

TAILSTOCK (metal) tail' stock: The casting on the lathe, fitted to the V ways, providing outer bearing and support for the work being turned.

TAIL TRIMMER (const.) tail trim' mer: A trimmer against a wall to which the ends of joist are nailed.

TAKE (graphics) take: A division of copy given to a composer to set-up into type.

TALC (paint. and dec.) talc: A hydrous magnesium aluminum silicate used as an extender in paints.

TALL OIL (paint. and dec.) tall oil: A blend of resin and oil acids obtained as a by-product from the sulfate process for making paper.

TAMP (const.) tamp: To settle earth firmly by pounding.

TAMPION (plumb.) tam' pi on: A cone shaped wooden tool used for swaging out the end of a lead pipe.

TANG (wood.) tang: The shank of a tool to which the handle is attached.

TANGENT (draft.) tan' gent: A line drawn to the surface of an arc or circle so that it contacts the arc at only one point. A trigonometric function of an angle in a right triangle equal to the opposite side divided by the adjacent side.

TANK (weld.) tank: See CYLINDER.

TANK CIRCUIT (elec.) tank cir' cuit: A parallel resonant circuit.

TAP (elec.) tap: A connection made to a coil at a point other than at its terminals.

TAP (metal) tap: A tool used to form an internal thread.

TAP

TAP DRILL (metal) tap drill: Drill used to make hole in metal prior to tapping.

TAPE (elec.) tape: Narrow, flexible strip of adhesive coated material, used to wrap and insulate electric wiring joints and splices.

TAPER (elec.) ta' per: The manner in which the resistance of a potentiometer varies.

TAPER (wood.) ta' per: A uniform change in size.

TAPER ANGLE (metal) ta' per an' gle: The included angle between tapered surfaces.

TAPER ATTACHMENT (metal) ta' per at tach' ment: An accessory for a lathe which provides a guiding mechanism for the cutting tool so that tapers may be machined.

TAPER, AUDIO (elec.) ta' per, au' di o: The resistance variation in a potentiometer corresponding to a semilogarithmic scale. Used to compensate for the inability of the human ear to respond equally to all frequencies in audio systems.

TAPE RECORDER (elec.) tape record'-er: An electronic recording device in which audio signals are converted to electric signals which are used to form a magnetic pattern on specially prepared tape.

TAPERED SHANK DRILL (metal) ta'-pered shank drill: A drill made with a tapered shank such as the Morse taper, to fit directly into the tapered hollow spindle of a drill press or lathe.

TAPER, LINEAR (elec.) ta' per, lin' e-ar: A uniform change in resistance over entire range of a potentiometer.

TAPER REAMER (metal) ta' per ream'-er: A typical reamer shaped to ream tapered holes.

TAPER TURNING (metal) ta' per turn'-ing: Work turned in a lathe so that the diameter is changing constantly from one end to the other.

TAPE TRANSPORT (elec.) tape trans'-port: The driving mechanism and reels of a tape recorder.

TAPING (automation) tap' ing: The process of recording a program or results on a magnetic or punched tape.

TAPPED TEE (plumb.) tapped tee: A soil pipe tee with its branch tapped to receive a threaded pipe.

TAPPER TAP (metal) tap' per tap: A special tap used in a nut tapping machine.

TAPPET (auto.) tap' pet: An adjusting screw in the valve train of an engine to assure proper clearances between valve stem and cam.

TAP WRENCH (metal) tap wrench: A T shaped holder for taps.

TAR (paint. and dec.) tar: A thick brown or black liquid with a characteristic odor – a residue from the distillation of wood, peat, coal, shale or other vegetable or mineral material.

T – ATTENUATOR (elec.) t – at ten'-u a tor: Two variable resistors connected in series with the load and a variable resistor from the junction of the two series resistors across the source. All resistors are gang controlled. The T – attenuator maintains at both pairs of terminals a constant resistance for any setting of the ganged variable resistors.

T–Bolt (metal) t–bolt: A bolt with a T shaped head for holding work to work table. Table has T slots to accommodate the bolts.

TEAK (wood.) teak: Wood from the East Indian tree. It is hard, yellowish brown and highly prized as a furniture wood.

TEE (plumb.) tee: A pipe fitting shaped like the letter T and providing connections for pipes of the same or different sizes.

TEEMING (metal) teem' ing: Pouring molten metals from ladle into molds.

TEFLON (elec.) tef' lon: A duPont tradename for a plastic insulating material highly resistant to humidity, pressure and shock.

TELECAST (elec.) tel' e cast: To broadcast a TV program.

TELECINE PROJECTOR (elec.) tel' e-cine pro jec' tor: A projector used in TV studios to televise motion picture films.

TELEGRAPHY (elec.) te leg' ra phy:

Communication by a code of electrical pulses. Ex: Morse Code.

TELEMETER (space) te lem' e ter: An electronic instrument that senses and measures a quantity, as that of speed, temperature or pressures of radiation, then transmits radio signals to a distant station, where, indicated or recorded they are interpreted by code.

TELEMETRY (elec.) te lem' e try: The transmission of measurements recorded on instruments by means of radio or telephone to a remote point.

TELEPHONE (elec.) tel' e phone: The instruments and system used to transmit voice and sound by means of electrical signals over interconnecting wires.

EXCHANGE, the telephone central switching location.

REPEATER, an amplifier installed at intervals along a telephone line to increase signal strength.

TELEPHONE LINES (elec.) tel' e phone lines:

Class AA. Response is flat within 2 db from 50–8000 cps.

Class A. Same as Class AA except frequency range is 100–5000 cps.

Class BB and B. Same as AA and A, but only leased for use on an hourly basis.

Class C. Lines with response of 200–3500 cps available on 24 hour basis.

Class D. Same as Class C, but available for use on hourly basis.

Class E. Ordinary voice lines. Response is 300–2500 cps.

TELEPHONY (elec.) te leph' o ny: The operation of a telephone or telephone system; telephone communications.

TELEPHOTO (elec.) tel' e pho to: A picture transmitted and reproduced by means of telegraph systems; a camera lens with a long focal length.

TELESCOPING GAUGE (metal) tel' e-scop ing gauge: A gauge for measure-ing inside diameter of holes. The gauge is inserted in hole and is permitted to expand to maximum measurement. The gauge is then locked, removed from hole and diameter is measured with a mi-crometer.

TELETRANSCRIPTION (e l e c .) tel' e-tran scrip' tion: See KINESCOPE RE-CORDING.

TELETYPE (elec.) tel' e type: A ma-chine which changes plain language into code and vice versa. It uses a keyboard similar to a typewriter.

TELEVISION (elec.) tel' e vi sion: A method of transmitting and receiving a visual scene by radio broadcasting.

TELEVISION CHANNEL (elec.) tel' e-vi sion chan' nel: An allocation in the frequency spectrum of 6 mc assigned to each television station for trans-mission of picture and sound informa-tion.

TEMPER (metal) tem' per: To relieve stresses and reduce brittleness by reheating hardened steel uniformly to 300-550 degrees.

TEMPERA (paint. and dec.) tem' per a: A water-thinned or water-emulsion paint.

TEMPERATURE (air cond.) tem' per-a ture: The degree of hotness or cold-ness of anything; the tendency of matter to transmit heat to matter in contact with it.

ABSOLUTE, The temperature ex-pressed in degrees above absolute zero.

DEW POINT, The temperature at which condensation starts if air is cooled at a constant pressure.

DRY BULB, The temperature indi-cated on an accurate thermometer when there is no heat flow to or from the thermometer bulb.

EFFECTIVE, The index expressing the ability of the human body to re-spond to changes in temperature, hu-midity and movement of air.

WET BULB, The temperature at which water can bring the air to sat-uration adiabatically at the same tem-perature, by evaporation; the temper-ature measured on a wet bulb psychrom-eter.

TEMPERATURE (e l e c .) tem' per a-ture:

ABSOLUTE, measured on scale from absolute zero (-273.16 C).

CENTIGRADE, measured on scale on which the freezing point of water is 0 degrees and the boiling point is 100 degrees.

FAHRENHEIT, measured on a scale on which the freezing point of water is 32 degrees and the boiling point is 212 degrees.

KELVIN, A temperature scale start-ing at absolute zero. It is based on the heat transfer of a CARNOT heat engine which is the most efficient type of engine.

TEMPERATURE COEFFICIENT OF RE-

SISTANCE (elec.) tem' per a ture co-ef fi' cient of re sis' tance: The amount of increase in resistance of a one ohm sample of conductor per degree of temperature rise above 0° centi-grade.

TEMPLATE (draft.) tem' plate: A thin plastic or metal sheet in which is cut the outline of curves, symbols and devices. The draftsman uses the tem-plate for rapidly drawing the required object.

TENON (wood.) ten' on: A projection or tongue cut on a piece of wood to fit into a mortise.

TENSILE STRENGTH (metal) ten' sile strength: The maximum load per cross sectional area sustained by a material during test.

TENSILE STRENGTH (weld.) ten' sile strength: Maximum pull stress in psi a specimen is capable of developing.

TENSION (elec.) ten' sion: Voltage; po-tential difference.

TERMINAL (elec.) ter' mi nal: A point of electrical connections.

TERMINAL STRIP (elec.) ter' mi nal strip: A strip of insulating material on which are mounted several terminals or tie points.

TERNARY ALLOY (metal) ter' na ry al' loy: A complex alloy of three dif-ferent metals.

TERNARY STEEL (metal) ter' na ry steel: Steel alloyed with a third ele-ment.

TERNEPLATE (plumb.) terne' plate: Sheet iron coated with an alloy of lead and tin.

TERRACE (const.) ter' race: A raised level space outside a building such as a lawn or flagstone terrace. A terrace usually has at least one vertical or sloping side.

TERRA COTTA (const.) ter' ra cot' ta: High quality baked clay.

TERRAZZO (const.) ter raz' zo: A floor made of cement containing fragments of colored stone. After the cement has hardened, the floor is ground and pol-ished with a machine.

TERTIARY COLORS (paint. and dec.) ter' ti ar y col' ors: Colors made by combining colors on color wheel that are adjacent like red and orange.

TERTIARY COLORS (paint. and dec.) ter' ti a ry col' ors: Colors obtained by mixing the secondary colors in pairs to produce olive, citrine and russet.

TESLA COIL (elec.) tes' la coil: A high frequency induction coil.

TEST (elec.) test:

CLIP, a spring clip fastened to the end of a wire to make a temporary connection to a circuit or terminal.

POINT, a designated point in a circuit at which a specified voltage, resistance or waveform should appear; a pointed metal end of a test probe.

PROD, a metal test point with an insulated handle.

TESTING (automation) test' ing: The trial of a product by actual operation or use, or subjecting the product to ex-ternal effects and treatments.

TEST PATTERN (elec.) test pat' tern: A drawing of circles, lines, wedges in geometric designs transmitted by a television station. It is designed to facilitate certain service adjustments on a TV receiver.

TEST STAND (space) test stand: A stand at which some mechanism or engine is tested out.

TETRODE (elec.) tet' rode: An electron tube with four elements including cathode, plate, control grid and screen grid.

TETRODE TRANSISTOR (elec.) tet' rode tran sis' tor: A transistor with four elements, usually using either two emitters or two bases.

TEXT (graphics) text: The body matter of a book.

TEXT LETTER (graphics) text let' ter: A type face with bold, heavy body strokes and sharp thin elongated serifs; Old English type face.

TEXTURE PAINT (paint. and dec.) tex'-ture paint: One which may be manipulated by brush, trowel or other tool to give various patterns.

THAWING (air cond.) thaw' ing: Changing ice to water by addition of heat.

T HEAD ENGINE (auto.) T head en' gine: An engine with valves located in block on each side of the cylinder.

THEODOLITE (const.) the od' o lite: An accurate surveyor's transit.

THERLO (elec.) ther' lo: An alloy used for shunts for instruments. It consists of copper, aluminum and manganese. It has a low temperature coefficient.

THERMAL AGITATION (elec.) ther' mal ag i ta' tion: Noise produced in a circuit as a result of electrons moving at random.

THERMAL EFFICIENCY (auto.) ther'-mal ef fi' cien cy: The relationship between the power output of an engine to energy in the fuel used to produce the power.

THERMAL HEATING (space) ther' mal heat' ing: Aerodynamic heating produced by supersonic travel through the atmosphere.

THERMAL RUNAWAY (elec.) ther' mal run' a way: In a transistor, the regenerative increase in collector current and junction temperature.

THERMIONIC EMISSION (elec.) therm-i on' ic e mis' sion: The emission of electrons from a heated cathode.

THERMIONICS (elec.) therm i on' ics: The branch of science which studies the emission of electrons by heat.

THERMISTOR (elec.) therm' is tor: A semiconductor device which changes resistivity with a change in temperature.

THERMIT (metal) ther' mit: A mixture of powdered aluminum and a metallic oxide. Used in thermit welding.

THERMIT WELDING (weld.) ther' mit weld' ing: Welding process based on the chemical reaction between aluminum and iron oxide.

THERMOCOUPLE (elec.) ther' mo couple: A device used to measure temperature based upon the principle that an electric current is produced when two dissimilar wires are joined together and the junction is heated.

THERMOCOUPLE METER (elec.) ther'-mo cou ple me' ter: A meter based on the principle that if two dissimular metals are welded together and the junction is heated, a dc voltage will develop across the open ends. Used for measuring radio frequency currents.

THERMODYNAMICS (air cond.) thermo dy nam' ics: The sciences of heat energy and its transformations to and from other forms of energy.

THERMODYNAMICS (automation) thermo dy nam' ics: The science of conversion of energy from one form to another, and the work that results from or is required to cause the transformation.

THERMOMETER (air cond.) thermom' e ter: An instrument for measuring temperature.

THERMONUCLEAR (space) ther mo nu' cle ar: Pertaining to nuclear reaction induced by heat, especially to nuclear fusion triggered by the intense heat and pressure of an atomic fission explosion.

THERMOPILE (elec.) ther' mo pile: An electrical device used to measure temperature difference.

THERMOPLASTICS (crafts) ther mo plas' tics: A group of plastics which soften when heated and remain permanently soft under heat.

THERMOSETTING (crafts) ther mo set' ting: A group of plastics which harden under certain heating conditions.

THERMOSETTING (paint. and dec.) therm o set' ting: Material which undergoes irreversible chemical reaction when heated and molded. Once formed, it cannot be reheated and reshaped.

THERMOSIPHON (auto.) ther' mo siphon: The natural circulation of a

cooling liquid depending upon expansion of the liquid when heated.

THERMOSTAT (air cond.) ther' mo stat: An automatic control device operating on changes in temperature.

THERMOSTAT (auto.) ther' mo stat: A temperature controlled valve in the cooling system of an engine to maintain a constant operating temperature.

THETA (θ) (elec.) the' ta: The angle of rotation of a vector representing selected instants at which a sine wave is plotted. The angular displacement between two vectors.

THICKNESS GAUGE (metal) thick' ness gauge: An assembly of a quantity of

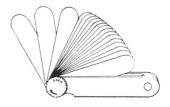

leaves of metal, each of a different thickness. Used for measuring clearances and fits.

T HINGE (const.) t hinge: A surface hinge shaped like the letter T.

THINNERS (paint. and dec.) thin' ners: Volatile liquids used to lower or otherwise regulate the consistency of paint and varnish.

THINWALL (elec.) thin' wall: Electrical tubing; conduit tubing.

THIRD ANGLE PROJECTION (draft.) third an' gle pro jec' tion: An object drawn as if placed in the third quadrant of the intersecting projection planes. The top view appears above the front view.

THIRD BRUSH GENERATOR (auto.) third brush gen er a' tor: A partially self-regulating generator which derives its field excitation from a third brush on its commutator.

THIRD-CLASS LEVER third-class le'-ver: A lever with the fulcrum at one

end and the weight at the other end. The applied force is between the fulcrum and the weight.

THIXOTROPIC PAINT (paint. and dec.) thix o trop' ic paint: Property exhibited by some paint of becoming fluid when shaken or disturbed. After cessation of mechanical disturbance, such as stirring or putting brush into paint, rigidity develops again.

THORIATED-TUNGSTEN (elec.) thor i-at' ed-tung' sten: A tungsten emitter coated with a thin layer of Thorium.

THORIUM (elec.) thor'i um: An element, atomic number 90. Used as cathode emitter material.

THREAD PITCH GAUGE (metal) thread pitch gauge: A gauge for measuring the number of threads per inch on a screw.

THREAD STOP (metal) thread stop: An adjustable depth stop used when cutting threads on a lathe.

THREADS, Types of (metal):

ACME, a type of worm thread, similar to a square thread, except that the included angle between the two adjacent faces is 29 degrees.

AMERICAN OR NATIONAL STAND-

ARD, similar to the V-thread except that the crest and the root of the grooves are made flat.

BUTTRESS THREAD, a thread with one face at right angles to the axis of the screw on one side and a 45° bevel on the other.

DARDELET THREAD, a thread similar to the acme thread but of less thread depth. The root of the thread of the screw and the crest of the thread in the nut are tapered at 6°. As the nut is tightened on the bolt, the tapered surfaces lock.

SQUARE THREAD, a square shaped thread, the face of which equals the space and depth.

WHITWORTH THREAD, the English modification of the V-thread. The angle between adjacent faces is 55° and the crest and root of the thread are rounded.

THREE-PHASE ALTERNATING CURRENT (elec.) three-phase al' ter nat-ing cur' rent: A combination of three alternating currents having their voltages displaced by 120° or one third of a cycle.

THREE-POINT PERSPECTIVE (draft.) three-point per spec' tive: A drawing of an object so that none of its principle edges is parallel to the picture plane. Each set of edges will have its separate vanishing point.

THREE-POINT SUSPENSION (auto.) three-point sus pen' sion: Suspended at three points; a method of mounting an automotive engine so that the weight of the engine is supported at three points.

THREE-SQUARE FILE (metal) three-square file: A common name for a triangular or three-cornered file used for saw sharpening.

THREE-WAY SWITCH (elec.) three-way switch: See SWITCH, THREE-WAY.

THREE-WIRE DISTRIBUTION (elec.) three-wire dis tri bu' tion: In dc circuits one wire is positive, the second wire negative and the third is neutral. Power may be taken from neutral and either positive or negative feeder.

THRESHOLD (const.) thresh' old: A specially shaped wood or metal strip under a door.

THRESHOLD OF AUDIBILITY (elec.) thresh' old of au di bil' i ty: See THRESHOLD OF SOUND.

THRESHOLD OF SOUND (elec.) thresh'- old of sound: The minimum sound at a particular frequency which can be heard.

THROAT (const.) throat: The opening in the top of a fireplace where the damper is placed.

THROAT OF A FILLET WELD (actual throat) (weld.) throat of a fil' let weld: Distance from the weld root to the weld face.

THROTTLE CRACKER (auto.) throt' tle crack' er: A device which partially opens the throttle during cranking or starting.

THROTTLE VALVE (auto.) throt' tle valve: A butterfly valve by which the operator may control the volume of air-fuel mixture supplied to the engine.

"THROUGH DRYING" (paint. and dec.) through dry' ing: Uniform drying of the entire paint film.

THROW (air cond.) throw: The distance at which the velocity of the stream of air from a supply opening falls to 50 ft. per minute.

THROWING (crafts.) throw' ing: The shaping of clay on a potter's wheel.

THRUST BEARING (auto.) thrust bear'- ing: A bearing used to take up end thrust and prevent excessive end play.

THRUST CHAMBER (space) thrust cham' ber: A rocket motor or engine.

THUMBNAIL PROOF (paint. and dec.) thumb' nail proof: Checking hardness of a finish by pressing thumbnail against it.

THUMB NUT (metal) thumb nut: A wing nut that can be operated by your thumb and forefinger.

THUMB PLANE (wood.) thumb plane: A name given to small wood planes used in model making. Pressure is applied to the plane by the thumb.

THYRATRON (elec.) thy' ra tron: A gas filled tube in which a grid is used to control the firing potential.

TICKLER (elec.) tick' ler: A coil used to feedback energy from output to input circuit.

TIE (const.) tie: A metal rod or timber used to bind parts together which tend to separate.

TIE ROD (auto.) tie rod: A rod between the front wheels of an automobile to permit them to act together when steering.

TIFFANY FINISH (paint. and dec.) tif'- fa ny fin' ish: A multi-color, blended finish, used mostly for wall decoration.

TIG (weld.) tig: Term used to describe gas tungsten arc welding (Tungsten Inert Gas).

TIGHT FIT (metal) tight fit: A fit between parts which requires a light pressure to assemble.

TILDE (graphics) til'de: A punctuation mark placed over ñ to show that it should be pronounced as "ny."

TILES (const.) tiles: Flat squares of fired clay used as roofing, floor and wall coverings, fireplace hearth and kitchen counter tops.

TIMBER (wood.) tim'ber: Trees; sawed lumber greater than five inches in both thickness and width.

TIME CONSTANT ($\frac{L}{R}$) (elec.) time con'-stant: The time period required for the current in an inductor to increase to 63.2% of maximum value or to decrease to 36.7% of maximum value.

TIME CONSTANT, RC
The time period required for the voltage across a capacitor in an RC circuit to increase to 63.2% of maximum value or to decrease to 36.7% of maximum value. Time (in seconds) = R (in ohms) x C (in farads).

TIMER (elec.) tim'er: A switching device arranged to start and stop a machine or operation at specific time intervals.

TIMING GEAR (auto.) tim'ing gear: The gears between the crankshaft and the camshaft which operates the valve mechanism. The gear ratio is 2 to 1 since the camshaft must revolve one half crankshaft speed.

TIMING MARKS (auto.) tim'ing marks:

Marks on the flywheel or dynamic balancer of an automotive engine to permit the mechanic to identify the ignition point of number 1 cylinder; marks on the timing gears to facilitate assembly of gears for proper valve timing.

TIME STUDY (automation) time stud'y: The time required for an operation as determined by production data.

TIN (crafts) tin: A soft, silvery white metal, malleable at room temperature, capable of a high polish and used as an alloy in tin foil, solder, type metals and tin plate. Symbol: Sn.

TINCTURE (paint. and dec.) tinc'ture: A dilute extract of a chemical or drug.

TINGE (paint. and dec.) tinge: Slight trace of color.

TINNING (weld.) tin'ning: Term applied to soldering where the metals to be soldered together are first given a coating of the soldering metal.

TIN PLATING (metal) tin plat'ing: A protective coating for sheet steel by passing through molten flux into a bath of molten tin.

TINT (paint. and dec.) tint: A light value of a color; one made by adding white to the color.

TIP (weld.) tip: Part of the torch at the end where the gas burns, producing the high temperature flame. In resistance welding the electrode ends are sometimes called tips.

TITANIUM (paint. and dec.) ti ta'ni um: A metal which is the basis for the pigment, titanium dioxide.

TITANIUM DIOXIDE (paint. and dec.) ti ta'ni um di ox'ide: White pigment used extensively in paint making. Comes in two forms, rutile and anatase. It is chemically inactive and is not affected by dilute acids, heat or light.

TITLE (draft.) ti' tle: A descriptive part of a drawing imparting information to identify it and other information.

TITLE (graphics) ti' tle: A type face possessing modern characteristics.

TITLE BLOCK (draft.) ti' tle block: An enclosed space on a drawing including name of drawing, number, draftsman's name, scales, dates and other information required.

TITRATION CONTROL (elec.) ti tra'- tion con' trol: An electronic device used to measure and control the acidity or alkalinity of solutions in chemical processing.

T JOINT (const.) t joint: A joint shaped like a letter T.

T JOINT (weld.) t joint: Joint formed by placing one metal against another at an angle of 90 deg. The edge of one metal contacts the surface of the other metal.

TNT (const.): Tri nitro tol' u ene; a high explosive.

TOBIN BRONZE (metal) to' bin bronze: A trade name for an alloy of copper, zinc, tin, iron and lead. It is widely used for ship fittings because of its high resistance to corrosion.

TOE DOGS (metal) toe dogs: Similar to grippers, but with adjusting screws.

TOE-IN (auto) toe-in: The amount the front wheels of a car are pointed inward at the front.

TOENAIL (const.) toe' nail: Driving a

nail at an angle, as around the base of a stud to fasten it to the sole plate.

TOE OF WELD (weld.) toe of weld: Junction of the face of the weld and the base metal.

TOGGLE BOLT (metal) tog' gle bolt: A type of expansive bolt used to fasten objects to a hollow wall. The nut on the bolt is compressed and inserted in the hole. When in place, the nut spreads out inside the wall, thereby permitting the tightening of the bolt and securing the object to the wall.

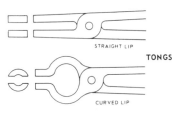

STRAIGHT LIP

TONGS

CURVED LIP

TOGGLE SWITCH (elec.) tog' gle switch: A switch which opens or closes a circuit by moving a lever or rocker button from one position to another.

TOLERANCE (draft.) tol' er ance: The amount of variation permitted in the size of a part.

TOLUENE (paint. and dec.) tol' u ene: See TOLUOL.

TOLUIDINE RED (paint. and dec.) to- lu' i dine red: Brilliant nonbleeding red pigment made from coal tar product.

TOLUOL (paint. and dec.) tol' u ol: Lacquer diluent made normally by coal tar distillation.

TON (refrigeration) (air cond.) ton: The rate of heat interchange of 12,000 Btu per hour; 200 Btu per minute.

TONE (paint. and dec.) tone: A gradation of color, either a hue, a tint, or a shade.

TONE ARM (elec.) tone arm: The pick-up arm on a phonograph.

TONE CONTROL (elec.) tone con' trol: An adjustable filter network to emphasize either high or low frequencies in the output of an audio amplifier.

TONGS (metal) tongs: Long handled plier-type tools for holding work while being forged. See illustration, page 334.

TONGUE (wood.) tongue: The projecting part along the edge of a board to fit into a groove in a tongue and groove joint.

TONGUE AND GROOVE (wood.) tongue and groove: A joint made by cutting a groove in one board and mating tongue in the other.

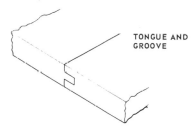

TONGUE AND
GROOVE

TOOL (automation) tool: The implement by which a product is held, cut, shaped or formed.

TOOL BASE (metal) tool base: The underside or bottom side of the tool bit.

TOOL BIT (metal) tool bit: A ground cutting tool.

TOOL BLANK (metal) tool blank: A piece of steel of a specified shape for making tool bits.

TOOL ENGINEERING (automation) tool en gi neer' ing: The design and re-

placement of tools which actually contact the work to shape it to a desired configuration. Also the design of holders and fixtures for cutting tools.

TOOL HOLDER (metal) tool hold' er: A piece of steel designed to hold a cutting tool in a lathe or miller.

TOOLING UP (automation) tool' ing up: The preparation of machines, jigs and fixtures, cutting tools, etc. for manufacturing an object. Ex: tooling up a production line for a specific product.

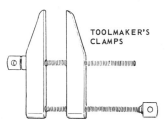

TOOLMAKER'S
CLAMPS

TOOLMAKER'S CLAMPS (metal) tool'- mak' er's clamps: Small metal parallel bar clamps.

TOOL POST (metal) tool post: The post on top of the carriage which holds the tool holder.

TOOL POST RING (metal) tool post ring: A concave, disk-like ring which fits over the tool post of a lathe. The rocker fits onto the ring and permits the tool holder to be clamped in a desired position.

TOOL POST ROCKER (metal) tool post rock' er: A small steel finger, straight on one side and curved on the other to fit the post ring. The tool holder is clamped between the rocker and the screw on the tool post. The rocker may be adjusted to provide the correct cutting tool height.

TOOLROOM WORK (automation) toolroom work: The shop in industry concerned with making a few-of-a-kind such as experimental models, tools, jigs, dies and fixtures and machine parts.

TOOL STEEL (metal) tool steel: Steels containing carbon in the .9% range.

"TOO MUCH DRAG" (paint. and dec.) too much drag: Refers to paint that has excessive "pull" or "drag" in its application.

TOOTH (paint. and dec.) tooth: Roughened or absorbent quality of a surface which affects adhesion and application of a coating.

TOP DEAD CENTER (auto.) top dead cen'ter: The upper limit of piston movement. Abbreviated, TDC.

TOPOGRAPHIC VECTORS (elec.) topo graph'ic vec'tors: Vectors arranged end to end.

TORCH (weld.) torch: The mechanism which the operator holds during gas welding and cutting, at the end of which the gases are burned to perform the various gas welding and cutting operations.

TOROID (elec.) to'roid: A doughnut shaped coil; a ring shaped solenoid.

TORQUE (tork) (elec.) torque: Forces producing twisting or rotating motion. It is measured in pound-feet.

TORQUE CONVERTER (auto.) torque con vert'er: A fluid coupling which provides varying drive ratios between the driving and driven members.

TORQUE TUBE (auto.) torque tube: A propeller shaft incased in a hollow tube. The tube is bolted to the final drive on one end and to the transmission at the other. The tube and its braces absorb the rear end torque and

prevent excessive differential housing movement.

TORQUE WRENCH (auto.) torque wrench: Special wrench with an indicator which shows force applied.

TORQUE WRENCH

TORR (space) torr: A suggested international standard term to replace "millimeter of mercury."

TORSIONAL BALANCER (auto.) tor'sional bal'anc er: See VIBRATIONAL DAMPENER.

TORUS (const.) to'rus: A half-round decorative molding.

TOUCHDOWN (space.) touch'down: Landing of a manned or unmanned space vehicle on the surface of a planet by any method, except gliding.

TOUGHNESS (metal) tough'ness: The characteristics of a material including strength and plasticity.

TOURMALINE (elec.) tour'ma line: A semiprecious crystalline mineral of a complex group of silicates.

TRACE (elec.) trace: The lines formed on the face of a cathode-ray tube as the electron beam moves.

TRACING (draft.) trac'ing: A copy of the original drawing made by tracing on transparent paper. The tracing is used to make prints.

TRACING CLOTH (draft.) trac'ing cloth: A translucent cloth used for more permanent tracings of a drawing.

TRACING PAPER (draft.) trac'ing pa'per: A thin translucent paper for drawings.

TRACK (automation) track: A path parallel to the edge of a tape on which information can be stored.

TRACK (elec.) track: The portion of a recording tape which records the sound.

TRACKING (elec.) track'ing: An alignment procedure used in radio service to assure that all tuned circuits follow the indicated dial frequency; following a satellite by radio.

TRACTION (auto.) trac'tion: Rolling friction; adhesiveness of a rolling wheel, such as a tire on the road.

TRAFFIC PAINT (paint. and dec.) traf'fic paint: A paint, usually white, red or yellow, used to designate traffic lanes, safety zones and intersections.

TRAIN (metal) train: An arrangement of gears and mechanisms for transferring power or changing of speed.

TRAMMEL (draft.) tram'mel: An instrument consisting of a straightedge

TRAMMEL POINTS

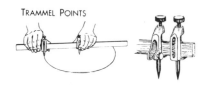

with two adjustable fixed points for drawing curves and ellipses.

TRAMP (auto.) tramp: The up and down movement of wheels in opposite directions.

TRANSCEIVER (elec.) trans ceiv'er: A combined transmitter and receiver.

TRANSCONDUCTANCE (Symbol g_m)

(elec.) trans con duc'tance: The grid plate transconductance of a vacuum tube expressed as the ratio of a small change in plate current to a small change in grid voltage while the plate voltage is held constant. It is measured in mhos.

TRANSCRIPTION (elec.) tran scrip'tion: The recording of a live program for later broadcasting.

TRANSDUCER (elec.) trans duc'er: A device by which one form of energy may be converted to another form, such as electrical, mechanical or acoustical.

TRANSFER CHARACTERISTIC (elec.) trans fer' char ac ter is' tic: The relation between input and output characteristics of a device.

TRANSFER MACHINE (automation) trans'fer ma chine': A machine into which is built the ability to handle or move the material from one station to another. Each station performs a series of operations on the part or piece.

TRANSFORMER (elec.) trans form'er: A device which transfers energy from one circuit to another by electromagnetic induction.

TRANSFORMER, 3 phase (elec.) transform'er:

DELTA CONNECTION: Coils form a closed loop in a delta configuration.

WYE OR STAR CONNECTION: Coils connected to a common center point in a Y configuration.

TRANSFORMER, CURRENT (elec.) trans form'er, cur'rent: A transformer used to reduce large currents to a small proportionate value for operation of meters.

TRANSFORMER, POTENTIAL (elec.)

trans form' er, po ten' tial: A transformer used to step-down high voltages to a low voltage for operation of meters, relays, and pilot lights.

TRANSFORMERS, TYPES (elec.) transform' ers:

ISOLATION, A transformer with a one to one turns ratio.

STEP-DOWN, A transformer with a turns ratio greater than one. The output voltage is less than the input voltage.

STEP-UP, A transformer with a turns ratio of less than one. The output voltage is greater than the input voltage.

TRANSIENT RESPONSE (elec.) tran'sient re sponse': The response to a momentary signal or force.

TRANSITE (const.) trans' ite: A Johns-Manville Co. trade name for a material made of asbestos fibers and Portland cement.

TRANSIT TIME (elec.) trans' it time: The time required for electrons to travel from cathode to plate in an electron tube.

TRANSITRON (elec.) tran' si tron: A Pierce oscillator in which the crystal is placed between the screen and suppressor grids.

TRANSISTOR (elec.) tran sis' tor: A semiconductor device derived from two words, transfer and resistor.

TRANSISTOR SOCKET (elec.) tran sis'tor sock' et: A small device in which the leads of a transistor are placed to provide ease in connection to circuit and to permit replacement of transistor.

TRANSLUCENT (const.) trans' lu cent: That which passes light but diffuses it so that objects cannot be identified; partially transparent such as frosted glass.

TRANSLUNAR SPACE (space) translu' nar space: That part of space conceived as a spherical layer centered on the Earth, with its lower limits at the distance of the orbit of the Moon, but extending several hundred thousands of miles beyond.

TRANSMISSION (air cond.) trans mis'sion: Heat transfer per unit of time.

TRANSMISSION (auto.) trans mis' sion: A gear box providing several gear ratios between engine speed and final drive, plus a reverse gear mechanism. Gear shifts may be manually or automatically controlled.

TRANSMISSION LINE (elec.) transmis' sion line: A wire or wires used to conduct or guide electrical energy.

TRANSMITTER (elec.) trans mit' ter: An all inclusive term applying to all equipment used for generating, amplifying and radiating a radio signal into space.

TRANSOM (const.) tran' som: A window above a door; a cross-piece in the middle of a window; a lintel.

TRANSOM BAR (const.) tran' som: The horizontal member between a transom and the top of a door.

TRANSPONDER (elec.) trans pon' der: A trigger-type beacon used in the IFF system (Identification of Friend or Foe) of target identification.

TRANSPORTATION (automation) transpor ta' tion: The movement of products and materials between plants and locations.

TRANSPOSITION (elec.) trans' po si_tion: The exchange of position of values in an equation such as from one side to the other with change of sign.

TRAP (plumb.) trap: A plumbing fix_ture placed in a drain pipe for the purpose of holding water to form a seal and prevent sewer gases from entering a building.

TRAPEZOID (draft.) trap' e zoid: A four sided geometric figure which has two sides parallel.

TRAP, WAVE (elec.) trap, wave: A resonant circuit placed in the lead_in to a radio receiver to attenuate un_desirable frequencies which would cause interference.

TRAVERSE (const.) trav' erse: To plane across the grain of the wood.

TRAY (plumb.) tray: A special sink used in a laundry.

TREAD (const.) tread: The horizontal step in a stairway.

TREADLE (metal) trea' dle: A foot operated part of a machine.

TREFOIL (crafts) tre' foil: An orna_mental figure resembling a threefold leaf.

TRELLIS (const.) trel' lis: Latticework of wood or metal, generally used to support plants and flowers.

T REST (wood.) t rest: The tool support for a wood turning lathe; a tool support for a grinding wheel.

TRF (elec.): Abbreviation for TUNED RADIO FREQUENCY.

TRIAD COLOR HARMONY (paint. and dec.) tri' ad col' or har' mo ny: Har_

mony obtained by using colors from three equidistant points of the color wheel. Red, yellow and blue make up a triad.

TRIANGLE (draft.) tri' an gle: A closed geometric figure having three sides and three angles.

Equilateral Triangle - A triangle with three equal sides.

Right Triangle - A triangle, one angle of which is a right angle.

Scalene Triangle - A triangle with three unequal sides.

Isosceles Triangle - A triangle with two equal sides.

TRIANGLES (draft.) tri' ang les: Flat plastic or wood triangles, either 45° or 30°-60° used with T square for drawing perpendicular and angular lines.

TRIANGULAR SCALE (draft.) tri an'_gu lar scale: A triangular shaped scale which combines several scales on one stick.

TRIANGULAR SCALE

TRICKLE CHARGE (elec.) trick' le charge: A low rate of charge applied to storage batteries to maintain peak condition.

TRIM (const.) trim: Moldings and boards of various designs to finish door and window openings.

TRIM ENAMEL PAINT (paint. and dec.) trim en am' el paint: Surface coating differing from ordinary house paint by faster drying, by having more gloss and showing fewer brush marks. Used mostly on trim, shutters and screens.

TRIMETRIC PROJECTION (draft.) tri-met'ric pro jec'tion: An object so drawn that no two axes make equal angles with the plane of projection, therefore each of the three axes have different ratios of fore-shortening when projected to the plane of projection.

TRIMMER (const.) trim' mer: A beam in floor framing that receives the ends of headers around a chimney or a stairwell.

TRIMMER (elec.) trim' mer: A small variable capacitor connected in parallel with a larger capacitor for minute ad-justments at the low capacity range.

TRIMO WRENCH (plumb.) tri' mo wrench: See PIPE WRENCH.

TRIMPOT (elec.) trim' pot: The trade name for a precision variable resistor manufactured by Bourns.

TRIODE (elec.) tri' ode: A three element vacuum tube, consisting of a cathode, grid and plate.

TRIP DOG (metal) trip dog: Adjustable lever or cam in the table feed mechan-ism of a machine which changes di-rection of feed.

TRIPHASE (elec.) tri' phase: See THREE PHASE.

TRIPLE POINT (air cond.) tri' ple point: The static point at which three sub-stances exist in equilibrium, such as gas, liquid and a solid.

TRIPOLI (crafts) trip' o li: Fine silica earth, used for polishing.

TRISECT (draft.) tri sect': To divide into three equal parts.

TRISTIMULUS VALUES (elec.) tri-stim' u lus val' ues: In color TV; the amount of each primary color that must be combined to match a sample color.

TRITON (elec.) tri' ton: An emitted particle consisting of a proton and two neutrons.

TRIVALENT (elec.) tri va' lent: A semiconductor impurity having three valence electrons. Acceptor impurity.

TROOSTITE (metal) troost' ite: A tran-sition structure element of steel below the hardness of Martensite.

TROPOSPHERE (elec.) trop' o sphere: The lower part of the Earth's atmos-phere in which clouds form and temper-ature decreases with altitude.

TROUBLE LAMP (auto.) trou' ble lamp: A light at the end of an extension cord to bring light to the place at which repairs are to be made. The lamp is usually equipped with a protective cage and reflector shield.

TROY WEIGHT: A weight measurement system used by jewelers and gold-smiths based on one pound equals 12 ounces.

    24 grains (g) = 1 pennyweight (dwt)
    20 dwt = 1 ounce (oz.)
    12 oz. = 1 pound (lb.)

TR SWITCH (elec.) tr switch: Abbrevia-tion for Transmit-Receive Switch. An electronic switch which disables the receiver during transmission.

TRUE COMPLEMENT COLOR HARMO-NY (paint. and dec.) true com' ple ment col' or har' mo ny: Two colors di-rectly across the color wheel from each other are true complements. Ex-amples are red and green, and orange and blue.

TRUE LENGTH (draft.) true length: The length of a line as viewed when the line is parallel to the plane of projection.

TRUE POWER (elec.) true pow' er: The actual power absorbed in a circuit.

TRUNCATE (draft.) trun' cate: To cut a geometric solid with a plane

TRUNK (elec.) trunk: Interconnecting wires and cables between switchboards and telephone exchanges.

TRUNNIONS (auto.) trun' nions: The arms of the cross-shaped member in a universal joint.

TRUSS (const.) truss: A structure of beams and steel rods arranged in a triangular shape to support loads over a long span as in roof construction.

TRUSSED BEAM (const.) trussed beam: A beam stiffened by a truss rod.

TRUSS ROD (const.) truss rod: A rod between the ends of a trussed beam, through which the strain due to downward pressure is transmitted.

TRY SQUARE (wood.) try square: A tool made by fixing a metal blade at a

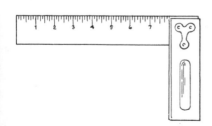

right angle to a heavier base or straight edge. Used for testing squareness of surfaces and joints.

T PLATE (metal) t plate: A metal plate shaped like a letter T. Used as reinforcement of a T joint between wooden parts. The plate has countersunk holes for wood screws or bolts.

T SLOT (metal) t slot: A slot cut in a table surface, shaped like an inverted T.

T SPLICE (elec.) t splice: Wires joined at right angles in the form of a letter T.

T SQUARE (draft.) t square: A straightedge with a T shaped head, used with a

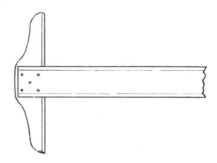

drawing board for drawing straight lines perpendicular to the edge of the board.

TUBE (plumb.) tube: A hollow cylinder for conducting liquids.

TUBE, TYPES OF (elec.)

    ACORN, a small high frequency tube shaped like an acorn. Leads from tube elements extend out radially from tube. It has no base.

    BALLAST, a resistor mounted in a tube envelope.

    BEAM POWER, a specially designed power amplifier tube, in which the electron stream is directed by beam forming plates. A substantial increase in power handling is realized.

    CATHODE-RAY TUBE, a tube in which the electron stream from emitter is directed toward the face of the tube, where it strikes a phosphor coating which fluoresces and produces a visible image on the face of the tube.

COLD CATHODE, a tube which has no heater. Emission is caused by other means.

CROOKES, a tube, filled with selected gases, used for observation and study of conduction of electricity through gases.

ELECTRON RAY, a tuning indicator tube, in which changes in control voltage may be observed on a fluorescent target.

GLOW DISCHARGE, a gas filled tube which depends upon glow discharge characteristics.

MIXER, a tube in the superheterodyne receiver in which the incoming signal is mixed with the local oscillator signal and produces an intermediate frequency output.

MULTIELECTRODE, a tube with more than three elements associated with a single electron stream.

PICTURE, the cathode-ray tube in a TV on which the picture is observed.

REMOTE CUTOFF, a tube with a variable amplification factor depending upon control grid voltage.

SHARP CUTOFF, a tube with a constant amplification factor.

VARIABLE MU, See REMOTE CUTOFF.

VOLTAGE REGULATOR, a gas tube which maintains a constant voltage drop over its operating range.

TUFTING (crafts) tuft' ing: In upholstery, it is the sewing at specified locations through both the material and the stuffing to hold the stuffing in place. Each tuft is usually covered with a button which also prevents the sewing thread from cutting through the material.

TUMBLE (space) tum' ble: To rotate above its horizontal axis, end-over-end.

TUMBLER GEAR (metal) tum' bler gear: An intermediate gear in a gear train used to reverse rotation.

TUMBLING (metal) tum' bling: A method of cleaning and shaping small parts by rolling in a rotating barrel-shaped machine with special abrasives.

TUMBLING (paint. and dec.) tum' bling: Method of finishing or polishing by using a tumbling barrel. Articles to be finished and finishing material are put into barrel which is turned or tumbled.

TUNE (elec.) tune: The process of bringing a circuit into resonance by adjusting one or more variable components.

TUNED AMPLIFIER (elec.) tuned am'-pli fi er: An amplifier employing tuned circuits for input and/or output coupling.

TUNED CIRCUIT (elec.) tuned cir' cuit: A circuit containing capacitance, inductance and resistance in series or parallel, which when energized at a specific frequency known as its resonant frequency, an interchange of energy occurs between the coil and the capacitor.

TUNER (elec.) tun' er: The stages of a radio receiver consisting of radio frequency amplifiers and detector.

TUNGAR RECTIFIER (elec.) tung' ar

rec' ti fi er: A General Electric trade name for a rectifier tube.

TUNG OIL (paint. and dec.) tung oil: Oil obtained from seeds of fruit of the tung tree.

TUNGSTEN (elec.) tung' sten: An element used as an emitter in a vacuum tube.

TUNING (elec.) tun' ing: The changing of the characteristics of a radio circuit so that a radio station is received with maximum strength and clarity; the adjustment of tuned circuits for a desired response.

TUNING FORK (elec.) tun' ing fork: A fork shaped instrument which vibrates an exact natural frequency.

TUNING INDICATOR (elec.) tun' ing in'- di ca tor: See TUBE, ELECTRON RAY.

TURBINE (auto.) tur' bine: An engine using the principle of a fluid force acting upon an incline plane such as the blade of a propeller or vanes on a wheel.

TURBOJET (space) tur' bo jet: A jet motor whose air is supplied by a turbine-driven compressor, the turbine being activated by exhaust gases from the motor.

TURN (elec.) turn: A complete loop of wire.

TURN (wood. - metal) turn: The process of shaping on a lathe.

TURNBUCKLE (metal) turn' buck le: A threaded connector by which tension on a rod or line may be adjusted.

TURNING GOUGE (wood.) turn' ing gauge: A roughing tool used in woodturning.

TURNING RADIUS (auto.) turn' ing ra'- di us: The radius of the arc in which an automobile can turn.

TURNING SAW (wood.) turn' ing saw: A thin metal blade attached to an H shaped frame for cutting heavy curves, scrolls and roundings.

TURNS RATIO (elec.) turns ra' tio: Ratio of number of turns of primary winding of a transformer to number of turns of secondary winding.

TURPENTINE (paint. and dec.) tur' - pen tine: Colorless, volatile liquid having a characteristic odor and taste. Obtained by distillation of the oleoresinous secretions found in pine trees.

"TURPS" (paint. and dec.) turps: Slang for turpentine.

TURRET (elec.) tur' ret: A tuning and frequency selection switch used in TV receivers.

TURRET LATHE (metal) tur' ret lathe: A lathe which is provided with a turret to carry several cutting tools in place of the tailstock.

TUSCAN RED (paint. and dec.) tus' can red: A red pigment consisting of a combination of iron oxides and a lake.

TUSCHE (graphics) tu' she: Substance similar to ink used in lithography for drawing and painting; used in etching and silk screen work as resist.

TUYERE (metal) tu yere': The air port to a cupola furnace. Air from the wind box is forced into the furnace through the tuyeres.

TWEETER (elec.) tweet' er: A high frequency loudspeaker.

TWIST DRILL (metal) twist drill: A drill with a helical fluted body.

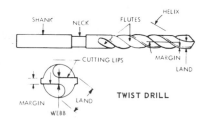

TWIST DRILL

TWISTED CABLE (elec.) twist' ed ca'- ble: Two or more electrical conductors twisted together.

TWO-COAT SYSTEM (paint. and dec.) two-coat sys' tem: Two-coat paint application for initial painting.

TWO CYCLE (auto.) two cy' cle: See TWO STROKE CYCLE.

TWO-PHASE (elec.) two-phase: Two a-c currents 90° out of phase with each other.

TWO-POINT PERSPECTIVE (draft.) two-point per spec' tive: A drawing of an object so that one set of parallel edges is vertical and has no vanishing point, while the other two sets of edges have vanishing points.

TWO STROKE CYCLE (auto.) two stroke cy' cle: An engine which requires two strokes to complete a cycle of operation.

T WRENCH (auto.) t wrench: A socket wrench with a T shaped handle.

TYMPAN (graphics) tym' pan: The packing placed on the platen of a job press, or the cylinder of a cylinder press, consisting of paper, pressboard, etc., and covered with a drawsheet, against which the form is printed; the tympan acts as a cushion for the paper being printed and equalizes type pressure.

TYMPAN-BALES (graphics) tym' pan-bales: Metal bands used to clamp the tympan to the platen.

TYPE-GAUGE (graphics) type-gauge: A metal strip, graduated in type sizes and used to measure the number of lines in a piece of matter.

TYPE-HIGH (graphics) type-high: In America, type height is .918 inches. It varies in foreign countries from .916 to .923 inches.

TYPE METAL (graphics) type met' al: An alloy consisting of five parts lead, two parts antimony and one part tin.

TYPOGRAPHY (graphics) ty pog' raph-y: The art of printing from type; the art of setting and arranging type.

TYPOTECT (graphics) ty' po tect: A typographical architect; the job planner and designer.

U BOLT (metal) u bolt: A bolt shaped like the letter U and threaded on both ends.

U CLAMP (metal) u clamp: A U shaped bolt used to fasten work on the table of a mill or planer.

UHF (elec.): Ultra High Frequency range; frequencies in the band between 300 and 3000 megacycles.

ULLAGE (space) ull' age: The amount a tank or container lacks of being full.

ULTRAMARINE BLUE (paint. and dec.) ul tra ma rine' blue: Blue pigment made by heating a mixture of china clay, sodium carbonate, carbon and sulphur.

ULTRASONIC (elec.) ul tra son' ic: See SUPERSONIC.

ULTRASONIC (space) ul tra son' ic: Speeds between sonic and hypersonic.

ULTRASONIC MACHINING (automation) ul tra son' ic ma chine' ing: An abrasive cutting operation in which the cutting tool in contact with the work is wetted by a slurry of fine abrasives. The tool is vibrated at ultrasonic frequencies causing the abrasive particles to cut the material.

ULTRAVIOLET (elec.) ul tra vi' o let: Invisible radiation waves with frequencies above the violet range and extending into the X-ray range.

ULTRAVIOLET LIGHT (paint. and dec.) ul tra vi' o let light: Light of short wave length which is invisible but has active chemical effect on finishing materials.

ULTRAVIOLET RAYS (weld.) ul tra vi'- o let rays: Energy waves that emanate from the electrodes and the welding flames of such a frequency that these rays are in the ultraviolet light spectrum.

UMBER (paint. and dec.) um' ber: A pigment obtained from the earth, which when raw is brown in color, when burnt it has a reddish hue. The color of umber is due to oxides of iron and of manganese.

UMBILICAL CORD (space) um bil' i- cal cord: A servicing cable fitted with a quick disconnect plug, through which equipment is controlled, monitored and tested while a missile is still attached to its launcher.

UMBRA (space) um' bra: Conical part of a shadow of a celestial body which geometrically excludes light from primary source.

UNBALANCED LOAD (elec.) un bal' - anced load: A greater load on one side of a line than on the other. Applies to distribution systems.

UNDAMPED WAVE (elec.) un damped' wave: A continuous wave of constant frequency and amplitude.

UNDERCOAT (paint. and dec.) un' der- coat: Second coat in three-coat work, or first coat in repainting.

UNDERCOATING (auto.) un' der coat- ing: The spraying of the undercarriage of an automobile with protective material to prevent rust and corrosion.

UNDERCOMPOUNDED (elec.) un der- com pound' ed: A compound wound generator in which the terminal voltage drops as the load increases.

UNDERCUT (weld.) un' der cut: A depression at the toe of the weld which is below the surface of the base metal.

UNDERCUT (wood.) un' der cut': A deep V cut made on one side of a tree in preparation for felling the tree. The undercut determines the direction in which the tree will fall.

UNDERCUT MICA (elec.) un' der cut mi' ca: The removal of mica below the surface of commutator segments so it will clear the brushes.

UNDERLAY (graphics) un' der lay: A cardboard backing placed behind type matter on the press to bring it up to the proper height for printing.

UNDERLOAD RELAY (elec.) un' der- load re' lay: A relay that activates another circuit when the load drops to a predetermined value.

UNDERSLUNG (auto.) un der slung': Having the automobile springs attached to the underside of the axles rather than on top.

UNDERTONE (paint. and dec.) un' dertone: A color covered up by other colors but when viewed by transmitted light, shows through the other colors modifying the effect.

UNDERWRITER'S LABORATORIES, INC. (elec.) un' der writ er's lab' o-ra to ries, inc.: A laboratory which tests devices and materials for compliance with the standards of construction and performance established by the Laboratories and with regard to their suitability for installation in accordance with the appropriate standards of the National Board of Fire Underwriters.

UNGROUNDED PAPER (paint. and dec.) un ground' ed pa' per: Wallpaper without a basic background color.

UNICONDUCTOR (elec.) u ni con duc'-tor: A single wire or group of unisulated wire which provide a single path of conduction.

UNIDIRECTIONAL (elec.) u ni di rec'-tion al: In one direction only.

UNIFILAR WINDING (elec.) u ni fi' lar wind' ing: A coil wound with a single conductor.

UNILATERAL CONDUCTOR (elec.) u-ni lat' er al con duc' tor: A device which conducts a current in one direction only.

UNILATERAL TOLERANCE (metal) u-ni lat' er al tol' er ance: The tolerance permitted on only one side of the basic dimension.

UNION (plumb.) un' ion: A device used to join two threaded pipes, which will permit a disconnect without dismant-tling the pipes.

UNIPHASE (elec.) u' ni phase: Single phase current or voltage.

UNIPOLAR (elec.) u' ni po' lar: One pole only.

UNISHEAR (metal) u' ni shear: A hand power shear for cutting straight and curved cuts in sheet metal.

UNIT CHARGE (elec.) u' nit charge: The quantity of electricity which exerts a force of one dyne upon an equal quantity of electricity one centimeter away.

UNIT MAGNETIC POLE (elec.) u' nit mag net' ic pole: A unit of measurement of magnetic strength. A unit pole repels a similar pole with a force of one dyne at a distance of one centimeter.

UNIT MEASUREMENT (elec.) u' nit mea' sure ment: The standard increments of measurements or quantity used as a means of comparison to other quantities.

UNITY COUPLING (elec.) u' ni ty cou'-pling: If two coils are positioned so that all lines of magnetic flux of one coil will cut across all turns of the second coil, it is called UNITY COUPLING.

UNIVERSAL CHUCK (metal) u ni ver'-sal chuck: See CHUCK, UNIVERSAL.

UNIVERSAL JOINT (auto.) u ni ver' sal joint: A double hinged joint made up of

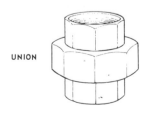

UNION

two Y shaped yokes and a cross-shaped member. See JOINT, UNIVERSAL.

UNIVERSAL MILLING MACHINE (metal) u ni ver' sal mill' ing ma chine': A milling machine which has both transverse and longitudinal feeds. The universal machine also has a swivel table. See also MILLING MACHINE.

UNIVERSAL MOTOR (elec.) u ni ver'- sal mo' tor: A series AC motor which operates also on DC. Fractional horsepower AC-DC motor.

UNIVERSAL TIME CONSTANT CHART (elec.) u ni ver' sal time con' stant chart: A graph with curves representing the growth and decay of voltages and currents in RC and RL circuits.

UNIVERSAL WORKTABLE (metal) u ni- ver' sal work' ta' ble: A table for a machine tool, which permits work to be rotated, as well as fed horizontally and vertically.

UNMODULATED WAVE (elec.) un mod- u lat' ed wave: See CONTINUOUS WAVE.

UNSAPONIFIABLE MATTER (paint. and dec.) un sa pon i fi' able mat' ter: Substance in resins and fats which does not unite with caustic alkali to form a soap.

UPHOLSTERER'S HAMMER (wood.) up- hol' ster er's ham' mer: See HAMMER.

UPHOLSTERY (crafts) up hol' ster y: The craft of fitting and covering furniture with decorative material. Also stuffing and cushioning furniture.

UP-MILLING (metal) up-mill' ing: A method of milling, when the cutter rotates so that the cutting force tends to lift the work into the cutter. Work moves opposite to cutting teeth.

UPPER AIR (space) up' per air: The atmosphere region embracing the ionosphere and the exosphere.

UPPER CASE (graphics) up' per case: Capital letters.

UPPER STAGE (space) up' per stage: A second or later stage in a multistage rocket.

UPSET (metal) up' set: The process of increasing the cross sectional area of a piece of stock by decreasing its length.

UPSETTING (metal) up set' ting: Thickening a metal part by mashing it down axially, either unconfined or into a die.

URANIUM (elec.) u ra' ni um: A radioactive element, number 92.

UREA-FORMALDEHYDE RESIN (paint. and dec.) u re' a-form al' de hyde res' in: Product obtained by chemical reaction between urea and formaldehyde in presence of catalyst.

UREA-MELAMINE RESINS (paint. and dec.) u re' a-mel' a mines res' ins: Melamine-formaldehyde resins which produce tough finish that approaches procelain.

UREA RESIN u re' a res' in: A group of synthetic resins used in laminating and treatment of textiles; adhesives made of these resins.

USF (metal) usf: Abbreviation for United States Form thread. These threads have the same form as National Coarse Thread (NC) but differ in pitch.

USGS (draft.): United States Geological Survey.

U.S.P. (paint. and dec.): Letters affixed to name of material to indicate that it conforms in grade to specifications of United States Pharmacopoeia and that it is approved for use in medicinal preparations. The material does not necessarily have to be chemically pure.

VACATIONS (paint. and dec.) vaca'tions: The uncoated portion of a finished object. Also known as "skips" and "holidays."

VACUUM (elec.) vac'u um: A space with nothing in it; a space left empty by removal of all matter usually found in the space.

VACUUM BRAKE (auto.) vac'u um brake: A mechanical breaking system used by trucks and heavy vehicles. The system is operated by a vacuum taken from the engine manifold.

VACUUM BREAKER (plumb.) vac'u um break'er: A device to prevent the formation of a vacuum in a pipe system.

VACUUM FORMING (automation) vac'u um form'ing: The process of drawing a sheet of material in a plastic state over a mold to form an object by means of vacuum.

VACUUM GAUGE (auto.) vac'u um gauge: An instrument used to test the vacuum in the intake manifold of an engine during operation.

VACUUM IMPREGNATED (elec.) vac'u um im preg na'ted: The coating and filling of spaces between electronic components with insulating materials by means of a vacuum.

VACUUM PLATING (metal) vac'u um plat'ing: A finishing process where parts are placed in an evacuated chamber where metal is vaporized onto the articles.

VACUUM SPARK ADVANCE (auto.) vac'u um spark ad vance': A diaphragm operated by manifold vacuum and linked to the breaker-point plate in the distributor of the engine. A change in manifold advances the ignition timing.

VACUUM SYSTEM (air cond.) vac u um sys'tem: A refrigeration system employing a vacuum to boil water at a desired temperature.

VACUUM TANK (auto.) vac'u um tank: A double tank system, using vacuum from engine to suck gasoline into tank from supply which then flows to the carburetor by gravity.

VACUUM TUBE (elec.) vac'u um tube: See ELECTRON TUBE.

VACUUM TUBE VOLTMETER, VTVM (elec.) vac'u um tube volt'me ter, VTVM: A voltmeter which uses vacuum tubes to perform the function of amplification and rectification. It operates on the principle that a change in grid voltage produces a proportional change in plate current.

VALENCE (elec.) va'lence: The chemical combining ability of an element in reference to hydrogen. The capacity of an atom to combine with other atoms to form molecules.

VALENCE BAND (elec.) va'lence band: The energy level of an atom closest to the nucleus.

VALLEY (const.) val'ley: The internal roof angle formed by two inclined sides of a roof.

VALLEY RAFTER (const.) val'ley raft'er: See RAFTERS.

VALUE (paint. and dec.) val'ue: Term used to distinguish dark colors from light ones. Dark values are known as shades; light values as tints.

VALUE ANALYSIS (automation) val' ue a nal' y sis: In automation, it is an intensified search for simplification to determine if the product can be produced in a simpler, cheaper, or more practical form.

VALVE (air cond.) valve: A device used to regulate the flow of air or liquid.

CHARGING, a valve used to permit addition of refrigerant to a system.

CHECK, a unidirectional valve; permits flow in one direction only.

EMERGENCY RELIEF, a valve to permit release of refrigerant in case of emergency.

EXPANSION, a valve used to control the flow of refrigerant in a cooling system.

FLOAT, a valve controlled by the liquid level.

KING, a valve between the receiver and the liquid main in a refrigeration system.

PRESSURE RELIEF, a relief valve activated by an excess pressure.

PURGE, a valve to drain a system.

REDUCING, a valve which maintains a constant pressure at its outlet regardless of a varying pressure at its input.

SAFETY, another name for a pressure relief valve.

VALVE (auto.) valve: A device used to open and close the port between the intake manifold and the combustion

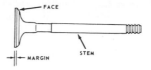

chamber or between the combustion chamber and the exhaust manifold. Valve operation is timed for proper engine operation.

VALVE (elec.) valve: British name for a vacuum tube.

VALVE FACE (auto.) valve face: The beveled edge of a valve which mates with the valve seat.

VALVE GRINDER (auto.) valve grind'- er: Tools and accessories used for refacing and reseating automotive valves.

VALVE KEEPER (auto.) valve keep' er: A device such as an open washer or sleeve which fits on the valve stem to hold the valve spring under compression.

VALVE LIFTER (auto.) valve lift' er: A special tool to relieve the valve spring pressure while removing or replacing valves; a metal or hydraulic rod or plunger which links the camshaft motion to the valve.

VALVE OVERLAP (auto.) valve o' ver- lap: The interval which may exist in some engines when both valves are partly open.

VALVE PORT (auto.) valve port: The opening into or from the combustion chamber of an engine, which is opened or closed by valve action. Air-fuel mixture enters and exhaust gases leave through the valve ports.

VALVE RETAINER (auto.) valve retain' er: See VALVE KEEPER.

VALVE SEAT (air cond.) valve seat: The fixed part of a valve mechanism upon which the valve face rests.

VALVE SEAT INSERTS (auto.) valve seat in' serts: A ring of special heat resistance metal inserted around a valve port. It is ground to properly seat the valve. Inserts extend the life of an engine.

VALVE SPRING (auto.) valve spring: A spring to hold valves closed when not activated.

VALVE TIMING (auto.) valve tim' ing: Adjustments made during engine assembly to insure that intake and exhaust valves open and close at proper intervals.

VANADIUM STEEL (metal) va na' di um steel: A steel alloyed with from .1 to .15 percent vanadium.

VAN ALLEN RADIATION BELTS (space) van al' len ra di a' tion belts: Two doughnut-shaped belts of high-energy charged particles, trapped in the Earth's magnetic field, which surround the Earth. Their minimum altitude ranges from approximately 100 miles near the Earth's magnetic poles to more than 1,000 miles at the equator. The maximum altitude of the outer belt extends to approximately 40,000 miles at the equator.

van de GRAAFF GENERATOR (elec.) van de Graff gen' er a tor: An electrostatic generator; a charge is generated on a hollow metal sphere at the top of the machine by a motor driven belt. The charge carried on the insulating belt is deposited on the sphere.

VANDYKE BROWN (paint. and dec.) vandyke brown: A brown pigment which consists of decomposed vegetable matter that has almost approached the coal state.

VANDYKE PRINT (graphics) van' dyke print: A silver print; a photographic image on inexpensive paper.

VANE PUMP (auto.) vane pump: A pump with vanes assembled into a rotor. As the rotor turns, the vanes are carried around as they press tightly against the inner surface of the pump casing. As a vane passes the inlet port, it pushes oil ahead of it to the outlet port.

VANISHING POINT (draft.) van' ish ing point: A point in the distance at which parallel lines seem to converge.

VAPOR (auto.) va' por: Mixture of gasoline and air; steam; gas.

VAPOR LOCK (auto.) va' por lock: The formation of vapor in a line which limits the flow of liquid. Ex: Vapor lock in a fuel line of an automobile engine.

VAPOR RECTIFIER (elec.) va' por rec'- ti fi er: A rectifier tube in which conduction takes place by ionization of mercury vapor.

VAR (elec.) var: The unit of measurement of reactive power. It is derived from volt-ampere reactive.

VARIABLE CAPACITOR (elec.) var' i- able ca pac' i tor: See CAPACITOR, VARIABLE.

VARIABLE INDUCTOR (elec.) var' i a- ble in duc' tor: A coil with some means of varying its self-inductance.

VARIABLE MU TUBE (elec.) var' i a- ble mu tube: A tube with an increased range of amplification due to its remote cutoff characteristics.

VARIABLE RESISTOR (elec.) var' i a-ble re sis' tor: A resistor which can be adjusted to different values.

VARIABLE SPEED GENERATOR (elec.) var' i a ble speed gen' er a tor: A generator which maintains constant voltage output under varying speeds by means of regulation circuits.

VARIATION (elec.) var i a' tion: The angle of declination.

VARIOCOUPLER (elec.) var i o cou'-pler: A radio frequency coupling trans-former which allows a variation in coupling, by mechanically changing the physical position of the coils.

VARIOMETER (elec.) var i om' e ter: A variable inductance made by a fixed coil and a rotating inner coil in series with each other. Rotation of inner coil varies the mutual inductance between the two coils.

VARISTOR (elec.) var' is tor: A two-electrode semiconductor device having a voltage-dependent nonlinear resis-tance.

VARMETER (elec.) var me' ter: An in-strument used to measure the reactive power of a circuit. It is calibrated in VAR units.

VARNISH (paint. and dec.) var' nish: A liquid composition which is convert-ed to a translucent or transparent solid film after application in a thin layer.

VARNISH (CLEAR) (paint. and dec.) var' nish (clear): Varnish which is transparent and contains no pigment.

VARNISH (wood.) var' nish: A solution of gums and oils which produce a hard glossy finish. Sometimes color is added.

VARNISH CAMBRIC (elec.) var' nish cam' bric: Cotton cloth coated with in-sulating varnish.

VARNISH-STAIN (paint. and dec.) var'-nish-stain: Interior varnish tinted with pigments or dyes.

VAULT (const.) vault: An arched ceil-ing or roof; a room covered by a vault.

V BELT (metal) v belt: A rubber and fabric belt with a V cross section for use on grooved pulleys.

V BLOCKS (metal) V blocks: Metal blocks, machined with a V on two sides. Used to clamp and hold a round shaft while machining it.

VECTOR (draft.) vec' tor: A straight line drawn to scale, showing the di-rection and magnitude of a force.

VECTOR DIAGRAM (elec.) vec' tor di'-a gram: A diagram showing direction and magnitude of several forces, such as voltage and current, resistance, reactance and impedance.

VEGETABLE OILS (paint. and dec.) veg' e ta ble oils: Oils obtained from the seeds or nuts of vegetable growth. Includes linseed, soybean, perilla, tung, castor, etc.

VEHICLE (paint. and dec.) ve' hi cle: In painting, it is the liquid used to carry the pigment.

VEINING (wood.) vein' ing: To cut shal-low narrow grooves on surface, simi-lar to fluting.

VELLUM (draft.) vel' lum: A type of tracing paper used in drafting.

VELOCITY (metal) ve loc' i ty: Revo-lutions per minute for rotating ma-chinery.

VELOCITY FACTOR (elec.) ve loc' i ty fac' tor: The velocity of propagation of a signal along a transmission line compared to the speed of light.

VELOCITY MODULATION (elec.) ve-loc' i ty mod u la' tion: Periodic changes in electon velocity; (alternate deceleration and acceleration) in an electron tube.

VELOCITY OF LIGHT (elec.) ve loc'-i ty of light: The velocity of light and electromagnetic waves is considered as 186,000 miles per second or 300,000,000 meters per second.

VELOCITY RATIO (metal) ve loc' i ty ra' tio: The ratio speed between the driving and driven pulley.

VENEER (const.) ve neer': The build-ing system where a frame building is covered with a skin or veneer of ma-terial such as stone or brick.

VENEER (wood.) ve neer': Wood sliced into thin sheets, used for decorative purposes.

VENEER PRESS (wood.) ve neer': A press used to hold veneers and ply-wood under pressure until adhesives or glues harden.

VENEER SAW (wood.) ve neer': A small back saw with fine teeth for cutting veneers and finish work.

VENETIAN BLIND (const.) ve ne' tian blind: A window blind or curtain made of a series of thin wooden or metal slats supported by a cloth tape. The blinds can be adjusted by pull cords.

VENETIAN RED (paint. and dec.) Ve-ne' tian red: Pigment with brick-red color, made synthetically by calcining copperas and whiting.

V ENGINE (auto.) v en' gine: An inter-nal combustion engine with two banks of cylinders at an angle to each other.

VENT (plumb.) vent: A vent pipe used to prevent the loss of the water seal in a trap from causes other than evap-oration. See BACK VENT.

VENTHOLES (metal) vent' holes: Holes made in a sand mold to allow gases to escape.

VENT PIPE (plumb.) vent pipe: A vent pipe from a plumbing fixture to the vent stack.

VENT STACK (plumb.) vent stack: A vertical pipe extending through the roof of a house, to which is attached all the vent pipes. The stack carries away undesirable gases and aids in main-taining the water seal in traps.

VENT SYSTEM (plumb.) vent sys' tem: A system of pipes to conduct air to and from a drainage system to prevent siphonage and back pressure.

VENTURI (auto.) ven' tu ri: A restric-tion in the main air passage of a car-buretor. It is used to produce a partial vacuum by increasing the velocity of the airflow.

VERANDA (const.) ve ran' da: A porch; a roofed open air portico on the side of a house.

VERDIGRIS (crafts) ver' di gris: A name referring to the greenish blue colors on metals such as brass and copper.

VERGE (const.) verge: The edge of the shingles projecting over the gable of a roof; also the projection along the eaves; an edge or margin.

VERGE BOARD (const.) verge board:

The board under the verge on a gable; a barge board.

VERMICULATED (const.) ver mic u-la' ted: Worm-eaten appearance; materials and stones made to look worm-eaten.

VERMILION (paint. and dec.) ver mil'-ion: Sulphide of mercury used as a pigment.

VERNIER (metal) ver' ni er: A small movable scale attached to a larger fixed scale, for obtaining fractional subdivisions of the fixed scale.

VERNIER (space) ver' ni er: Named after Pierre Vernier (1580-1637), French mathematician. Small rocket engines or gas nozzles mounted on the outside of a missile which can be tilted by commands from the flight control system to control the roll, pitch and yaw attitudes during propelled flight.

VERNIER CALIPER (metal) ver' ni er cal' i per: A steel scale or bar, with a fixed and a sliding jaw, for extremely accurate inside and outside measurements. Caliper employs vernier scales for measuring.

VERTEX (draft.) ver' tex: The intersection of two lines; the point of a V.

VERTICAL (draft.) ver' ti cal: Perpendicular to the horizon.

VERTICAL BORING MILL (metal) ver'-ti cal bor' ing mill: A machine tool, on which the work is mounted on a revolving work table. The tool is fed into the work and may be controlled both vertically and horizontally. Similar to a lathe in a vertical position.

VERTICAL POLARIZATION (elec.) ver' ti cal po lar i za' tion: An antenna positioned vertically so that its

electric field is perpendicular to the Earth's surface.

VERTICAL POSITION (welding) ver' ti cal po si' tion: Types of weld where the welding is done on a vertical seam and on a vertical surface.

VERY HIGH FREQUENCIES, VHF (elec.) ver' y high fre' quen cies, vhf: The band of radio frequencies from 30 to 300 megacycles.

VERY LOW FREQUENCIES, VLF (elec.) ver' y low fre' quen cies, vlf: The band of frequencies from 10 to 30 kilocycles.

VESTIBULE (const.) ves' ti bule: A small room used as an entranceway into a larger room or a building.

VESTIGIAL SIDEBAND (elec.) ves tig'-i al side' band: A method of radio transmission where some of the sideband frequencies are filtered out in order to reduce the bandwidth of the transmitted signal.

VFO (elec.): Abbreviation for Variable Frequency Oscillator.

VIADUCT (const.) vi' a duct: A masonry bridge structure for carrying a road or railway over a gorge or valley.

VIBRATING REED METER (elec.) vi-bra' ting reed me' ter: A type of frequency meter employing reeds with natural vibration frequencies.

VIBRATIONAL DAMPENER (auto.) vi-bra' tion al damp' en er: A mechanism fastened to the end of an engine crankshaft to absorb torsional vibration.

VIBRATOR (elec.) vi' bra tor: A magnetically operated interrupter, similar to a door bell or buzzer, to change a steady state dc to a pulsating dc.

VIDEO SIGNAL (elec.) vid' e o sig' nal: The electrical signal from the studio camera used to modulate the TV transmitter.

VIDICON (elec.) vi' di con: A small TV camera tube, less complicated than an image orthicon. Its resolution is less and it requires greater illumination of scene.

VIGNETTE (graphics) vi gnette': A picture with no definite border and shading off gradually to its edges.

VINYL RESIN (paint. an dec.) vi' nyl res' in: Resin or polymer produced by reaction between acetylene and acetic acid in presence of mercuric catalyst.

VIRTUAL CATHODE (elec.) vir' tul cath' ode: An electrical plane due to a space charge existing between the screen and plate of a beam-forming electron tube. Its effect is similar to a suppressor grid in a pentode.

VISCOSIMETER (air cond.) vis co sim'- e ter: A device for measuring the viscosity of a liquid.

VISCOSITY (air cond.) vis cos' i ty: The internal fluid resistance of a liquid.

VISCOSITY (paint. and dec.) vis cos' i- ty: Internal friction of a fluid which influences its rate of flow or exhibits resistance to change of form.

VISCOSITY RATING (auto.) vis cos' i ty rat' ing: The time required for a definite amount of oil to flow through a hole of definite diameter at a given temperature. Results are compared to standards set up by the SAE.

VISCOUS FRICTION (auto.) vis' cous fric' tion: The tendency of an oil or liquid to resist flowing. The friction between layers of oil.

VISE, BENCH (metal) vise, bench: See Bench Vise.

VISUALIZING (draft.) vis' u al iz ing: The ability to see the complete object from two or more views.

VITREOUS ENAMEL (metal) vit' re ous en' am el: Fired on, low porosity, glassy coating for metal. Also called porcelain enamel.

VITRIFIED BRICK (const.) vit' ri fied brick: A very hard building brick turned to the point of vitrification.

VITRIFIED SOIL PIPE (plumb.) vit'- ri fied soil pipe: A hard baked clay pipe used in drainage and sewer lines.

VIXEN FILE (metal) vix' en file: A flat file with curved teeth.

VODAS (elec.): Abbreviation for Voice Operated Device.

Anti-Singing. It is an automatic device used in radio telephony, which shifts the sending station to transmit and the receiver to standby when activated by an audio signal from a telephone set. When voice signal ceases, the sending station is shifted to receive so that answer may be received.

VOICE COIL (elec.) voice coil: The small coil attached to the speaker cone, to which the signal is applied. The reaction between the field of the voice coil and the fixed magnetic field causes mechanical movement of the cone.

VOIDS (const.) voids: Vacant spaces between materials such as in coal or gravel.

VOLATILE (paint. and dec.) vol' a tile: Said of a liquid that evaporates.

VOLATILE LIQUID (air cond.) vol'a-tile liq'uid: A liquid which readily evaporates at room temperature and atmospheric pressure.

VOLATILITY (auto.) vol a til'i ty: The ease with which a liquid or fuel changes from liquid to vapor.

VOLT (elec.) volt: (symbol E in electricity, symbol V in semiconductor circuits) The unit of measurement of electromotive force or potential difference.

VOLTA, ALESSANDRO (1745—1827) (elec.): A famous Italian scientist who proved the discoveries of Galvani's "animal electricity" were "metallic electricity." The voltaic cell and voltaic pile were among his major contributions to the science. He also invented the electrophorus for producing a static charge of electricity.

VOLTAGE (elec.) volt'age: See ELECTROMOTIVE FORCE.

VOLTAGE DIVIDER (elec.) volt'age di-vid'er: A tapped resistor or series resistors across a source voltage to produce multiple voltages.

VOLTAGE DOUBLER (elec.) volt'age doub'ler: A rectifier circuit which produces double the input voltage.

VOLTAGE DROP (elec.) volt'age drop: The voltage measured across a resistor. The voltage drop is equal to the product of the current times the resistance in ohms. E = IR.

VOLTAGE MULTIPLIER (elec.) volt'age mul'ti pli er: Rectifier circuits which produce an output voltage at an even multiple greater than the input voltage, usually doubling, tripling or quadrupling.

VOLTAGE REGULATOR (auto.) volt'age reg'u la tor: A circuit relay, actuated by a shunt voltage coil, which inserts resistance in the generator field circuit and reduces output if output voltage attempts to exceed a predetermined value.

VOLTAGE REGULATOR TUBE (elec.) volt'age reg'u la tor tube: A cold cathode gas filled tube which maintains a constant voltage drop independent of current, over its operating range.

VOLTAIC CELL (elec.) vol ta'ic cell: A cell produced by suspending two dissimular elements in an acid solution. A potential difference is developed by chemical action.

VOLT-AMPERE (elec.) volt-am'pere: The unit of measurement of apparent power.

VOLTMETER (elec.) volt'me ter: A meter used to measure voltage.

VOLUME (elec.) vol'ume: The intensity of a sound.

VOLUMETER (plumb.) vo lu'me ter: A flushometer valve.

VOLUMETRIC EFFICIENCY (auto.) vol-u met'ric ef fi'cien cy: The relationship between the quantity of air-fuel mixture taken into an engine on intake stroke to the actual piston displacement.

VOLUME UNIT (elec.) vol'ume u'nit: See VU.

VOLUTE (const.) vo lute': Spiral ornamentation on Ionic and Corinthian columns.

VOM (elec.): A common test instrument which combines a voltmeter, ohmmeter and milliammeter in one case.

VOSSOIR (const.) vos soir': An arch stone; a wedge shaped stone in an arch.

VPL (draft.): Vanishing Point Left.

V-PLANE (draft.) v-plane: The vertical plane in orthographic projection which shows the frontal view.

VPR (draft.): Vanishing Point Right.

V-R TUBE (elec.) v-r tube: A gas filled, cold cathode tube used for voltage regulation.

V-THREAD (metal) v-thread: A helical V-shaped section cut around the periphery of a cylinder.

V TVM (elec.): Vacuum Tube Volt Meter.

VU (elec.): A number numerically equal to the number of decibels above or below the reference volume level. Zero Vu represents a power level of one milliwatt dissipated in a 600 ohm load or a voltage of .7746 volts.

VULCANIZE (auto.) vul' can ize: To heat rubber under pressure to mold into desirable shapes and characteristics.

V-WAYS (metal) v-ways: Accurately machined V's on the bed of a lathe to assure alignment of headstock, tailstock and carriage.

WAINSCOTING (const.) wain' scot ing: A wooden covering, usually panelling, on lower portion of a wall. Usually finished differently from remainder of the wall.

WALKIE-TALKIE (elec.) walk' ie-talk'-ie: A small portable combination of a radio transmitter and a receiver. It is used for field communication over medium distances.

WALLBOARD (const.) wall' board: Any

of the manufactured wall coverings in sheet form, made of wood pulp, gypsum and other material.

WALLBOARD (paint. and dec.) wall'-board: Term refers to such boards as pressed cellulose fibers, plasterboard, cement-asbestos board, plywood, used in place of plaster in interior surfaces.

WALL BOX (elec.) wall box: A metal box used in house wiring to enclose a switch or receptacle.

WALL PLATE (const.) wall plate: A horizontal timber in a wall used as a bearing for joists and girders.

WALL SECTION (draft.) wall sec' tion: A cross sectional drawing of a wall showing heights and methods of construction.

WALL SIZE (paint. and dec.) wall size: Solution such as glue, starch, casein, shellac, varnish or lacquer, used to seal or fill pores of wall surface to stop suction, counteract chemicals or stains and prepare surface for paint, paper, or fabric.

WALNUT, BLACK (wood.) wal' nut, black: One of the most beautiful hardwoods native to the United States. It is chocolate brown in color, straight grained, very durable and easy to work. It is used for gun stocks, veneers and cabinetmaking.

WANDERING (auto.) wan' der ing: Condition where steering wheel tends to turn first in one direction then other, interfering with directional control.

WANE (const.) wane: The natural irregular edge of a board cut from an unsquared log.

WARDING FILE (metal) ward' ing file: A thin flat file used by the locksmith.

WARM AIR DUCT (air cond.): A pipe or duct used to convey warm air to or from a room.

WARM COLORS (paint. and dec.) warm col'ors: Colors in which red-orange predominates. This term is applied not only because of the association with fire, heat and sunshine, but because they are actually warmer than cool colors.

WARMING COLORS (paint. and dec.) warm'ing col'ors: Any color except green may be "warmed" by adding red. Green is warmed by adding yellow.

WARPED (const.) warped: A board twisted out of shape during seasoning.

WASHBURN & MOEN GAUGE (metal) wash'burn & moen gauge: (Also Steel Wire Gauge). The accepted standard for sizing steel and iron wire and drill rod.

WASH COAT (paint. and dec.) wash coat: A very thin coat of finishing material, usually shellac.

WASHING (paint. and dec.) wash'ing: Rapid dissolution or emulsification of a paint film when wet with water.

WASTE (metal) waste: Refuse from cotton mills consisting of fine soft cotton fibers matted together. Used for cleaning machinery.

WATER COOLING (auto.) wa'ter cool'-ing: Used in automotive engines, where the heat of combustion is transferred to circulating water in jackets or passageways around a cylinder. The water is air cooled in a radiator before re-circulation.

WATER GLASS (const.) wa'ter glass: A concentrated and viscous solution of sodium or potassium silicate in water. Used as an adhesive, protective coating and for fireproofing.

WATER GLASS (paint. and dec.) wa'ter glass: Silicate of soda; a white powdery substance, soluble in water and dries to a hard transparent film when exposed to air.

WATER JACKET (auto.) wa'ter jack'et: A passage or container containing a cooling liquid around combustion chambers and valves of engine to limit temperatures.

WATER MAIN (plumb.) wa'ter main: The main water supply pipe serving a building. It is usually buried in the street near the building.

WATERMARK (graphics) wa'ter mark: A manufacturing mark left on paper. It is visible when the paper is held up to light.

WATER PAINT (paint. and dec.) wa'ter paint: Paint in which water is used as thinner.

WATER PUMP (auto.) wa'ter pump: A vane pump used to circulate the coolant through an automotive engine. It is usually driven by the fan belt.

WATER PUTTY (wood.) wa'ter put'ty: Any of several powder compounds, which when mixed with water make a putty for filling holes and cracks.

WATER SOFTENER (plumb.) wa'ter sof'ten er: A device or chemical for removing calcium and magnesium sulfates or bicarbonates from water.

WATER SPOTTING (paint. and dec.) wa'ter spot'ting: Spotty changes in the color or gloss of a paint film. May be caused by various factors, such as emulsification or the solution of water soluble components.

WATER STAIN (paint. and dec.) wa' ter stain: Stain soluble in and mixed with water.

WATER TABLE (const.) wa' ter ta' ble: A projecting board and molding placed around the exterior wall of a house to shed rain water; the level of water below the ground.

WATER-THINNED PAINT (paint. and dec.) wa' ter-thinned paint: A paint whose thinner is mainly water.

WATER VAPOR (air cond.) wa' ter va'-por: Refers to steam in the atmosphere.

WATER WHITE (paint. and dec.) wa' ter white: Transparent and colorless like water.

WATT (elec.) watt: Unit of measurement of power.

WATT, JAMES (1736-1819) (elec.): A Scottish inventor who improved the steam engine and produced the first condensing steam engine. He invented the governor for regulating the speed of the steam engine. In 1874 he obtained a patent for a steam locomotive.

WATTAGE RATING (elec.) watt' age rat' ing: The amount of heat that can be dissipated by a component or device.

WATT-HOUR (elec.) watt-hour: Unit of energy measurement, equal to one watt per hour.

WATT-HOUR METER (elec.) watt-hour me' ter: A meter which indicates the instantaneous rate of power consumption of a device or circuit.

WATTLESS POWER (elec.) watt' less pow' er: The power not consumed in an a-c circuit due to reactance.

WATTMETER (elec.) watt' me ter: A meter used to measure power in watts.

WATT-SECOND (elec.) watt-sec' ond: A unit of measurement of electrical energy representing the work required to maintain a one ampere current through one ohm of resistance for one second.

WAVE (elec.) wave: A disturbance in a medium which is a function of time and space or both. Energy may be transmitted by waves. Ex: audio and radio waves.

WAVE, ELECTROMAGNETIC (elec.) wave, e lec tro mag net' ic: A wave which has both an electric and a magnetic field. Ex: radio wave.

WAVEFORM (elec.) wave' form: The shape of a wave derived from plotting its instantaneous values during a cycle against time.

WAVE FRONT (elec.) wave front: The most forward point on an advancing wave.

WAVE GUIDE (elec.) wave guide: A hollow tube, cylindrical or rectangular in shape, used to direct or guide r-f energy.

WAVELENGTH (elec.) wave' length: The distance bwtween a point on the loop of a wave to the corresponding point on an adjacent wave.

WAVELENGTH (color term) (paint. and dec.) wave' length: Computed distance between vibrations of light that produces visible color sensation on eye. In visible spectrum red-orange has longest wave length; violet the shortest. Wave lengths shorter than violet are called ultra-violet; wave lengths longer than red-orange are called infrared.

WAVE METER (elec.) wave me' ter: A meter used to measure the frequency of a wave.

WAVE, SAWTOOTH (elec.) wave, saw'-tooth: See SAWTOOTH WAVE.

WAVE TRAIN (elec.) wave train: A series of wave cycles of short duration.

WAVE TRAP (elec.) wave trap: A type of band reject filter.

WAVINESS (draft.) wav' i ness: Surface undulations of greater magnitude than roughness irregularities.

WAX (air cond.) wax: A substance which separates from some lubricants and oil-refrigerant mixtures when cooled.

WAX (paint. and dec.) wax: Substance derived from vegetable, animal and mineral matter used in painting industry mostly for making polishes.

WAX FINISH (wood.) wax fin' ish: A finish for wood by rubbing with a prepared wax.

WAYS (metal) ways: V or flat longitud-inal guides upon which a work table may slide or to hold various machine sub assemblies in proper alignment. Ex: V ways of a lathe bed.

WEAK-SIGNAL DETECTOR (elec.) weak-sig' nal de tec' tor: A detector designed to handle signal voltages hav-ing amplitudes of less than one volt.

WEAR AND TEAR: Depreciation due to use of.

WEATHER (wood.) weath' er: To mark, finish, scratch dry or damage a surface to make it appear as if exposed to weather for a long time.

WEATHER STRIP (const.) weath' er strip: Strips of metal or fabric around doors and windows to seal and prevent drafts.

WEB (metal) web: A thin metal section between parts of a casting.

WEBBER BLOCKS (metal) web' ber blocks: A set of gauge blocks manu-factured by the Webber Gage Co.

WEBER'S LAW (elec.) we' ber's law: The minimum change in stimulus neces-sary to produce a perceptible change in response is proportional to the stim-ulus already existing.

WEBER, WILHELM EDUARD (1804-1891) (elec.): A German theo-logian who made significant discoveries in electricity.

WEDGE (wood.) wedge: A V shaped piece of wood or metal used to exert pres-sures, such as splitting wood.

WEDGING (crafts.) wedg' ing: Working clay by cutting into sections over a taut wire to get it into condition for use.

WEE-GEE BOARD (auto.): A device used to check toe-in of front wheels of an automobile.

WEEP (air cond.) weep: To give off or leak slowly, as in drops.

WEEPHOLE (const.) weep' hole: A small hole in a wall to permit water drain-age.

WEIGHTLESSNESS (space) weight' less-ness: The absence of any apparent gravitational pull on an object. Any object deprived of support and freely falling in a vacuum is weightless.

WELD (elec.) weld: The joining of metals together by heat in which the parent metals are brought to their melting points. A welding rod is gen-erally used to add metal to the joint.

WELDING (weld.) weld' ing:

FUSION, welding without pressure. The melting and flowing of parent metals together.

OXYACETYLENE, welding by using oxyacetylene gas and oxygen. Also used in cutting.

RESISTANCE, an electric welding method where the parts to be welded are held together under pressure and a high current is run through the contact point. The metal heats at the contact point and the metals join together.

SPOT, a form of resistance welding used with thin sheets of metal. The metal is placed between two electrodes under pressure and the current applied. Spot welding joins the metal over a relatively small area or in spots.

TRANSFORMER, a specially designed transformer to provide the large currents needed for resistance welding.

WELDING (welding) weld' ing: Art of fastening metals together by means of interfusing the metals.

WELDING FLUX (weld.) weld' ing flux: A compound used during welding to clean and prevent oxidation and increase flowability and fusion of the joint.

WELDING PROCESSES (weld.) weld' ing pro' cess es:

BUTT WELD, between two pieces having their ends or edges squarely together.

CONTINUOUS WELD, one of unbroken continuity.

FILLET WELD, weld in a corner between two pieces intersecting at 90°.

FLAT WELD, weld on horizontal plane.

INTERMITTENT WELD, a series of short beads at regular intervals.

LAP WELD, along the edges of overlapping pieces.

OVERHEAD WELD, on the underside of horizontal plane.

TACK WELD, a temporary intermittent weld to aid in assembling parts for additional welding.

WELDING ROD (welding) weld' ing rod: Wire which is melted into the weld metal.

WELDING SEQUENCE (weld.) weld' ing se' quence: Order in which the component parts of a structure are welded.

WELDMENT (weld.) weld' ment: Assembly of component parts joined together by welding.

WELD METAL (weld.) weld met' al: Fused portion of base metal or fused portion of the base metal and the filler metal.

WELL POINT (plumb.) well point: A pointed pipe and screen which is driven into the ground for a well. Water enters the pipe through the screen.

WELSH PLUGS (auto.) welsh plugs: Small disks of sheet metal used to cover holes left by core prints during casting of a cylinder block.

WESTERN FRAME (const.) west' ern frame: A method of framing a building in which studs extend only from one floor to the next. Studs have a length of one story only.

WESTERN UNION SPLICE (elec.) west'-ern un' ion splice: A standard splice made by twisting two wires together.

WESTON CELL (elec.) west' on cell: A standard dry cell.

WET BULB DEPRESSION (air cond.) wet bulb de pres' sion: The difference between wet bulb and dry bulb temperatures.

"WET EDGE TIME" (paint. and dec.) wet edge time: The length of time before a "stretch of paint" sets up without showing lap marks when the painter applies the next "stretch."

WET-FUEL ROCKET (space) wet-fuel rock' et: A liquid rocket.

WET ROT (wood.) wet rot: Decay of lumber due to heat and moisture.

WET VENT (plumb.) wet vent: The portion of the vent pipe system through which liquid wastes flow.

WHEATSTONE BRIDGE (elec.) wheat'- stone bridge: A bridge circuit used for precision measurement of resistors.

WHEEL BALANCE (auto.) wheel bal'- ance: A service procedure of balancing out unequal forces on a wheel by attaching counterweights.

WHEEL BALANCER (auto.) wheel bal'- anc er: A machine for balancing automotive wheels. The machine spins the wheel and indicates the location and amount of weight to be placed on the wheel.

WHEELBASE (auto.) wheel' base: The distance between the center of the front wheel to the center of the rear wheel of an automobile.

WHEEL DRESSER (metal) wheel dress'- er: A tool for reshaping, cleaning and sharpening a grinding wheel.

WHEEL PULLER (auto.) wheel pull' er: A screw pressure device for pulling a wheel from an axle.

WHEELWRIGHT wheel' wright: One who builds or repairs wagons.

WHETTING (metal) whet' ting: Finish sharpening of a tool on a fine oil stone to improve its cutting edge.

WHITE COAT (const.) white coat: The finish coat of plaster; the slipped coat; skimcoat.

WHITE DOT GENERATOR (elec.) white dot gen' er a tor: A television service instrument. The generator will cause a pattern of white dots to appear on the CRT which may be varied in number and size. The instrument is useful in adjusting the convergence of beams from the electron gun in a color TV.

WHITE IRON (metal) white iron: Extremely hard cast iron caused by rapid chilling in a metallic mold.

WHITE LEAD (paint. and dec.) white lead: Basic carbonate white lead is a compound of lead, carbon dioxide and water. Lead is melted and cast into disks or "buckles" which are about six inches in diameter. The buckles are placed in porcelain pots each containing dilute acetic acid. The pots are covered with boards and layers of tanbark. Heat and carbonic acid generated by fermentation of the tanbark, with the acid vapors, combine to transform the lead into basic carbonate white lead.

WHITE LEAD (Carter Process) (paint. and dec.) white lead: In the Carter Process melted lead is blown into fine granules by a jet of air or superheated steam. The powdered lead is placed in revolving drums or cylinders and subjected to the action of air and carbon dioxide gas from burning coal.

WHITE LEAD (Basic sulphate) (paint. and dec.) white lead: White pigment obtained from lead sulphide ore by a process of fuming or burning.

WHITE LIGHT (elec.) white light: A mixture of red, green and blue color in proper proportions.

WHITE METAL (metal) white met'al: A bearing metal called babbitt, which is an alloy of tin, lead, antimony and copper.

WHITE OAK (wood.) white oak: A heavy close grain wood of remarkable strength and durability. The hardest of American oak trees.

WHITE PEAK (elec.) white peak: The maximum excursion of the white picture signal in TV in the white direction.

WHITEWASH (const.) white'wash: Slaked lime and water applied with a brush.

WHITEWASH (paint. and dec.) white'-wash: One of the oldest kinds of paint and decoration. Whitewash is made with casein, trisodium phosphate and lime paste.

WHITING (const.) whit'ing: Powdered chalk; a paste form of chalk and oil used as putty.

WHITING (paint. and dec.) whit'ing: See CALCIUM CARBONATE.

WHITNEY KEYS (metal) whit'ney keys: A square key rounded at both ends. Sizes are described in the Pratt and Whitney Key System.

WHORL (crafts) whorl: Spiral scroll design.

WIEN BRIDGE (elec.) wien bridge: A bridge circuit used to measure frequencies in the audio range. The circuit

is adjusted to null point with an ac signal applied. The adjustable element may be calibrated in cycles per second.

WIGGLER (metal) wig'gler: A sharp pointed rod supported in a universal joint, for checking the centering of work in a lathe.

WIGGLER

WINCH (const.) winch: A hand powered hoisting machine attached to a crane. It consists of a rope drum driven by reduction gears to increase its mechanical advantage.

WIND (const.) wind: A bending or twisting of a wall or board.

WINDERS (const.) wind'ers: Stair tread wider on one end than on the other, and used on curved portions of the staircase.

WINDLASS (metal) wind'lass: See WINCH.

WIND LOAD (const.) wind load: The load on a structure due to wind pressures.

WINDOW (const.) win'dow: An opening in the wall of a building structure, closed with glass in a frame with provisions for opening. Its purpose is to admit light and for ventilation.

WINDOW (space) win'dow: Strips of frequency-cut metal foil, wire or bars usually dropped from aircraft or expelled from shells or rockets as a radar countermeasure.

WINDOW FRAME (const.) win'dow frame: The frame that holds the sash.

WINDOW SILL (const.) win'dow sill:

The bottom horizontal member of a window frame.

WIND SHAKE (wood.) wind shake: A defect in lumber caused by wind stresses on the tree before cutting. It appears as splits or separations.

WIND TUNNEL (space) wind tun' nel: A tunnel through which a stream of air is drawn at controlled speeds for aerodynamic tests and experimentation.

WING NUT (metal) wing nut: A nut with ear-like projections so that it may be easily turned with the fingers; a thumb nut.

WIPED JOINT (plumb.) wiped joint: A joint between the ends of two lead pipes made by wiping a ball of solder around the joint.

WIPER (metal) wip' er: A cam having a sliding motion.

WIPING CONTACTS (elec.) wip' ing con' tacts: Contacts, such as in a switch, which rub between two other contacts.

WIPING STAIN (paint. and dec.) wip' ing stain: See PIGMENT OIL STAIN.

WIRE (elec.) wire: A single, solid conductor.

WIRE CLOTH (metal) wire cloth: A fabric made of woven wire.

WIRED EDGE (metal) wired edge: The edge of sheet metal strengthened by being formed over a wire.

WIRE EDGE JOINT (wallpaper) (paint. and dec.) wire edge joint: Joint made by trimming both selvedges and lapping one edge slightly over the other.

WIRED RADIO (elec.) wired ra' di o:

The transmission of radio signals along wires instead of through the air.

WIRE GAUGE (elec.) wire gauge: A numerical system of expressing wire size.

WIRE GLASS (const.) wire glass: Window glass imbedded with coarse mesh wire to prevent scattering fragments if broken.

WIREPHOTO (elec.) wire' pho to: See FACSIMILE.

WIRE RECORDER (elec.) wire re cord'- er: A recorder which employs a magnetic wire as a recording medium.

WIREWOUND (elec.) wire' wound: This term refers to fixed and variable resistors using resistance wire, such as Nichrome, wound on a ceramic form.

WIRING DIAGRAM (elec.) wir' ing di'- a gram: A diagram showing electrical devices by symbols and their interconnections.

WITHERING (paint. and dec.) with' ering: Withering or loss of gloss is often caused by varnishing open-pore woods without filling pores, use of improper undercoating and applying the top coat before undercoat has dried.

WITHES (const.) withes: A dividing partition between two flues in one chimney.

WITH THE GRAIN (graphics) with the grain: Parallel to or in the direction of the fibers in the paper.

WOBBULATOR (elec.) wob bu la' tor: A circuit using a motor driven variable capacitor to frequency modulate the output of an oscillator.

WOLFRAMITE (metal) wolf' ram ite: A

German alloy of aluminum and tungsten with small percentages of copper and zinc.

WOOD ALCOHOL (paint. and dec.) wood al' co hol: Poisonous alcohol obtained by destructive distillation of wood.

WOODCUT (g r a p h i c s) wood' cut: A printing plate made of wood on which the image is left in relief.

WOOD FINISHING (wood.) wood fin' ish- ing: The preparation of a wood surface and the application of a finish, such as paint, stain or varnish.

WOOD FLOUR (wood.) wood flour: Fine- ly ground wood used as a filler for linoleum flooring.

WOODRUFF KEY (metal) wood' ruff key: Serving the same purpose as the flat key, but semicircular in shape.

WOOD SCREWS (wood.) wood screws: A wood fastener. These are made of various types of material such as steel, aluminum and brass; they are manufactured in a wide variety of wire sizes and lengths with round, flat, oval and special heads. They are sized by number 0 to 30, the larger the num- ber, the larger diameter of the screw body. Their lengths are specified in inches, 1/4 to 6 inches.

WOOFER (elec.) woof' er: A large loud- speaker designed for reproduction of low frequency sounds. It is used in high fidelity amplifier systems.

WORK (auto.) work: Work is done when a force moves the position of a body against an opposing force.

WORK (automation) work: The effort expended in producing a useful product or service. It may include machine power, man power and brain power.

WORK (elec.) work: When a force moves through a distance, work is done. It is measured in foot-pounds and

Work = Force x Distance.

WORK FUNCTION (elec.) work func'- tion: The amount of work required to cause emission. Work required to over- come attractive forces between ma- terials and emitted electrons.

WORK HARDENING (metal) work hard'- en ing: An increase in hardness of metal resulting from cold working.

WORKING DEPTH (m e t a l) work' ing depth: The depth of a gear tooth from the addendum line to the clearance line; the total tooth depth minus the clearance.

WORKING DRAWINGS (draft.) work' ing draw' ings: The complete set of draw- ings consisting of detail sheets and assembly drawings necessary to manu- facture a given object or machine.

WORKING LOAD (metal) work' ing load: The normal load for which a machine or device was designed; the average load.

W O R K I N G O P E R A T I O N S (automa- tion) work' ing op er a' tions: The division of manufacturing concerned with the creation of the product.

WORKING SKETCH (draft.) work' ing sketch: A freehand drawing showing dimensions and other information nec- essary to make a finished drawing.

WORKING VOLTAGE (elec.) work' ing volt' age: The maximum voltage that can be steadily applied to a capacitor without danger of arc-over.

WORM AND GEAR STEERING (auto.) worm and gear steer' ing: A method of transmitting steering power from steering wheel to the front wheels. A worm at the end of the steering gear shaft mates with a worm gear on the cross shaft which moves the steering arm.

WORM GEARING (metal) worm gear'-ing: Transmission of power by worms and worm gears.

WORM'S-EYE VIEW (draft.) worm's-eye view: A perspective view looking up at an object.

WORM THREADS (metal) worm threads: Acme type threads with a 29 degree included angle, but deeper than standard threads.

WOVE PAPER (graphics) wove pa' per: A paper free of watermark lines found on a laid paper.

WOW (elec.) wow: A low frequency flutter resulting from variations in turntable speeds.

WRECKING BAR (wood.) wreck' ing bar: A steel bar one to three feet in length, with a flat chisel point on one end and curved to a claw on the other.

WRENCH (metal) wrench: One of many varieties and types of tools used to turn nuts. Some wrenches are for fixed sizes and others are adjustable.

WRINGING FIT (metal) wring' ing fit: Class 5 fit; a metal to metal fit.

WRINKLE FINISH (paint. and dec.) wrin'-kle fin' ish: A varnish or enamel film which exhibits fine wrinkles on ridges. Used extensively as a novelty finish.

WRIST PIN (auto.) wrist pin: See PIS-TON PIN.

WROUGHT IRON (metal) wrought iron: Almost pure iron; iron with all its carbon and impurities removed.

WWV and WWVH (elec.): National Bureau of Standards Radio Stations in Washington D.C. and Hawaii respectively.

WYE CONNECTION (elec.) wye connec' tion: A method of connecting three-phase alternators and transformers so that the end of each coil or winding has a common neutral point. The circuit configuration resembles the letter Y.

X (elec.): The symbol for reactance measured in ohms.

X (space): Symbol for "experimental." When used as a prefix with the designation of an aerospace vehicle, it indicates that the designated item is an experimental model of the specified vehicle.

XANTHIC (paint. and dec.) xan' thic: Containing yellow, or pertaining to yellow color.

X-AXIS (elec.) x-ax' is: The axis drawn through the corners of a hexagonal crystal.

X-AXIS (draft.) x-ax' is: The horizontal axis of a graph.

X_C (elec.): Capacitive reactance.

X-CUT CRYSTAL (elec.) x-cut crys' tal: A crystal cut perpendicular to the X axis.

XEROGRAPHY (elec.) xe rog' raph y: A dry electrical and mechanical process of reproduction based on the use of photoconductive materials.

XEROGRAPHY (graphics) xe rog' raph-y: A dry printing process by the electrostatic method.

X$_L$ (elec.): Inductive reactance.

X MEMBER (auto.) x mem' ber: A re-enforcement frame made of pressed-steel and shaped like the letter X. Used to strengthen a main frame assembly.

X RAYS (elec.) x rays': Nonluminous electromagnetic radiation of extremely short wave length, produced by bombardment of a target substance by a stream of electrons moving at a great velocity.

XYLENE (paint. and dec.) xy' lene: See XYLOL.

XYLOGRAPHY (graphics) xy log' raph-y: The art of wood engraving or taking impressions from wood engravings.

XYLOL (paint. and dec.) xy' lol: Coal tar distillate used in the paint industry as a solvent, solvent ingredient and as a process material in synthetic enamel.

Y (elec.): Symbol for ADMITTANCE measured in mhos.

Y (space): Symbol for "prototype." When used as a prefix in the designation of an aerospace vehicle, indicates that the vehicle is a prototype model which is produced in limited numbers for operational tests.

YAGI ANTENNA (elec.) ya' gi an ten' na: A dipole with two or more director elements.

YANKEE SCREWDRIVER (wood.) yan'-kee screw' driv er: The Stanley Trade Name for a spiral ratchet screwdriver.

YARD (const.) yard: The open space surrounding a building; an area near a building designated for a special purpose such as service yard, lumber-yard, etc.

YARNING IRON (plumb.) yarn' ing iron: An offset calking tool.

Y-AXIS (elec.) y-ax' is: The axis drawn perpendicular to the faces of a hexagonal crystal.

Y-AXIS (draft.) y-ax' is: The vertical axis of a graph.

YAW (space) yaw: The lateral or oscillatory movement of an aircraft or rocket about its transverse axis.

Y CONNECTION (elec.) y con nec' tion: A method of connecting three-phase electrical circuitry.

Y-CUT CRYSTAL (elec.) y-cut crys' tal: A crystal cut perpendicular to the Y-axis.

YELLOW BRASS (metal) yel' low brass: An alloy of 70 percent copper and 30 percent zinc.

YELLOW OCHER (crafts) yel' low o'-cher: A color pigment for paint derived from mineral earth ocher.

YELLOW PINE (wood.) yel' low pine: The wood from either the long leaf or short leaf pine. The long leaf pine is dense, heavy and strong. The short leaf pine is brittle and less expensive.

YIELD POINT (metal) yield point: A point during the tensile testing of materials when there is a definite increase in length with no increase in load.

YIELD STRENGTH (weld.) yield strength: Stress in psi at which a specimen assumes a specified limiting permanent set.

YOKE (elec.) yoke: Coils placed around the neck of a TV picture tube for magnetic deflection of beam.

YOUNG'S MODULUS (metal) Young's mod' u lus: See MODULES OF ELASTICITY.

Y-SIGNAL (elec.) y-sig' nal: In TV. The luminescence signal.

YO-YO (wood.) yo-yo: A slang term used to describe a flexible steel rule, contained in a metal case.

Z (elec.): Symbol for IMPEDANCE measured in ohms.

Z-AXIS (elec.) z-ax' is: The optical axis of a crystal.

ZEBRANO (wood.) ze bran' o: Zebra wood; a hard, heavy wood, light brown in color with parallel stripes of dark brown. Excellent for expensive furniture and paneling.

ZENER DIODE (elec.) ze' ner di' ode: A silicon diode which makes use of the breakdown properties of a PN junction. If a reverse voltage across the diode is progressively increased, a point will be reached when the current will greatly increase beyond its normal cut-off value. This voltage point is called the Zener voltage.

ZENER VOLTAGE (elec.) ze' ner volt'-age: The reverse voltage at which the breakdown occurs in a Zener diode.

ZEOLITE (plumb.) ze' o lite: A chemical compound which will change its composition, dependent upon the concentration of other chemicals in solution in its presence.

ZERO BEAT (elec.) zer' o beat: The point at which two mixed signals have the same frequency and their algebraic difference is zero.

ZERO GRAVITY (space) zer' o grav' i-ty: The complete absence of gravitational effect.

ZERO POTENTIAL (elec.) zer' o poten' tial: Zero voltage.

ZERO REFERENCE LEVEL (elec.) zer' o ref' er ence lev' el: The power level selected as a reference for computing the gain of an amplifier or system.

ZIG-ZAG RULE (wood.) zig-zag rule: A folding rule that closes in a zig-zag fashion.

ZINC (metal) zinc: A bluish-white metal used chiefly for galvanizing and making alloys.

ZINC (paint. and dec.) zinc: Ore obtained from mines; used extensively as paint pigment.

ZINC (LEADED) (paint. and dec.) zinc: Basic lead sulphate united with zinc oxide.

ZINC CHROMATE (Zinc Yellow) (paint. and dec.) zinc chro' mate: Metal priming pigment with important rust-inhibitive properties.

ZINC DUST (paint. and dec.) zinc dust: Finely divided zinc metal, gray in color. Used primarily in metal primers.

ZINC ENGRAVING (graphics) zinc engrav' ing: A printing plate made of zinc, on which the image is in relief and the background etched away.

ZINC ETCHING (graphics) zinc etch'-ing: Line engraving on zinc.

ZINC OXIDE (crafts) zinc ox' ide: A white powder derived from zinc carbonate. It is used as pigment for white paint.

ZINC SULPHIDE (paint. and dec.) zinc sul'phide: Compound of zinc used as white pigment in paints.

ZINC WHITE (crafts) zinc white: Zinc oxide used as pigment.

ZINOX (crafts) zi'nox: Hydrated oxide of zinc used in enamels.

ZOOM (elec.) zoom: A term used in televising, where the size of the televised scene or object is changed during camera operation, by moving the camera closer to the scene or by special variable focus lenses.

ZOOMAR (elec.) zoo'mar: A special variable focus lens used on a television camera to enlarge the televised object or scene.

ZYGLO (metal) zy'glo: A fluorescent penetrant inspection technique for detecting flaws in nonmagnetic metals.